CONDUCTION HEAT TRANSFER

MEMBRANE ANALOGY

Surface ordinates of a dilated soap film representing the temperature field in a circular region generating uniform heat.

ADDISON-WESLEY SERIES IN MECHANICAL ENGINEERING

JOHN F. LEE and ALI BULENT CAMBEL, *Consulting Editors*

CONDUCTION HEAT TRANSFER

by

P. J. SCHNEIDER

Department of Mechanical Engineering
University of Minnesota

ADDISON-WESLEY PUBLISHING COMPANY, Inc.

READING, MASSACHUSETTS

"To found the theory, it was in the first place necessary to distinguish and define with precision the elementary properties which determine the action of heat. I then perceived that all the phenomena which depend on the action resolve themselves into a very small number of general and simple facts; whereby every physical problem of this kind is brought back to an investigation of mathematical analysis. From these general facts I have concluded that to determine numerically the most varied movements of heat, it is sufficient to submit each substance to three fundamental observations. *Different bodies in fact do not possess in the same degree the power to contain heat, to receive or transmit it across their surfaces, nor to conduct it through the interior of their masses.* These are the three specific qualities which our theory distinguishes and shows how to measure."

J. B. J. Fourier, 1822

CONTENTS

PREFACE

The study of conduction heat-transfer is principally concerned with the *distribution of temperature* and *temperature history* within solid structures. In certain problems the determination of the temperature field will constitute a complete solution. Examples of this sort occur in the design of electrical coils, turbine blades, rocket-engine nozzles, and all such structures which must operate within allowable temperature limits. The design of high-temperature systems such as supersonic vehicles and nuclear reactors involves the additional problem of high thermal stressing, but here again the computation of thermal stresses depends directly on knowledge of the existing temperature distribution. In still other applications the heat flow through such structures as plane-wall, tube, and extended-surface heat-exchanges is of chief interest, and occasionally there is need to compute both the temperature field and the flow. We shall always be preoccupied with the temperature, however, because in all cases it is the temperature distribution which determines the heat transfer and thermal stress, and in general the latter two cannot be obtained without the first, except by recourse to direct experiment.

There are essentially four available methods for the evaluation of these temperature fields: (1) *analytical*, (2) *graphical*, (3) *numerical*, and (4) *experimental*. The formal analytical approach involves the derivation of a mathematical solution for the temperature as a function of space or space-time coordinates. The solution must satisfy the characteristic differential equation from which it was derived and certain initial and boundary conditions imposed by the particular problem itself. In nearly all cases the practical system must be simplified in order for this approach to be successful at all, and while solutions obtained under these circumstances are by no means "exact," the formal approach is still to be regarded as the preferred method of computation whenever possible. Graphical techniques are based on properties of the characteristic field equations and numerical principles; they have the singular advantage of giving a rapid first approximation to a temperature field. The numerical method is based on finite differences, and is therefore an approximate computational technique. Students invariably prefer this method; it is straightforward, flexible, and it will frequently give a good approximate solution to a problem which would otherwise be awkward or entirely intractable by formal analytical means. Like the graphical method, however, numerical techniques lack the possible parameterization of an exact solution. The final method of direct experiment is ordinarily reserved for that class of problems which cannot be handled successfully or at least conveniently by the analytical, graphical, or numerical approach. This method can range anywhere from actual temperature measurements at points in a model of the prototype structure to the use of analogic experiments which take advantage of the mathematical analogy between heat flow and other familiar potential-field phenomena.

The text considers all four of these methods for several practical reasons. First, it is necessary to become acquainted with more than one approach, since all problems cannot be handled successfully by any one method. Secondly, by introducing the student to the power and limitations of each method he comes to realize that for each new problem there is a most realistic method of solution with regard to conservation of time, labor, expense, talent, and accuracy. Thus while one approach might be the best for one problem, for another it might be the very worst.

The text is designed for use in the first of a three-semester sequence of graduate-level courses on conduction, convection, and radiation, and for use as a supplementary text in the usual undergraduate course covering the three modes of heat transfer in one semester. The reader will find that the text encompasses a variety of familiar engineering systems, and that the analysis of these systems is presented with a conspicuous lack of the mathematical rigor ordinarily awarded solutions in potential field theory. At this level, then, the student is not called upon to demonstrate the uniqueness of his solutions, but simply to verify that such solutions converge and satisfy an appropriate differential equation and required initial and boundary conditions. In order to gain admittance to the main body of analytical material beyond the simple one-dimensional systems of Chapter 2, the student will be obliged to consider in some detail general solutions of the Bessel and Legendre differential equations in Chapter 3 and the developments in Fourier series and integrals contained in Chapter 5. In an undergraduate course this will represent some spadework, while a course on the graduate level will assume acquaintance with this material and a brief review will suffice. Aside from this, the reader is expected to have only the usual undergraduate background in the calculus and ordinary differential equations, and little or no acquaintance with the properties and integration of partial-differential equations.

A large number of numerical examples are presented within the text material, and a sufficient number of problems are included at the end of each chapter to make some selection possible. In nearly all of these exercises the answer is included in the statement of the problem itself.

The reader who is already conversant with heat-conduction literature will appreciate that this present text has little claim to originality. Rather, the chief contribution of any text author is to select, abstract, and reframe in teachable form that material which he finds most suitable for exemplifying the principles and techniques of the field. In this undertaking the present author has epitomized the work of many first and subsequent writers. The references on which he drew most heavily, and accordingly to which he feels particularly obliged, are those of, Allen, Carslaw and Jaeger, Churchill, Dusinberre, Ingersoll and Zobel, Jakob, and Relton. The author takes additional pleasure in singling out and acknowledging his use of individual papers by Boelter, Dusinberre, Ellerbrock, Fend, Gardner, Gelissen, Green, Harper, Heisler, Higgins, Ikeda, Jakob, Kayan, Kaye, Langer, Langmuir, Lawson, Livingood, Lutz, McNall, Moore, O'Brien, Olson, Rosenthal, Sunatani, Weinbaum, Wilson, and Wolfenstein. Many of these writers contributed reprints and additional illustrations, and this includes the Division of Research Information of the NACA and Technical Information Service of the USAEC. Finally, the author is pleased to give special acknowledgment to Professor A. D. Moore, University of Michigan, who generously solved a problem by his fluid-mapping techniques for illustration in Chapter 13, to Professor J. F. Lee, University of North Carolina, and Professor B. T. Chao, University of Illinois, for friendly technical advice, and to Professor W. M. Rohsenow, Massachusetts Institute of Technology, for general assistance and for many valuable suggestions which have found their way into the final manuscript.

P. J. SCHNEIDER

Minneapolis, Minnesota
January, 1955

CHAPTER 1

INTRODUCTION

In this first chapter we examine the fundamental laws, characteristic differential equations, and thermal properties that are peculiar to the natural process of conduction heat transfer.

1-1 Concept of heat conduction. The phenomenon of heat conduction in solids is commonly interpreted as a simple molecular interchange of kinetic energy. Thus if the molecules of conducting material at one end of a rod are heated they are set into rapid motion and these, in communicating by elastic impact with their neighbors of lower kinetic energy, set the latter into more violent motion, and so on throughout the length of rod. An alternate picture of heat conduction is derived from the concept of electron drift; good conductors of heat are also good conductors of electricity, and since the conduction of electricity is postulated on the theory of free electron drift it appears rational to ascribe heat conduction primarily to the mobility of free or valence electrons. In both theories the thing in transition is referred to as *heat*, and the process of transition itself is known as *conduction*.

While the actual mechanism of heat conduction in solids is not thoroughly understood, the basic laws which govern the phenomenon are known to be consistent with classical thermodynamics, and the particular law which characterizes the transfer phenomenon itself can be established directly by experimental evidence. Our chief concern here will not be with the mechanism, but rather with the application of these phenomenological laws to practical heat-transfer systems.

1-2 The fundamental law. A consequence of the second law of thermodynamics and of experience is that heat can be exchanged between two systems only if the two systems are at different temperatures, and that the direction of this heat transfer is from the high- to the low-temperature system. The fundamental conditions for heat transfer by conduction within a solid body therefore require (a) *that a temperature gradient exist,* and (b) *that the resulting flow be in a direction of decreasing temperature.* If the flow proceeds at a constant rate, then the first law of thermodynamics tells us that this heat energy must also be conserved along the flow path.

The basic law which quantitatively defines heat conduction is generally attributed to the French mathematician Jean Fourier (1768–1830). With reference to Fig. 1–1, the one-dimensional form of the Fourier law states that the quantity of heat dQ conducted in the x-direction of a homogeneous

1

solid in time $d\theta$ is a product of the conducting area A *normal* to the flow path x, the temperature gradient $\partial t/\partial x$ *along* this path [the limiting value of $(t_2 - t_1)/(x_2 - x_1)$, which is negative], and a property k of the conducting material known as the *thermal conductivity*. Expressed analytically,

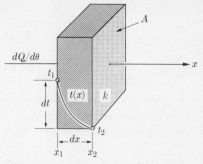

Fig. 1-1. Linear heat conduction.

$$\frac{dQ}{d\theta} = -kA\,\frac{\partial t}{\partial x}, \qquad (1\text{--}1)$$

in which the negative sign is arbitrarily affixed in order that Q be positive. The type of process (1–1) in which the temperature t appears as a function of a time coordinate θ as well as a space coordinate x is known as *transient conduction*, in contrast to *steady conduction*, where t is a function of x alone. In the case of steady conduction, we have simply $dQ/d\theta = Q/\theta = q$, wherewith

$$q = -kA\,\frac{dt}{dx}. \qquad (1\text{--}2)$$

It is important to keep in mind that the temperature gradient is taken in the direction of flow, and the conducting area is interpreted as that normal to the flow direction. It should also be mentioned here that k is not necessarily *uniform* (a constant) for any one material, but may be non-uniform as, say, a function of local temperature t, as k_t.

The most elementary solution of the Fourier equation is that for steady flow in *linear* conductors, where A does not vary with x. Thus by a simple separation of variables in (1–2),

$$q\int_{x_1}^{x_2} dx = kA\int_{t_2}^{t_1} dt,$$

we have for a total path length $x_2 - x_1 = L$,

$$q = k\,\frac{A}{L}\,(t_1 - t_2). \qquad (1\text{--}3)$$

Note that for this case the temperature function $t(x)$ in Fig. 1–1 is linear.

In the transient state of heat conduction, the quantity of heat entering and leaving a volume element of the body is not the same at any given instant, and the first law of thermodynamics tells us that this difference is used to increase the internal energy E of the element. This *internal energy change* is in amount

$$dE = CwV\,\frac{\partial t}{\partial \theta}\,d\theta, \qquad (1\text{--}4)$$

where C is identified as the *thermal capacity* of the material in question (heat energy required to raise the temperature of a unit weight of the material by one degree), w is the *specific weight* of the material, and V is its *volume*. We adopt a consistent set of engineering units for these quantities, as in Table 1–1.

TABLE 1–1

BRITISH GRAVITATIONAL UNITS

$\mid A \mid$	$= ft^2$	$\mid q \mid$	$= Btu/hr$
$\mid C \mid$	$= Btu/lb\text{-}°F$	$\mid t \mid$	$= °F$
$\mid k \mid$	$= Btu/hr\text{-}ft\text{-}°F$	$\mid V \mid$	$= ft^3$
$\mid L \mid$	$= ft$	$\mid w \mid$	$= lb/ft^3$
$\mid Q \mid$	$= Btu$	$\mid \theta \mid$	$= hr$

1–3 General differential equation for the temperature field. The Fourier law (1–1) defines transient heat flow in a linear conductor, and from this is derived the general partial-differential equation satisfied by the transient temperature field in a three-dimensional volume.

Consider an infinitesimal rectangular parallelepiped of conducting material as in Fig. 1–2. We treat the general case where this volume $V = dxdydz$ is to generate internal heat as a function of local temperature in amount q_t''' Btu/hr-ft^3, and where the thermal conductivity of the conducting material is also nonuniform, as k_t. The total quantity of heat entering the differential face surface $dydz$ at x is given by (1–1) as

$$dQ_x = -dydz\left(k_t \frac{\partial t_x}{\partial x}\right) d\theta.$$

Here the gradient is expressed as a partial derivative, since t is also a function of y and z. To determine the corresponding quantity of heat leaving the element at $x + dx$, let $F(x,t) = k_t \partial t_x/\partial x$ and allow x to increase by dx. Then by expanding $F(x + dx,t)$ in a Taylor's series and neglecting all terms after the first two, we have

$$F(x + dx,t) = F(x,t) + \frac{\partial F}{\partial x}\,dx$$

$$= k_t \frac{\partial t_x}{\partial x} + \frac{\partial}{\partial x}\left(k_t \frac{\partial t}{\partial x}\right) dx,$$

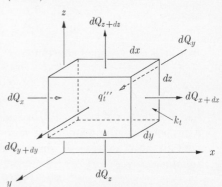

Fig. 1–2. General heat conduction through differential element of nonuniform thermal conductivity and generating nonuniform heat.

whereby

$$dQ_{x+dx} = -dydz\left[k_t\frac{\partial t_x}{\partial x} + \frac{\partial}{\partial x}\left(k_t\frac{\partial t}{\partial x}\right)dx\right]d\theta,$$

and in like manner for analogous conduction terms in the y- and z-directions. The total quantity of heat which goes to increasing the internal energy of the volume element is given by (1–4) as

$$dE = Cwdxdydz\frac{\partial t}{\partial \theta}d\theta,$$

and evidently the total heat dQ_g generated in the volume element is

$$dQ_g = q_t'''Vd\theta = q_t'''dxdydzd\theta.$$

The eight heat components must now be combined in such a way that the total energy is conserved. This is to say that

$$dQ_x + dQ_y + dQ_z + dQ_g = dQ_{x+dx} + dQ_{y+dy} + dQ_{z+dz} + dE,$$

or finally,

$$\frac{\partial}{\partial x}\left(k_t\frac{\partial t}{\partial x}\right) + \frac{\partial}{\partial y}\left(k_t\frac{\partial t}{\partial y}\right) + \frac{\partial}{\partial z}\left(k_t\frac{\partial t}{\partial z}\right) + q_t''' = Cw\frac{\partial t}{\partial \theta}. \tag{1–5}$$

The most general partial-differential equation for heat conduction is of this same form but with k_t, C, w, and q_t''' replaced by $k(x,y,z,t)$, $C(x,y,z,t)$, $w(x,y,z,t)$, and $q'''(x,y,z,t,\theta)$, which includes spatial and time as well as temperature dependence. On the other hand, (1–5) does include the majority of special cases having practical interest. For example, if the thermal conductivity of the system is uniform, then by (1–5) the temperature field $t(x,y,z,\theta)$ must satisfy the *general heat-conduction equation*

$$\frac{\partial^2 t}{\partial x^2} + \frac{\partial^2 t}{\partial y^2} + \frac{\partial^2 t}{\partial z^2} + \frac{q_t'''}{k} = \frac{1}{\alpha}\frac{\partial t}{\partial \theta}, \tag{1–6}$$

in which the grouped constant

$$\alpha = \frac{k}{Cw} \tag{1–7}$$

has dimensions of $|\alpha| = \text{ft}^2/\text{hr}$ and is referred to as the *thermal diffusivity*, a property of the conducting material. Further, if the system does not contain heat sources or sinks, then $t(x,y,z,\theta)$ must satisfy the *Fourier equation*

$$\frac{\partial^2 t}{\partial x^2} + \frac{\partial^2 t}{\partial y^2} + \frac{\partial^2 t}{\partial z^2} = \frac{1}{\alpha}\frac{\partial t}{\partial \theta}, \tag{1–8}$$

or if sources or sinks are present but the temperature is steady, then $t(x,y,z)$ must satisfy the *Poisson equation*

$$\frac{\partial^2 t}{\partial x^2} + \frac{\partial^2 t}{\partial y^2} + \frac{\partial^2 t}{\partial z^2} + \frac{q_t'''}{k} = 0. \tag{1–9}$$

Finally, for steady conduction in systems free of sources and sinks, $t(x,y,z)$ must satisfy the *Laplace equation*

$$\frac{\partial^2 t}{\partial x^2} + \frac{\partial^2 t}{\partial y^2} + \frac{\partial^2 t}{\partial z^2} = 0. \tag{1–10}$$

Particular solutions of these general partial-differential equations and still others in one form or another will constitute the principal developments in Chapters 2, 4, 6, 8, 9, 10, and 11. Similar developments for analogous equations expressed in terms of finite differences are considered in Chapters 7 and 12.

1–4 Change of coordinates. Physical systems having either cylindrical or spherical geometry are most conveniently handled by a suitable change of independent variables. In this respect we need to consider the transformation of (1–8) from a system of rectangular coordinates to systems of cylindrical and spherical coordinates, as in Fig. 1–3.

Cylindrical coordinates. The systems of rectangular and cylindrical coordinates are connected by the relations (Fig. 1–3a) $x = r \cos \varphi$, $y = r \sin \varphi$, and $z = z$, and the transformation from the former to the latter involves differentiation of the composite function $t = t(r,\varphi)$, where both r and φ are functions of x and y. For the first derivatives, we have

$$\frac{\partial t}{\partial x} = \frac{\partial t}{\partial r}\frac{\partial r}{\partial x} + \frac{\partial t}{\partial \varphi}\frac{\partial \varphi}{\partial x},$$

$$\frac{\partial t}{\partial y} = \frac{\partial t}{\partial r}\frac{\partial r}{\partial y} + \frac{\partial t}{\partial \varphi}\frac{\partial \varphi}{\partial y},$$

and, by the same rule, for the second derivatives,

$$\frac{\partial^2 t}{\partial x^2} = \frac{\partial t}{\partial r}\frac{\partial^2 r}{\partial x^2} + \frac{\partial^2 t}{\partial r^2}\left(\frac{\partial r}{\partial x}\right)^2 + 2\frac{\partial^2 t}{\partial r \partial \varphi}\frac{\partial r}{\partial x}\frac{\partial \varphi}{\partial x} + \frac{\partial^2 t}{\partial \varphi^2}\left(\frac{\partial \varphi}{\partial x}\right)^2 + \frac{\partial t}{\partial \varphi}\frac{\partial^2 \varphi}{\partial x^2},$$

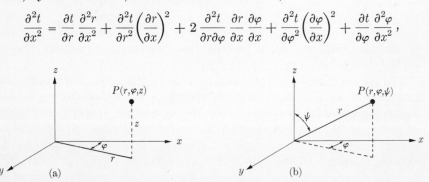

Fig. 1–3. Cylindrical and spherical coordinates.

$$\frac{\partial^2 t}{\partial y^2} = \frac{\partial t}{\partial r}\frac{\partial^2 r}{\partial y^2} + \frac{\partial^2 t}{\partial r^2}\left(\frac{\partial r}{\partial y}\right)^2 + 2\frac{\partial^2 t}{\partial r \partial \varphi}\frac{\partial r}{\partial y}\frac{\partial \varphi}{\partial y} + \frac{\partial^2 t}{\partial \varphi^2}\left(\frac{\partial \varphi}{\partial y}\right)^2 + \frac{\partial t}{\partial \varphi}\frac{\partial^2 \varphi}{\partial y^2}.$$

But evidently $\partial r/\partial x = \cos \varphi$, $\partial^2 r/\partial x^2 = \sin^2 \varphi/r$, $\partial r/\partial y = \sin \varphi$, $\partial^2 r/\partial y^2 = \cos^2 \varphi/r$, $\partial \varphi/\partial x = -\sin \varphi/r$, $\partial^2 \varphi/\partial x^2 = 2 \cos \varphi \sin \varphi$, $\partial \varphi/\partial y = \cos \varphi/r$, and $\partial^2 \varphi/\partial y^2 = -2 \cos \varphi \sin \varphi$, whereby

$$\frac{\partial^2 t}{\partial x^2} = \frac{\partial t}{\partial r}\frac{\sin^2 \varphi}{r} + \frac{\partial^2 t}{\partial r^2}\cos^2 \varphi - 2\frac{\partial^2 t}{\partial r \partial \varphi}\frac{\cos \varphi \sin \varphi}{r} + \frac{\partial^2 t}{\partial \varphi^2}\frac{\sin^2 \varphi}{r^2}$$
$$+ 2\frac{\partial t}{\partial \varphi}\cos \varphi \sin \varphi,$$

$$\frac{\partial^2 t}{\partial y^2} = \frac{\partial t}{\partial r}\frac{\cos^2 \varphi}{r} + \frac{\partial^2 t}{\partial r^2}\sin^2 \varphi + 2\frac{\partial^2 t}{\partial r \partial \varphi}\frac{\cos \varphi \sin \varphi}{r} + \frac{\partial^2 t}{\partial \varphi^2}\frac{\cos^2 \varphi}{r^2}$$
$$- 2\frac{\partial t}{\partial \varphi}\cos \varphi \sin \varphi.$$

Adding these second partial derivatives and using the identity $\sin^2 \varphi + \cos^2 \varphi = 1$, we have

$$\frac{\partial^2 t}{\partial x^2} + \frac{\partial^2 t}{\partial y^2} = \frac{\partial^2 t}{\partial r^2} + \frac{1}{r}\frac{\partial t}{\partial r} + \frac{1}{r^2}\frac{\partial^2 t}{\partial \varphi^2},$$

and therefore the corresponding cylindrical form of (1–8) reads

$$\frac{\partial^2 t}{\partial r^2} + \frac{1}{r}\frac{\partial t}{\partial r} + \frac{1}{r^2}\frac{\partial^2 t}{\partial \varphi^2} + \frac{\partial^2 t}{\partial z^2} = \frac{1}{\alpha}\frac{\partial t}{\partial \theta}. \tag{1–11}$$

Spherical coordinates. The systems of rectangular and spherical coordinates are connected by the relations (Fig. 1–3b) $x = r \sin \psi \cos \varphi$, $y = r \sin \psi \sin \varphi$, and $z = r \cos \psi$. By following a procedure identical to that used in the cylindrical transformation, we arrive at the corresponding spherical form of (1–8), which reads

$$\frac{1}{r}\frac{\partial^2}{\partial r^2}(rt) + \frac{1}{r^2 \sin \psi}\frac{\partial}{\partial \psi}\left(\sin \psi \frac{\partial t}{\partial \psi}\right) + \frac{1}{r^2 \sin^2 \psi}\frac{\partial^2 t}{\partial \varphi^2} = \frac{1}{\alpha}\frac{\partial t}{\partial \theta}. \tag{1–12}$$

If the temperature field in question has "azimuthal symmetry," then $\partial^2 t/\partial \varphi^2 = 0$ in either (1–11) or (1–12).

The partial-differential equations of Articles 1–3 and 1–4 represent the first step in an analytical solution wherewith the temperature gradient can be computed at any point in a conducting system. In a certain number of problems the heat flow through the system is of chief interest, and in general this calculation must always be preceded by an evaluation of the existing temperature field. In short, our task is to *select or derive the differential equation which the temperature field must satisfy, and then arrive by formal methods of integration at a particular solution or combination of particular solutions which satisfies the initial and boundary conditions imposed by the special circumstances of the problem itself.*

It is to be understood that by an *initial condition* we mean the temperature state of the system at the instant taken as the time coordinate $\theta = 0$. A *boundary condition*, on the other hand, is a description of surface conditions at any time $\theta = \theta$. Thus for a system initially at a uniform temperature t_i throughout, the initial condition is expressed as $\{t = t_i \text{ at } \theta = 0\}$. Boundary conditions are of various types: for a system having a uniform boundary temperature t_b, the *isothermal* boundary condition is $\{t = t_b \text{ at } x = b\}$; if the system is insulated against external heat exchange, then the *adiabatic* boundary condition becomes $\{\partial t/\partial x = 0 \text{ at } x = b\}$; and so on.

EXAMPLE 1–1. Derive solutions for the temperature distribution through the wall of a long hollow cylinder and hollow sphere operating with steady and uniform surface temperatures t_1 on the inner surface r_1, and t_2 on the outer surface r_2.

Solution. With steady and uniform surface temperatures, $\partial t/\partial\theta = 0$ and $\partial^2 t/\partial\varphi^2 = 0$ within the cylinder, and in addition $\partial^2 t/\partial z^2 = 0$ because the tube is long. Then by (1–11), the cylinder temperature must depend only on r and satisfy the total differential equation

$$\frac{d^2 t}{dr^2} + \frac{1}{r}\frac{dt}{dr} = 0.$$

By substituting $u = dt/dr$, separating variables, and integrating twice, we find the general solution of this differential equation to be

$$t = C_1 \ln r + C_2,$$

where the constants of integration C_1 and C_2 are to be evaluated by the boundary conditions that $t = t_1$ at $r = r_1$ and $t = t_2$ at $r = r_2$. This gives the particular solution for the dimensionless temperature distribution as

$$\frac{t - t_1}{t_2 - t_1} = \frac{\ln (r/r_1)}{\ln (r_2/r_1)}, \quad (r_1 \le r \le r_2). \tag{1–13}$$

In the case of a hollow sphere with steady and uniform surface temperatures, t again depends only on r, so that by (1–12),

$$\frac{1}{r}\frac{d^2}{dr^2}(rt) = \frac{d^2 t}{dr^2} + \frac{2}{r}\frac{dt}{dr} = 0.$$

The general solution of this total differential equation is found to be

$$t = \frac{C_1}{r} + C_2,$$

and from this follows the particular solution for the dimensionless temperature distribution as

$$\frac{t - t_1}{t_2 - t_1} = \frac{(1 - r_1/r)}{(1 - r_1/r_2)}, \quad (r_1 \le r \le r_2). \tag{1–14}$$

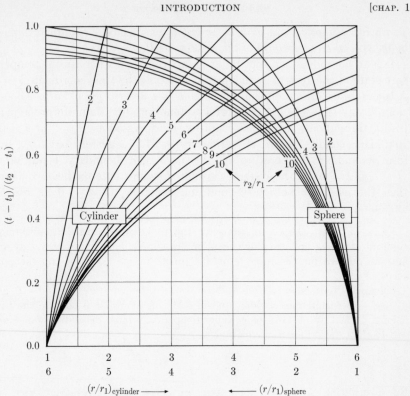

Fig. 1–4.   Temperature uniformity in hollow cylinders and spheres.

The temperature-difference ratio $(t - t_1)/(t_2 - t_1)$ is referred to as the *temperature uniformity*. By comparing the two solutions (1–13) and (1–14) in Fig. 1–4, we see that hollow cylinders have a generally higher temperature uniformity than do hollow spheres. This is important from the standpoint of *thermal stresses*.

1–5 Thermal stresses in elastic structures. The reader is already familiar with a large class of practical problems for which complete solutions are represented by a calculation of the temperature field and heat flow. It is well to point out here, however, that these calculations are not always an end in themselves, but rather that such information is also required for the calculation of thermal stresses in problems of applied mechanics. Thus if a solid structure is constrained so that it cannot freely expand or contract, it will be subject to thermal stressing if either heated or cooled. If the structure is not constrained, then thermal stresses may still result from the nonuniform temperature field within the structure; whether this temperature field is steady or transient, in both cases the elements of the structure do not expand uniformly and mutual interference gives rise to thermal stressing.

As an illustration, the problem of determining the distribution of stress in the cross section of a long tube has a general solution which cannot be carried to a particular solution until the nonuniform temperature profile $t(r)$ is first obtained as in Example 1–1. Of more familiar importance, the modern nuclear reactor represents a structure which is subject to extremely high thermal stresses, and here again the necessary prediction of such stresses must always rely on knowledge of the existing temperature field.

THERMAL PROPERTIES

In the analysis of conduction heat transfer the accuracy of analytical results can be seriously jeopardized by incomplete knowledge of the thermal properties of the system. For this reason it is important to have some feeling for the physical significance and variation of these properties, for the methods by which they are experimentally determined, and the limitations of these measurements.

1–6 Thermal conductivity. Thermal conductivity is a specific property of conducting material which has been defined by (1–2) for a homogeneous solid as the quantity of heat conducted across a unit area normal to the flow path in unit time and for unit temperature gradient along the flow The conductivity is an inverse measure of resistance to heat flow in much the same way as electrical conductivity is inversely proportional to electrical resistivity. For a given conducting area A and flow-path length L, this *internal thermal resistance* is

$$R = \frac{1}{k}\,(L/A),\qquad(1\text{–}15)$$

and the reciprocal of R is correctly referred to as the *internal thermal conductance*

$$K_i = k(A/L),\qquad(1\text{–}16)$$

Measurement. Experimental measurements of thermal conductivities can be accomplished by a variety of methods, all based on the observation of the temperature gradient across a given area of the material conducting

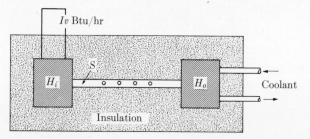

Fig. 1–5. Thermal conductivity by Searle's method.

heat at a known rate.   Each of these methods has certain unique limitations, and the choice of one over another is governed largely by the physical structure of the material in question, by the general temperature level at which the conductivity is to be measured, and by whether the material is a good or poor conductor.   For example, if the specimen is a relatively high-conductivity metal, then k for moderate temperature levels can be measured with simple apparatus but with only marginal precision by the *Searle method*, shown schematically in Fig. 1–5.   By Searle's method a known rate of heat is conducted through a specimen S of the material in the form of a rod of cross-sectional area A placed between an electric heat source H_i generating heat in amount $q = Iv$ Btu/hr, where I is the source current and v the source voltage, and a cooling-fluid heat sink H_0.   The entire assembly is embedded in a low-conductivity insulation such as hair felt, silica aerogel, or powdered Santocel in order to minimize lateral heat leakage from the exposed surface of the specimen and thus ensure a more nearly constant temperature gradient throughout the length of rod.   After a sufficient time has elapsed to establish steady conduction, temperatures at a number of stations along the rod are recorded by thermocouples, and this gives the average linear temperature gradient $\Delta t/\Delta x$.   The average value of k is then computed directly from q, A, and $\Delta t/\Delta x$ as in (1–2).

In measuring the thermal conductivity of poor conductors, the specimens are taken in the form of sheets in order that the heat-flow path be short and the conducting area large, i.e., to increase the conductance (1–16).   Here again a good deal of caution must be taken in order to reduce heat leakage, which is the principal source of error.

The most accurate method in this respect, and one which has been standardized by the ASTM and used by such research and testing organiza-

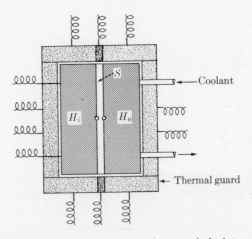

Fig. 1–6.   Thermal conductivity by guarded-plate method.

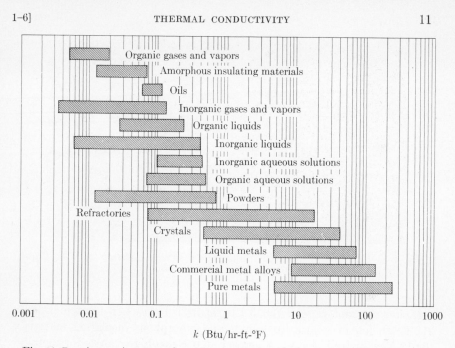

Fig. 1–7. Approximate order of magnitude of thermal conductivity for various substances.

tions as the National Bureau of Standards, is the so-called *guarded-plate method*, illustrated schematically in Fig. 1–6. By this method electrically heated thermal guards are placed adjacent to the exposed surface of the source H_i, specimen S, and sink H_0. These thermal guard plates are independently maintained at the same temperature as the adjacent surfaces, so that ideally no heat leakage occurs from source, sink, or specimen boundaries. This ensures that q from the source used in the computation of k for the specimen is equal to and not less than that actually passing through S.

A fairly complete outline of many other available methods for conductivity measurements is given by Worthing and Halliday (1),* and the reader is referred to Wilkes (2) for a description of more recent techniques developed in the Heat Measurements Laboratory of M.I.T.

Variation. An examination of Fig. 1–7 reveals that the numerical values of thermal conductivity vary over a large range, depending on the chemical *composition*, the physical *structure*, and the *state* of the substance in question. Crystalline materials, for example, exhibit high conductivities at low temperatures, while for gases of low density the conductivity may approach zero. In general, the sequence is from lowest values of k for inorganic and

———————
*Arabic numbers in parentheses refer to similarly numbered references at the end of each chapter.

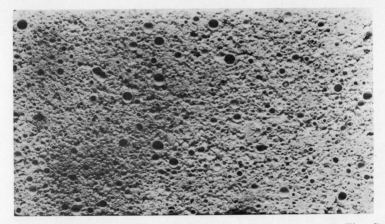

Fig. 1–8.   Refractory material of high porosity.   (*Courtesy of The Carbo-rundum Company*)

organic gases and vapors (0.005 Btu/hr-ft-°F for carbon tetrachloride at 212°F) to higher values for liquids and amorphous insulating materials (0.012 Btu/hr-ft-°F for silica aerogel at 0°F) to high values for metallic substances in the pure state (241 Btu/hr-ft-°F for silver at 32°F).

Heat conduction in gases and vapors is largely a matter of molecular diffusion of kinetic energy, so that low conductivities can be expected by the simple logic of a density effect.   In contrast to this, theory proposes that heat propagation in liquids is associated with a type of longitudinal vibration similar to the mechanism of sound propagation.   This theory also suggests an explanation for the high conductivity of many crystalline substances, which are favored in this respect by their molecular structure.

The variation in thermal conductivity for different nonhomogeneous materials is explained on the basis of a *porosity effect*.   For instance, in cellular materials such as common rock-wool insulation the conductivity of the homogeneous rock material is substantially higher than that of the wool, with its multiple air spaces of relatively low conductivity.   Another example of this is the modern refractory Alfrax BI, an electrically fused aluminum oxide of high porosity, as seen in Fig. 1–8.   In addition to the porosity or apparent density effect, the configuration and geometry of these air cells must be considered.   Materials having well-defined cellular porosity exhibit better insulating characteristics than materials with the same apparent density but with extruded air cells in which heat is also propagated by free convection.

In addition to these effects, the thermal conductivity of a solid is also subject to several other common nonuniformities.   Thus in the case of metals the influence of impurities is to change the conductivity from that in the pure state, and evidently in the case of porous materials the conductivity can be expected to change substantially if exposed to atmospheric humidity. Another nonuniformity which is common to grained materials is the *anisotropic* property of different conductivities in different directions. As a matter of fact, the thermal conductivity of many substances is sensitive to such a large number of effects that for a given material it is often necessary to resort to a direct experimental measurement of k rather than refer to published data.

Temperature dependency. The thermal conductivity of many substances has a marked dependence on local temperature. In a large number of the problems to be considered in later chapters, we disregard this nonuniformity because of the analytical difficulties of taking it into account in an exact solution. This is permissible if the temperature dependency is not severe, and/or if the temperature range under consideration is not large.

As an approximation in cases of large temperature ranges the conductivity is considered to vary linearly with temperature (as it does for many solids), so that an arithmetic-mean conductivity can be selected by interpolating between available values at the extremes of the expected temperature range. If k_t does not vary linearly with temperature, then a mean conductivity between t_1 and t_2 is determined by

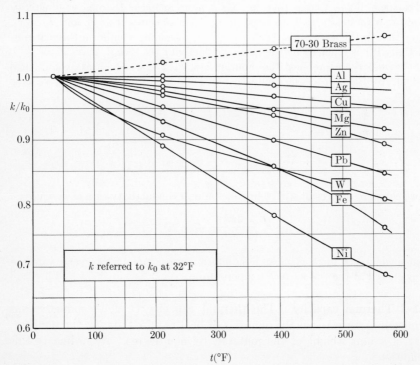

Fig. 1–9. Temperature dependency of thermal conductivity for some pure metals.

$$k = \frac{1}{t_2 - t_1} \int_{t_1}^{t_2} k_t dt, \tag{1–17}$$

providing the nonlinear function k_t is at hand. In some cases this function may take the form $k_t = k_0(1 \pm at \pm bt^2 \pm \cdots)$, while for most practical situations the nonuniformity can be expressed without substantial error by the linear function

$$k_t = k_0(1 \pm \beta_0 t), \tag{1–18}$$

where k_0 is the known conductivity at the reference temperature t_0.

In general, the temperature coefficient of thermal conductivity β_0 is negative for the pure homogeneous metals, while for metallic alloys β_0 becomes positive, as shown in Fig. 1–9. For a few ferrous metals, binary alloys, and even liquids, the conductivity increases with temperature in the lower range and then commences to fall off in the higher temperature range, so that an extrapolation of values may not be permitted even though a linear function is assumed. This is the case with ordinary water.

EXAMPLE 1–2. A long tube having a positive linear thermal conductivity operates with steady and uniform surface temperatures t_1 at r_1 and t_2 at r_2. Show that in this case q can be computed by assuming a uniform thermal conductivity if k is replaced by the mean conductivity $(k_{t_1} + k_{t_2})/2$.

Solution. By expressing the Fourier law (1–2) in cylindrical coordinates and substituting $2\pi r$ for the conducting area and $k_t = k_0(1 + \beta_0 t)$ for k, we have

$$q \int_{r_1}^{r_2} \frac{1}{r} dr = 2\pi k_0 \int_{t_2}^{t_1} (1 + \beta_0 t) dt,$$

whereby

$$q = \frac{2\pi}{\ln (r_2/r_1)} k_0 \left[1 + \frac{\beta_0}{2} (t_1 + t_2) \right] (t_1 - t_2).$$

If we compare this result with q for the uniform conductivity case as given by

$$q = \frac{2\pi k}{\ln (r_2/r_1)} (t_1 - t_2),$$

then evidently k for the linear nonuniform case is simply the mean value of k_t evaluated at the two surface temperatures.

1–7 Thermal capacity. The thermal capacity C of a conductor was defined in Article 1–2 as the quantity of heat required to raise the temperature of a unit weight of the material by one degree. According to this definition,

$$C = \frac{Q}{wV \Delta t}. \tag{1–19}$$

Again, a variety of methods are available for the precise measurement of constant-pressure thermal capacities. One common procedure is to drop a specimen at a known temperature into a calorimeter of predetermined thermal capacity containing water at a known temperature and of predetermined weight. The unknown thermal capacity of the specimen is then computed from a heat balance between the heat gained

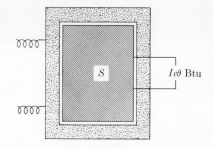

Fig. 1–10. Thermal capacity by guarded-plate method.

by the water and calorimeter and that gained by the specimen. Here again unaccounted-for heat losses represent a source of serious error.

The guarded-plate method of Article 1–6 can also be used with slight modification as a direct and accurate means of measuring thermal capacities. In this case the guarded specimen S (Fig. 1–10) is heated directly by an electric source supplying $Q = Iv\theta$ Btu's in θ hours of heating time. The observed change in temperature of the specimen during this time interval is then identified with the Δt in (1–19).

The thermal capacity of many solids is essentially independent of temperature. A good example of this is the aforementioned Alfrax BI refractory having a thermal capacity of $C = 0.20$ Btu/lb-°F between 32 and 1500°F. If a significant temperature nonuniformity exists, then a mean capacity is determined from C_t, as in (1–17). On the other hand, C_t is usually linear, an example being Carbofrax, a silicon carbide refractory for which $C_t = 0.197(1 + 0.000353t)$.

1–8 Thermal diffusivity. The properties making up the thermal diffusivity (1–7) suggest an interpretation for this derived property in terms of *heating time*. In a transient heating process the thermal capacity of the conducting material dictates the quantity of heat absorbed and the thermal conductivity of the conducting material sets the rate of this heat addition. The reciprocal of the diffusivity, $1/\alpha = \text{hr/ft}^2$, is then a measure of the time required to heat this material to some required temperature level, and evidently this time is directly proportional to the square of the conducting path length. Thus the ratio of heating times for two materials of the same thickness will be inversely proportional to their respective diffusivities, $\Delta\theta_1/\Delta\theta_2 = \alpha_2/\alpha_1$, and the ratio of heating times for two materials of the same diffusivity will be directly proportional to the square of their respective thicknesses, $\Delta\theta_1/\Delta\theta_2 = L_1^2/L_2^2$.

Values of the diffusivity for various materials can either be measured directly or computed from experimentally determined values of k, C, and w.

TABLE 1–2

THERMAL PROPERTIES OF PURE METALS AT 32°F

Metal	w (lb/ft³)	k (Btu/hr-ft-°F)	C (Btu/lb-°F)	$1/\alpha$ (hr/ft²)
Aluminum	(169)	117	0.181	0.262
Copper	(558)	224	0.092	0.230
Iron	(492)	36	0.106	1.280
Lead	(710)	20	0.031	1.072
Magnesium	(109)	89	0.242	0.295
Nickel	(557)	34	0.105	1.733
Silver	(660)	241	0.056	0.153
Tin	(457)	38	0.054	0.657
Tungsten	(1210)	92	0.032	0.423
Zinc	(446)	65	0.092	0.628

In Table 1–2 we compare the magnitude of the thermal conductivity, thermal capacity, and reciprocal thermal diffusivity for a number of pure metals at the same temperature.*

1–9 Surface conductance. An analysis of internal conduction considers not only the thermal resistance of the body itself (Article 1–6), but the separate resistance at the surface of the body as well. We examine briefly the control of this thermal resistance to boundary heat exchange by the transport process of thermal convection, where heat is conveyed in part by the movement of a fluid stream and in part by conduction within the fluid.

Consider a plane wall losing heat by free or forced convection to an ambient gas. In a plane normal to the wall face, the temperature of the gas varies from a high value of the face temperature at the wall, t_w, to the lower free-stream temperature of the gas, t_g, at some distance from the wall. This temperature distribution in the ambient gas can be seen experimentally by either Schlieren or interference photography. Figure 1–11 is an example of the latter. The interference method exhibits shifts in optical interference lines which are proportional to the density variation from point to point in the gas, and thus also proportional to the temperature variation.

By an examination of Fig. 1–11 we see that near the wall face the temperature gradient is nearly uniform, and that the temperature itself becomes uniform only at a considerable distance from the solid surface. According

*The reader is urged to consult Jakob (3) for a more comprehensive discussion of the theory and additional sample data on the thermal property values of gases and vapors, liquids, building and insulating materials, crystalline and refractory materials, and metals and alloys.

to the Langmuir film concept, we
imagine that the entire thermal resistance to heat exchange between wall
and gas is concentrated in a static film
of gas close to the solid surface and
including the region of linear temperature drop. Although the film thickness is not sharply defined, it is approximated by extending the linear
temperature distribution down to the
free-stream fluid temperature, as in
Fig. 1–11. If the temperature gradient were truly uniform all the way
up to the approximated film thickness
δ_g, then the heat conducted through
this film would be given by (1–3) as

$$q = \frac{k_g}{\delta_g} A (t_w - t_g).$$

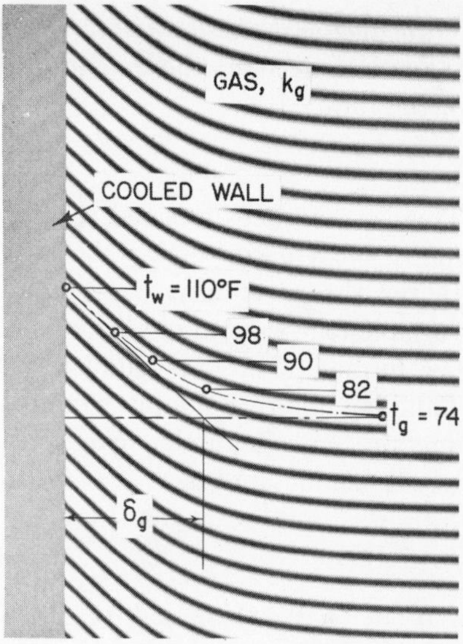

Fig. 1–11. Temperature distribution
in ambient gas for convective-cooling
of a plane vertical wall. (*Interfero-
gram by courtesy of C. D. Coulbert*)

Owing to the difficulty of interpreting and measuring an effective film
thickness, it is usual practice to combine the quotient k_g/δ_g into a single
property h, and therewith express general boundary heat exchange as
simply

$$q = hA (t_1 - t_2), \tag{1–20}$$

where now A is identified as the particular boundary area involved. The
coefficient h has dimensions of $|h| = $ Btu/hr-ft^2-°F and, while generally
known under a variety of names, it will be consistently referred to in this
text as the *unit surface conductance*. In this special way the *surface conductance* itself becomes

$$K_s = hA. \tag{1–21}$$

The unit surface conductance is actually a complicated function of the
thermal, physical, and dynamical properties of the conducting system and
ambient medium. Its evaluation for a given system operating under a
given set of conditions has been the main objective of a vast amount of
theoretical and experimental research effort. The values of h ordinarily
encountered vary over a large range of approximately 100,000-fold, grow-
ing from low values of 0.2 Btu/hr-ft^2-°F for free convection of air across
pipes, to high values of 6500 for liquid metals in pipes, on up to maximum
values of 20,000 for dropwise condensation of steam on plates. For our
present purposes we simply select appropriate values of h as needed.

Conduction Nusselt number. Whenever the conductance of the surface is taken into account there arises a dimensionless *conduction Nusselt number* of the form

$$N_u = h\delta/k. \tag{1-22}$$

This is sometimes referred to as the *Biot number* to distinguish it from a *convection Nusselt number* $N_u = h\delta/k_f$, where k_f is the fluid conductivity. In the theory of heat convection the Nusselt number is the dependent variable (the wanted quantity), while in heat conduction the Nusselt number formed with the conductivity of the body is simply a parameter. Thinking in terms of a plate of area A and thickness δ, we see that the conduction Nusselt number can be interpreted as the ratio of surface to internal conductance as $N_u = h\delta/k = (hA)/(kA/\delta) = K_s/K_i$.

REFERENCES

1. A. G. Worthing and D. Halliday, *Heat.* New York: John Wiley, 1948, pp. 160–198.
2. G. B. Wilkes, *Heat Insulation.* New York: John Wiley, 1950, pp. 36–71.
3. M. Jakob, *Heat Transfer*, Vol. I. New York: John Wiley, 1949, pp. 68–117.

PROBLEMS

1–1. Is the natural process of heat conduction thermodynamically reversible or irreversible? If reversible, give a formal argument including the special conditions under which one might expect it to be irreversible, and if irreversible give a formal argument including the special conditions under which one might expect it to be reversible.

1–2. A plane wall of infinite dimensions in the y- and z-directions and of thickness L is of uniform thermal conductivity k and generates uniform heat q'''. The wall faces at $x = 0$ and L are maintained at steady and uniform temperatures t_1 and t_2 respectively. (a) Show by derivation that the solution for the dimensionless temperature *profile* in this wall is given by

$$\frac{t - t_1}{t_2 - t_1} = (1 + \xi)\left(\frac{x}{L}\right) - \xi\left(\frac{x}{L}\right)^2, \quad (0 \le x \le L),$$

where $\xi = q'''L^2/2k(t_2 - t_1)$. (b) Prove that the difference in heat being conducted across faces $x = 0$ and L is equal to the total heat generated (Btu/hr) in the wall. (c) Plot a family of dimensionless temperature profiles in the wall for a unit-increment range of the parameter $\xi = 0$ to 5.

1–3. If the wall face at $x = L$ in problem 1–2 is adiabatic (perfectly insulated), then prove that the difference between the maximum temperature occurring in the wall and the face temperature at $x = 0$ is equal to one-half of the total heat generated divided by the internal thermal conductance of the wall.

1–4. Repeat the proof of Example 1–2 for a hollow sphere.

1–5. In a determination of the unknown uniform thermal conductivity of an insulating material by the guarded-plate method, the 120-volt electric heat source drew 2.5 amp and the measured temperature drop across a $\frac{3}{4}''$ thick specimen of the material in the form of a $15''$ square was $67.2°F$. Show that a large insulating wall of this material of thickness $L = 6''$ would allow 244 Btu/hr for each square foot of face surface to be conducted through it if its isothermal face surfaces were maintained at steady temperatures $t_1 = 100°F$ and $t_2 = 300°F$.

1–6. With reference to problem 1–5, (a) Show that the thermal resistance of the test specimen is $0.066°F$-hr/Btu. (b) If the test specimen were found to be of nonuniform thermal conductivity $k_t = 0.4 \, (1 + 0.0012t + 6 \times 10^{-7}t^2)$ Btu/hr-ft-°F, then show that the insulating wall would have an average thermal conductance of 1.01 Btu/hr-°F for each square foot of face surface.

1–7. The unknown thermal capacity of a material of specific gravity 1.72 is to be determined by the guarded-plate method using a 120-volt electric heat source drawing 10 amp. At the beginning of the heating period the temperature of a 1 ft^3 specimen is recorded as $77°F$, and following 10 min of heating the temperature of the specimen is found to be $116°F$. (a) Show that the thermal capacity of the material is 0.163 Btu/lb-°F. (b) What pure metal would require 15 min and 6 sec of heating time for the same temperature change? (c) If the thermal capacity of the material in (a) were actually nonuniform as $C_t = dQ/wVdt = 0.163(1 + 0.005t)$ Btu/lb-°F, then show that it would take 4070 Btu to raise the temperature of the specimen from $77°F$ to $212°F$.

1–8. The thermal conductivity of the material in (a) of problem 1–7 is 82 Btu/hr-ft-°F. Show that a wall of the metal in (b) would require 38% more time to heat up to some prescribed temperature than a wall of the same thickness but of the material in (a).

1–9. A plane wall in a building is exposed on the inside surface to ambient air at a uniform temperature of $76.3°F$ and on the outside surface to ambient air at $21.2°F$. The unit surface conductances on the inner and outer faces of the wall are known to be 1.6 and 6.4 Btu/hr-ft^2-°F respectively. (a) If a thermocouple registers the inner face temperature as $67.1°F$, then show that the outer face temperature must be $23.5°F$. (b) If a long tube of inner radius $0.8''$ and outer radius $1.5''$ has the same unit surface conductances as the plane wall in (a), then show that the inner and outer surface conductances are 0.67 and 5.02 Btu/hr-°F for each foot length of tube.

1–10. A plane infinite wall of uniform thermal conductivity k and of thickness $2L$ generates uniform heat q'''. The wall is exposed on both face surfaces to an ambient gas at a uniform and steady temperature t_g, and the unit surface conductance at each face is h. Show by derivation that the solution for the dimensionless temperature profile in this wall is given by

$$\frac{2k}{L^2 q'''} \, (t - t_g) = 1 - \left(\frac{x}{L}\right)^2 + \frac{2k}{Lh}, \quad (-L \le x \le L).$$

(Choose the origin of the x-axis at the wall center, and note that one of the boundary conditions requires that the heat gained by the gas be equal to that conducted across the face surfaces.)

CHAPTER 2

STEADY ONE-DIMENSIONAL SYSTEMS

In this chapter we examine a number of elementary systems in which the permanent state of temperature and steady heat flow are functions of a single space coordinate. General systems of composite walls, tubes, and spherical shells are considered, along with the particular problem of one-dimensional heat transfer in conduction-cooled turbine blades.

2–1 Composite structures. As an extension of the simple single-wall structures dealt with in Example 1–1, we now consider *composite* structures made up of two or more layers of different materials. These systems are of considerable practical interest, and are classified as either a *series* composite structure such as an insulated wall, tube, or sphere, or as a *parallel* composite structure as found, for example, in a wall with "through metal" (bolts, ribs, and the like). In both cases the system is exposed to an external heat source and sink, so that free-face surface temperatures are unknown, and this means that surface resistances must be accounted for as well as the individual resistances within the structure itself.

In the analysis of composite systems it is generally assumed (a) that the temperature distribution is steady and one-dimensional, (b) that all materials are of uniform thermal conductivity and free of internal heat sources and sinks, and (c) that all interface contact resistances are negligible. To assume a steady and one-dimensional temperature profile within the structure implies that all unit surface conductances and ambient temperatures are uniform as well.

The subject of *thermal contacts* is avoided here for simplicity only. It is well to keep in mind, however, that these interface contact resistances may actually represent an appreciable fraction of the total over-all fluid-to-fluid resistance.

The mechanism of heat transfer across a solid-to-solid thermal contact is difficult to describe analytically. The process is complicated by a dependence on such things as the unit pressure and total force exerted on the contacting surfaces, the physical nature of the contact bond (type of finish as it affects the type and distribution of surface irregularities, hardness, the possibility of plastic flow, etc.), the quantity and physical properties of the fluid trapped between the contacting surfaces, the mean temperature of the interface, and so on. Experimental data for such wet contact joints indicate that at low pressures the true solid conductance constitutes only a minor part of the total solid-fluid parallel conductance of the joint, while at high contact pressures the reverse is generally true.

Çetinkale and Fishenden (1) describe measurements of the thermal contact conductance for steel, brass, and aluminum surfaces ground to various degrees of roughness, and with air, spindle oil, or glycerol between the contacting surfaces. In these experiments, in which the mean interface temperature was 180°F, the range of joint conductances corresponding to a contact pressure range from 19 to 800 lb/in^2 was from 550 to 12,500 Btu/hr-ft^2-°F. Reasonable agreement was also obtained between these experimental results and an approximate analytical solution for which the surface roughness, the thermal conductivities of the metal and fluid, the applied pressure, the hardness of the softer metal, and the mean contact temperature must be known.

2–2 Series composite wall. Consider a simple series wall made up of two homogeneous materials whose mean thermal conductivities are k_1 and k_2, as in Fig. 2–1. There is a continuous heat exchange between the gas heat source g at a mean temperature t_g and the gas heat sink G at a mean temperature t_G, and if the steady state is assumed, then this heat energy q must be conserved through each layer of the same normal conducting area A. This is expressed analytically by (1–3) for the internal heat conduction and (1–20) for the surface heat exchange as

$$q = h_g A (t_g - t_\mathrm{I}) = k_1 \frac{A}{L_1} (t_\mathrm{I} - t_\mathrm{II}) = k_2 \frac{A}{L_2} (t_\mathrm{II} - t_\mathrm{III}) = h_G A (t_\mathrm{III} - t_G).$$

By rearranging each of these four equations as functions of the temperature-difference terms and adding, we have $(t_g - t_G) = (q/A)(1/h_g + L_1/k_1 + L_2/k_2 + 1/h_G)$, and this result can be reinterpreted in terms of internal and surface resistances according to (1–15) and the reciprocal of (1–21) as

$$q = \frac{t_g - t_G}{R_g + R_1 + R_2 + R_G}. \tag{2–1}$$

Thus, *in a series structure the separate resistances are to be added.*

For purposes of computation the R's can be based on one square foot of conducting area as long as we remember that q is then the number of Btu/hr per square foot of face surface. It is generally more convenient, however, to replace (2–1) with

$$q = UA(t_g - t_G), \tag{2–2}$$

in which the *thermal transmittance* U is evidently given by

$$U = 1/(1/h_g + L_1/k_1 + L_2/k_2 + 1/h_G). \tag{2–3}$$

The denominator in (2–3) represents the sum of the *thermal resistivities.*

If it is required to determine the temperature of any interface surface in the composite wall, successive equations must be written for the temperature drop through each layer up to and including the surface in question.

Thus, for the interface II in Fig. 2–1,

$$t_{II} - t_I = -q(L_1/k_1 A).$$

But t_I is known only as $t_I = t_g - q/h_g A$, so that

$$t_{II} = t_g - \frac{q}{A} (1/h_g + L_1/k_1).$$

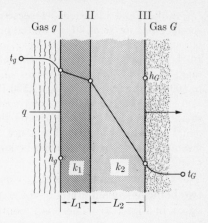

Fig. 2–1. Steady one-dimensional heat transfer through a series composite wall.

EXAMPLE 2–1. A steam-to-liquid heat-exchanger surface of 500 in² face area is constructed of $\frac{1}{4}''$ nickel with a $\frac{3}{64}''$ plating of copper on the steam side. The resistivity of a water-scale deposit on the steam side is estimated to be 0.01 hr-ft²-°F/Btu, and the steam- and liquid-side unit surface conductances are known to be 961 and 108 Btu/hr-ft²-°F respectively. If the heating steam is at 231°F and the heated liquid at 166°F, determine (a) the over-all steam-to-liquid heat exchange, (b) the temperature drop across the scale deposit, and (c) the temperature at the copper-nickel interface.

Solution. (a) By (2–3) the transmittance for this system (Table 1–2) becomes

$$U = \frac{1}{\dfrac{1}{961} + 0.01 + \dfrac{3/64}{12 \times 224} + \dfrac{1/4}{12 \times 34} + \dfrac{1}{108}}$$

$$= \frac{1}{0.00104 + 0.01 + 0.00002 + 0.00061 + 0.00926} = 47.8,$$

so that by (2–2) the over-all heat exchange is

$$q = 47.8 \times \frac{500}{144} (231 - 166) = 10{,}790 \text{ Btu/hr.}$$

(b) Knowing the resistivity of the scale deposit, we have for the temperature drop across it

$$\Delta t_s = 10{,}790 \left(\frac{0.01}{500/144} \right) = 31.1°F.$$

(c) Lastly, the copper-nickel interface temperature is computed to be

$$t_{cn} = 231 - \frac{10{,}790}{500/144} (0.00104 + 0.01 + 0.00002) = 196.6°F,$$

and checked as

$$t_{cn} = 166 + \frac{10{,}790}{500/144} (0.00926 + 0.00061) = 196.6°F.$$

The required area for a series-flow heat-exchange surface designed to operate between a given external source-sink temperature difference is determined by the transmittance, and in turn this transmittance is a function of the separate thermal resistivities of the system. In the case of a single wall we can combine the unit surface conductances h_g and h_G into what is called a *combined surface transmittance* $U_s = 1/(1/h_g + 1/h_G)$. Then the over-all transmittance for this system will be $U = 1/(1/U_s + L_1/k_1)$. Here we see that in the event of a very low surface transmittance, changing either the thickness or thermal conductivity of the wall material will have little effect on the over-all transmittance. In the event of a very high surface transmittance, the reverse is true; i.e., in this case the surface resistance no longer controls the over-all resistance.

The isolated effect of wall thickness, thermal conductivity, and surface transmittance is suggested in Fig. 2–2 for the most common commercial metals, listed in descending order of their conductivities. We see that decreasing the wall thickness increases the over-all transmittance (decreasing the required surface area A), but that this effect is much less

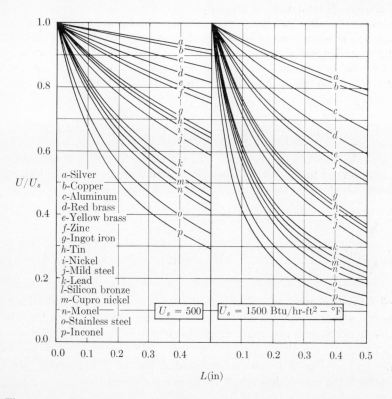

Fig. 2–2. Over-all heat transfer through single commercial-metal walls. Effect of thickness, thermal conductivity, and combined surface transmittance.

pronounced for wall materials of high conductivity than for wall materials of low conductivity. Such changes in the system of Example 2–1 would be more or less ineffective, since in that system the over-all transmittance was controlled by the relatively low surface transmittance and high resistivity of the scale deposit. Figure 2–2 also demonstrates that the general effect of increasing surface transmittance is to make the effect of changing wall thickness and conductivity more pronounced.

EXAMPLE 2–2. A large iron furnace with plane walls $L_1 = 1''$ operates full time $\theta = 8760$ hr/yr with inner and outer ambient temperatures of $t_g = 575°F$ and $t_G = 80°F$ respectively, and with an inner unit surface conductance of $h_g = 50$ Btu/hr-ft^2-°F. The furnace is to be insulated on the outer surface with an insulating material of thermal conductivity $k_2 = 0.05$ Btu/hr-ft-°F, for which the original cost plus cost of installation totals $C = \$5/\text{ft}^3$. The annual fixed charge against C (maintenance, interest, depreciation, insurance, and taxes) is to be taken as $C' = 15\%$, and the fuel cost for the furnace is known to be $C'' = 20\not c$ per 10^6 Btu. If the unit surface conductance on the outer insulation face is estimated to be $h_G = 1.6$ Btu/hr-ft^2-°F, then compute the most economical insulation thickness L_{2_e}.

Solution. This is a practical situation where the net saving by insulation is a maximum at some value of insulation thickness beyond which the additional saving by further insulation does not offset the added cost of its application.

Let q_a and q_b represent the furnace heat loss with and without insulation respectively. The net saving, N.S., due to insulating is then

$$\text{N.S.} = (q_b - q_a)\theta C'' - (CL_2)C'$$

$$= \left[q_b - \frac{(t_g - t_G)}{(1/h_g + L_1/k_1 + L_2/k_2 + 1/h_G)} \right]\theta C'' - (CL_2)C'$$

for each square foot of face surface. By equating to zero the first derivative of N.S. with respect to L_2, $d(\text{N.S.})/dL_2 = 0$, we find that the particular insulation thickness for which the net saving is a maximum (Table 1–2) is

$$L_{2_e} = \sqrt{\frac{k_2 \theta C''(t_g - t_G)}{CC'}} - k_2(1/h_g + L_1/k_1 + 1/h_G)$$

$$= \sqrt{\frac{0.05 \times 8760 \times 0.2(575 - 80)}{10^6 \times 5 \times 0.15}} - 0.05\left(\frac{1}{50} + \frac{1}{12 \times 36} + \frac{1}{1.6}\right) = 2.5 \text{ in.}$$

2–3 Graphical method. Temperature profiles in composite-wall structures can also be obtained graphically, and this includes cases for which surface temperatures are unknown, as in Article 2–2.

To develop a graphical method, we note that the broken temperature profile $t(x)$ in Fig. 2–1 can be represented by the linear profile $t(\eta) = C_1\eta + C_2$ if the new independent variable η is defined by

$$\eta = \frac{x}{k},$$

and if we interpret η at any interface station as being the sum of the individual η's through each composite resistance up to the interface in question. Then if $t = t_g$ at $\eta = \eta_g = 0$ and $t = t_G$ at $\eta = \eta_G$, we have

$$\frac{t - t_g}{t_G - t_g} = \frac{\eta}{\eta_G} \cdot \tag{2–4}$$

Now imagine the surface resistivity on each exposed face of the composite wall to be replaced by a "fictitious" composite layer of thickness L_f and thermal conductivity k_f. If the internal resistivity of this fictitious layer is to be the same as the actual surface resistivity, then $k_f/L_f = h$. The coordinate through the fictitious layers becomes $\eta_f = x/hL_f = 1/h$, and through the actual layers $\eta = x/k$.

EXAMPLE 2–3. A plane composite wall is made up of three metals: (1) $\frac{1}{4}''$ lead, (2) $\frac{1}{2}''$ aluminum, and (3) $\frac{1}{4}''$ tin. The lead and tin faces are exposed to ambient gases at $t_g = 400°F$ and $t_G = 200°F$ respectively, and the unit surface conductance on both faces is $h_g = h_G = 1500$ Btu/hr-ft²-°F. Determine graphically the temperature profile in the wall.

Solution. We first plot (2–4) as in Fig. 2–3(a). If $x = 0$ is taken at the outer face of the left-hand fictitious layer representing the surface resistivity $1/h_g$, then the initial η is zero, and the remaining η's are computed (Table 1–2) as

$$\eta_g = 0, \qquad\qquad \eta_{III} = \eta_{II} + \frac{0.50}{12 \times 117} = 0.002064,$$

$$\eta_I = \eta_g + \frac{1}{1500} = 0.000666, \qquad \eta_{IV} = \eta_{III} + \frac{0.25}{12 \times 38} = 0.002612,$$

$$\eta_{II} = \eta_I + \frac{0.25}{12 \times 20} = 0.001708, \qquad \eta_G = \eta_{IV} + \frac{1}{1500} = 0.003278.$$

By computing the ratios η/η_G, locating the corresponding temperatures in Fig. 2–3(a), and then transposing these graphically to the actual wall, we obtain the required broken temperature profile $t(x)$ shown in Fig. 2–3(b).

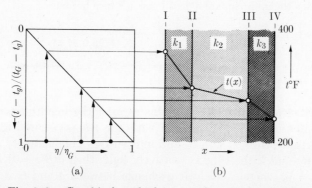

(a)   (b)

Fig. 2–3. Graphical method for a series composite wall.

2–4 Parallel composite wall.

In the case of parallel flow paths the total internal conductance is to be taken as the sum of all internal conductances (1–16) as

$$K_{i_j} = K_{i_1} + K_{i_2} + \cdots,$$

and in this way the *over-all conductance* for the system becomes

$$UA = \frac{1}{1/h_g A + 1/K_{i_j} + 1/h_G A}. \quad (2\text{–}5)$$

It is important to recognize that the result (2–5) is only a crude approximation. Actually the temperature distribution in all parallel structures is at least two dimensional, and for this reason we must assume that all materials in the structure are separated from each other by infinitely thin adiabatic planes.

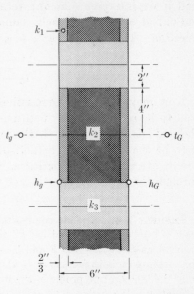

Fig. 2–4.   A parallel composite wall.

EXAMPLE 2–4.   Compute the heat gain through an insulated wall built up as in Fig. 2–4 if mean thermal conductivities are $k_1 = 1.0$, $k_2 = 0.5$, and $k_3 = 1.3$ Btu/hr-ft-°F, unit surface conductances are uniform as $h_g = 1.6$ and $h_G = 76.0$ Btu/hr-ft²-°F, and uniform ambient temperatures are $t_g = 83$ and $t_G = 32$°F.

Solution.   The total internal conductance for each symmetrical section of this parallel composite structure is

$$K_{i_j} = 2\left[1.0\left(\frac{8}{\frac{2}{3}}\right)\right] + 0.5\left(\frac{8}{\frac{1.4}{3}}\right) + 2\left[1.3\left(\frac{2}{6}\right)\right] = 25.7 \text{ Btu/hr-°F};$$

and from this the approximate over-all conductance becomes

$$UA = \frac{1}{(1/1.6 \times 1) + (1/25.7) + (1/76.0 \times 1)} = 1.48.$$

The total heat gain is therefore $q = 1.48(83 - 32) = 75.5$ Btu/hr for each one-foot deep symmetrical section of the wall.

2–5 Series composite tube.

In this case let the longitudinal axis of a hollow composite cylinder coincide with the z-axis, as in Fig. 2–5. If ambient temperatures t_g and t_G and unit surface conductances h_g and h_G are uniform, and if the tube is relatively long, then $\partial t/\partial \varphi = 0$ (Fig. 1–3) and $\partial t/\partial z = 0$, whereby all heat exchange between g and G will be conducted through the tube wall in an essentially radial direction.   This allows

us to apply the one-dimensional
Fourier law (1–2) in analogous cylindrical form

$$q = -kA_r \frac{dt}{dr}, \qquad (2\text{–}6)$$

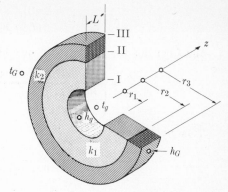

where now (Example 1–2) the conducting area A is a function of the
radius r as $A_r = 2\pi rL$. Then by separating variables in (2–6) and inte-
grating between some t_1 at r_1 and t_2 Fig. 2–5.   A series composite tube.
at r_2, we have

$$q = \frac{2\pi kL}{\ln (r_2/r_1)} (t_1 - t_2). \qquad (2\text{–}7)$$

Application of (2–7) to the particular system of Fig. 2–5 becomes

$$q = 2\pi r_1 Lh_g(t_g - t_{\mathrm{I}}) = \frac{2\pi k_1 L}{\ln (r_2/r_1)} (t_{\mathrm{I}} - t_{\mathrm{II}}) = \frac{2\pi k_2 L}{\ln (r_3/r_2)} (t_{\mathrm{II}} - t_{\mathrm{III}})$$

$$= 2\pi r_3 Lh_G(t_{\mathrm{III}} - t_G),$$

or again, by addition of temperature-difference terms and transposition,

$$q = \frac{2\pi L(t_g - t_G)}{\dfrac{1}{h_g r_1} + \dfrac{\ln (r_2/r_1)}{k_1} + \dfrac{\ln (r_3/r_2)}{k_2} + \dfrac{1}{h_G r_3}}.$$

The thermal transmittance for this structure can be based on any convenient area A, and in practice this is obviously the outer surface area A_3.
Thus, in analogy to (2–2),

$$q = UA_3(t_g - t_G), \qquad (2\text{–}8)$$

and in comparison with (2–3),

$$U = \frac{1}{\dfrac{r_3}{h_g r_1} + \dfrac{r_3}{k_1} \ln \dfrac{r_2}{r_1} + \dfrac{r_3}{k_2} \ln \dfrac{r_3}{r_2} + \dfrac{1}{h_G}}. \qquad (2\text{–}9)$$

EXAMPLE 2–5.   An iron pipe of $\frac{3}{4}''$ inner diameter and with $\frac{1}{2}''$ walls is
covered with a $\frac{1}{8}''$ layer of insulation whose outer surface is exposed to 76°F
ambient air.   The pipe transports a 380°F liquid with an inner unit surface
conductance of 120 Btu/hr-ft²-°F.   What is the thermal transmittance for this
system if a thermocouple embedded halfway through the pipe registers 341°F?
Solution.   The temperature of a point halfway through the pipe is evidently
given by

$$t_{1/2} = t_g - \frac{q}{2\pi L}\left[\frac{1}{h_g r_1} + \frac{1}{k_1}\ln\left(\frac{r_1 + r_2}{2r_1}\right)\right],$$

and from this the net heat exchange between g and G becomes

$$\frac{q}{L} = \frac{6.28(380 - 341)}{\left[\dfrac{8 \times 12}{3 \times 120} + \dfrac{1}{36}\ln\left(\dfrac{\frac{3}{8} + \frac{7}{8}}{2 \times \frac{3}{8}}\right)\right]} = 872 \text{ Btu/hr-ft}.$$

Then by (2–8)

$$U = \frac{q/L}{2\pi r_3(t_g - t_G)} = \frac{872}{6.28\,(\frac{1}{12})(380 - 76)} = 5.5 \text{ Btu/hr-ft}^2\text{-}°\text{F}.$$

2–6 Critical radius. We have seen that the radial heat flow through a tube is inversely proportional to the logarithm of the outer radius, while the heat dissipation from the outer surface is directly proportional to this radius. This dual effect of increasing resistance to radial heat conduction and simultaneous increase in cooling surface area as r increases suggests that for a single-wall tube a particular outer radius exists for which the heat loss or gain is a maximum. It is apparent that the radius ratio r_2/r_1 is also significant. Thus for a fixed but small inner radius r_1, increasing the wall thickness by increasing r_2 will affect the logarithmic term in

$$q = \frac{2\pi L(t_g - t_G)}{\dfrac{1}{h_g r_1} + \dfrac{1}{k_1}\ln\dfrac{r_2}{r_1} + \dfrac{1}{h_G r_2}}$$

more than an equal increase in wall thickness for a tube of larger inner radius.

If we consider r_1 fixed and thereby $q = q(r_2)$, then q will be a maximum at that particular value of r_2 for which

$$\frac{dq}{dr_2} = \frac{-2\pi L(t_g - t_G)(1/k_1 r_2 - 1/h_G r_2^2)}{\left(\dfrac{1}{h_g r_1} + \dfrac{1}{k_1}\ln\dfrac{r_2}{r_1} + \dfrac{1}{h_G r_2}\right)^2} = 0,$$

and from this the *critical outer radius* is found to be

$$(r_2)_c = \frac{k_1}{h_G}. \tag{2–10}$$

These ideas are illustrated quantitatively in Fig. 2–6 for a single-wall tube having a zero inner surface thermal resistivity $1/h_g$. In this case $t_I = t_g$, and the net heat exchange can be represented dimensionlessly by

$$\frac{q}{2\pi k_1 L(t_g - t_G)} = \frac{1}{\ln\,(r_2/r_1) + (k_1/h_G r_1)(r_1/r_2)},$$

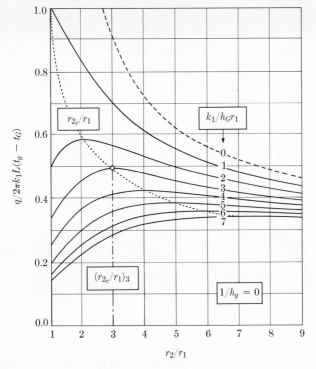

Fig. 2–6. Effect of radius ratio on the heat transfer through single-wall tubes.

with $k_1/h_G r_1$ as a dimensionless parameter. The curve for $k_1/h_G r_1 = 0$ encompasses the case where both inner and outer surface resistivities are zero, in which instance the critical outer radius is infinite, and the curve for $k_1/h_G r_1 = 1$ is a special case for which a critical outer radius occurs only under the fictitious condition of zero wall thickness. We see, as suggested above, that for a given inner radius the magnitude of the critical outer radius increases if either the thermal conductivity of the tube is increased or the outer unit surface conductance is decreased.

The existence of a critical outer radius suggests that under certain realistic conditions, and contrary to what one usually expects, the heat loss from an insulated pipe can actually be decreased by decreasing the insulation thickness. The inverse case is examined in problem 2–7, where the dissipation to ambient air of heat generated within a copper wire is found to increase by increasing the thickness of electrical insulation on the copper conductor. In both situations, $r_2 < r_{2_c}$ originally (Fig. 2–6).

2–7 Effect of nonuniform thermal conductivity. Consider again, as in Example 1–2, the case of a long single-wall tube whose inner and outer surfaces r_1 and r_2 are maintained at uniform temperatures t_1 and t_2. We want to examine the temperature profile in this tube when the thermal conductivity of the wall material varies linearly with local temperature, as in (1–18). In this case $t(r)$ must satisfy (1–5) with $q_t''' = 0 = \partial t/\partial\theta$ and expressed in cylindrical coordinates, as in (1–11), with $\partial^2 t/\partial\varphi^2 = 0 = \partial^2 t/\partial z^2$;

$$\frac{d}{dr}\left(k_t \frac{dt}{dr}\right) + \frac{1}{r}\frac{d}{dr}\,(k_t t) = 0. \tag{2–11}$$

In order to integrate (2–11) we use the *Kirchhoff transformation*, which introduces an auxiliary variable u together with a constant k_c defined by the differential equation

$$k_c \frac{du}{dr} = k_t \frac{dt}{dr}, \tag{2–12}$$

which must in turn be satisfied by the condition that $u = t$ for at least two values of r. In the present case this is fulfilled by

$$u = t_1 \quad \text{at} \quad r = r_1,$$
$$u = t_2 \quad \text{at} \quad r = r_2. \tag{2–13}$$

This is the general Kirchhoff method, which we shall use for cases of non-uniform thermal conductivity, its application being limited to systems in which two isothermal surfaces are present for the boundary conditions on the transformation.

To take advantage of the Kirchhoff method, the differential equation (2–11) must be rederived in terms of (2–12). Identifying the various elements in the heat balance and introducing (2–12), we have

$$q_r = -k_t A_r \frac{dt_r}{dr} = -2\pi r k_c \frac{du}{dr},$$

and (Article 1–3)

$$q_{r+dr} = -k_t A_{r+dr} \frac{d}{dr}\, t_{r+dr} = -2\pi(r+dr)\left[k_t \frac{dt_r}{dr} + \frac{d}{dr}\left(k_t \frac{dt}{dr}\right)dr\right]$$

$$= -2\pi(r+dr)k_c\left(\frac{du}{dr} + \frac{d^2 u}{dr^2}\,dr\right).$$

Then in the steady state, $q_r - q_{r+dr} = 0$, so that

$$\frac{d^2 u}{dr^2} + \frac{1}{r}\frac{du}{dr} = 0. \tag{2–14}$$

The particular solution of (2–14) is known from Example 1–1 to be (1–13), or

$$u = t_1 + (t_2 - t_1) \frac{\ln (r/r_1)}{\ln (r_2/r_1)}. \tag{2-15}$$

The original dependent variable $t = t(u)$ is now retrieved by a semidefinite integration of (2–12). For the case of linearly increasing conductivity,

$$k_c \int_{u=t_1}^{u} du = \int_{t_1}^{t} k_t dt = k_0 \int_{t_1}^{t} (1 + \beta_0 t) dt,$$

whereby

$$\frac{\beta_0}{2} t^2 + t - \left[t_1 + \frac{\beta_0}{2} t_1^2 - \frac{k_c}{k_0} (t_1 - u) \right]. \tag{2-16}$$

The constant k_c is then determined by carrying the above integration through to both limits as

$$k_c \int_{u=t_1}^{t_2} du = k_0 \int_{t_1}^{t_2} (1 + \beta_0 t) dt,$$

such that

$$k_c = k_0 \left[1 + \frac{\beta_0}{2} (t_1 + t_2) \right]. \tag{2-17}$$

By solving the quadratic (2–16) for t and substituting therein the expressions for u and k_c given by (2–15) and (2–17), we obtain the final solution for the temperature profile $t = t(r)$ as*

$$t = \frac{1}{\beta_0} \left\{ (1 + \beta_0 t_1)^2 - [(1 + \beta_0 t_1)^2 - (1 + \beta_0 t_2)^2] \frac{\ln (r/r_1)}{\ln (r_2/r_1)} \right\}^{\frac{1}{2}} - \frac{1}{\beta_0}. \tag{2-18}$$

Note that here again the temperature profile is independent of the general conductivity level.

The influence of nonuniform thermal conductivity is exhibited in Fig. 2–7 for a tube with surface radii $r_1 = \frac{1}{4}''$ and $r_2 = 1''$ and uniform surface temperatures $t_1 = 100°F$ and $t_2 = 0°F$. Here we see the orientation of 20°F isothermals for the case of uniform conductivity $k_t = k_0$ [see (1–13)] as compared with corresponding isothermals for the cases of linearly increasing conductivity ($\beta_0 = 0.005/°F$) and linearly decreasing conductivity ($\beta_0 = -0.005/°F$). A comparison of the uniform and nonuniform cases also shows that for the same set of surface temperatures this nonuniformity causes a percent increase $(+\beta_0)$ or decrease $(-\beta_0)$ in the heat transfer, $\Delta q\%$, which depends only on these surface temperatures and the tempera-

---

*The reader can verify this particular solution by obtaining it directly from

$$\frac{q}{2\pi L} \int_r^{r_1} \frac{1}{r} dr = k_0 \int_{t_1}^{t} (1 + \beta_0 t) dt,$$

where q is given by Example 1–2.

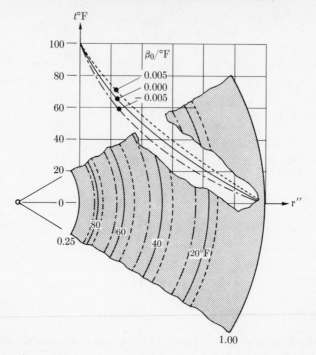

Fig. 2–7. Effect of nonuniform thermal conductivity on the temperature distribution through a single-wall tube.

ture coefficient of thermal conductivity. Thus, by the results of Example 1–2 for $+\beta_0$,

$$\Delta q\% = 100 \left[\frac{q(\beta_0) - q}{q} \right] = 50\beta_0(t_1 + t_2) = 50 \times 0.005 \times 100 = 25\%.$$

Finally, since thermal stresses are determined by the temperature gradient at any point (the more severe the gradient, the higher the thermal stress), it is clear that a nonuniform conductivity can have an appreciable effect on not only the temperature distribution and heat transfer, but the magnitude and distribution of thermal stresses as well.

2–8 Series composite spherical shell. This is another case of pure radial conduction if unit surface conductances and ambient temperatures are uniform so that (Fig. 1–3) $\partial t/\partial\varphi = 0 = \partial t/\partial\psi$. Then by integrating (2–6) across a single spherical shell of variable conducting area $A_r = 4\pi r^2$, we have

$$q = \frac{4\pi k r_1 r_2}{(r_2 - r_1)} (t_1 - t_2). \tag{2–19}$$

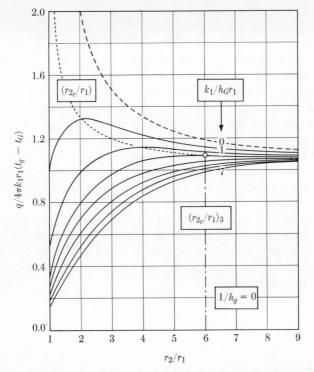

Fig. 2–8.   Effect of radius ratio on the heat transfer through single-wall spheres.

Application of (2–19) to a series composite spherical shell similar to Fig. 2–5 leads to

$$q = \frac{4\pi(t_g - t_G)}{\dfrac{1}{h_g r_1^2} + \dfrac{(r_2 - r_1)}{k_1 r_1 r_2} + \dfrac{(r_3 - r_2)}{k_2 r_2 r_3} + \dfrac{1}{h_G r_3^2}},$$

and from this the thermal transmittance based on the outer surface, as in (2–9), reads

$$U = \frac{1}{\dfrac{(r_3/r_1)^2}{h_g} + \dfrac{(r_2 - r_1)(r_3^2/r_1 r_2)}{k_1} + \dfrac{(r_3 - r_2)(r_3/r_2)}{k_2} + \dfrac{1}{h_G}} . \qquad (2\text{–}20)$$

The critical outer radius for a single-wall spherical shell is found to be twice that for a tube (2–10), or

$$(r_2)_c = \frac{2k_1}{h_G}, \qquad (2\text{–}21)$$

and the effect of radius ratio for the special case of $1/h_g = 0$ is represented dimensionlessly by

$$\frac{q}{4\pi k_1 r_1 (t_g - t_G)} = \frac{1}{1 - (r_1/r_2) + (k_1/h_G r_1)(r_1/r_2)^2},$$

as in Fig. 2–8 for comparison with Fig. 2–6.

2–9 Parallelepiped shells. Heat conduction through a parallelepiped shell such as a furnace, or more generally a room, is not a case of one-dimensional flow, and this is particularly true of the edges and corners of the structure. All such cases are found to be intractable by exact analytical means, and for this reason the heat transfer can only be computed from approximate experimental data. We consider such cases in this chapter only because the computations are, in a certain sense, of the one-dimensional type.

Langmuir* has investigated the heat flow in a parallelepiped shell by the approximate experimental method of *electrical analogy*, as discussed in Chapter 13. Some of these experimental results are presented as empirical formulas for the *effective* conducting area to be used in the integrated Fourier law for a plane wall, as

$$q = k \frac{A_{\text{eff}}}{\delta} (t_i - t_o), \tag{2–22}$$

where δ is the uniform thickness of all six walls, and t_i and t_o are the inner and outer face surface temperatures, which are assumed to be uniform. Thus, by experiment, where l_i is an inside wall-to-wall length, A_i and A_o are total inside and outside surface areas, e_i is an inside edge length, and L_i is the largest l_i:

     I. *For all $l_i > \delta/5$,*

$$A_{\text{eff}} = A_i + 0.54\delta\sum e_i + 1.20\delta^2. \tag{2–23}$$

     II. *For two $l_i > \delta/5$ and one $l_i < \delta/5$,*

$$A_{\text{eff}} = A_i + 0.46\delta\sum e_i + 0.35\delta^2. \tag{2–24}$$

     III. *For one $l_i > \delta/5$ and two $l_i < \delta/5$,*

$$A_{\text{eff}} = 6.41\delta L_i/\ln (A_o/A_i). \tag{2–25}$$

     IV. *For all $l_i < \delta/5$,*

$$A_{\text{eff}} = 0.79\sqrt{A_i A_o}. \tag{2–26}$$

In (2–23) and (2–24) the second term represents a correction for the edges and the third term a correction for the corners. *The $\sum e_i$ in (2–24) does not include the four edges for which l_i is less than $\delta/5$.*

---

*Cf. Ref. 20, Chapter 13.

The empirical formula (2–23) can also be used for the practical case of a parallelepiped structure whose six walls are not of equal thickness. In such a case the effective area and heat flow are computed separately for each wall, and this means that the edges will be counted in twice and the corners counted in thrice. This can easily be taken care of by simply using half the edge correction and a third of the corner correction, so that for each wall j:

V. *For all $l_i > \delta/5$,*

$$A_{eff_j} = A_i + 0.27\delta\sum e_i + 0.4\delta^2. \tag{2-27}$$

EXAMPLE 2–6. The inside of a rectangular fireclay kiln is 3′ wide, 3′ long, and 2′ high, the side walls are $\delta_s = 9''$ thick, the floor $\delta_f = 10''$ thick, and the ceiling is $\delta_c = 7''$ thick. Compute the hourly heat loss from this kiln if its mean thermal conductivity is 0.6 Btu/hr-ft-°F, and inside and outside surface temperatures are a uniform 420°F and 110°F respectively.

Solution. This case is covered by (2–23), since all l_i exceed all $\delta/5$. But all six walls are not of the same thickness, so we compute their separate effective areas, by (2–27), as

$$\tfrac{1}{4}A_{eff_s} = 2 \times 3 + 0.27(\tfrac{9}{12})(2 \times 3 + 2 \times 2) + 0.4(\tfrac{9}{12})^2 = 6 + 2.02 + 0.23 = 8.25,$$

$$A_{eff_f} = 3 \times 3 + 0.27(\tfrac{10}{12})(4 \times 3) + 0.4(\tfrac{10}{12})^2 = 9 + 2.70 + 0.28 = 11.98,$$

$$A_{eff_c} = 3 \times 3 + 0.27(\tfrac{7}{12})(4 \times 3) + 0.4(\tfrac{7}{12})^2 = 9 + 1.89 + 0.14 = 11.03.$$

The conductances of side walls, floor, and ceiling are therefore $K_s = 0.6(4 \times 8.25)/(\tfrac{9}{12}) = 26.40$, $K_f = 0.6(11.98)/(\tfrac{10}{12}) = 8.63$, and $K_c = 0.6(11.03)/(\tfrac{7}{12}) = 11.35$, and by these the total hourly heat loss becomes

$$q = q_s + q_f + q_c = (26.40 + 8.63 + 11.35)(420 - 110) = 14{,}378 \text{ Btu/hr.}$$

It is to be kept in mind that this is only an approximate answer based on an empirical formula and the unrealistic assumption that surface temperatures in such a structure would be uniform.

2–10 Conduction cooling of turbine blades. It is well known that maximum cycle temperatures in the modern gas turbine are primarily limited by the high-temperature failure characteristics of the turbine blades (Fig. 2–9) which operate under a high weight centrifugal loading and are subject to gas-bending, vibratory, and thermal stressing as well. Thus one of the most important problems encountered in increasing maximum cycle temperatures, and therewith obtaining the indicated large improvements in gas-turbine performance, is that of providing some means of preventing turbine-blade failure due to overheating.

A solution to this problem appears to lie in one of two possibilities: either the development of turbine-blade materials capable of extended operation under severe conditions of temperature and stress, or the use of

Fig. 2–9.   Turbine rotor and blade assembly.   *(Courtesy of the NACA)*

direct or indirect methods of cooling blades made of presently available materials.   Several artificial cooling methods involve the use of radiation exchange between the high-temperature blades and adjacent low-temperature shields, or the use of blades coated with a suitable heat-resistant ceramic.   Turbine blades may also be cooled directly by forcing a cooling fluid through passages within the blade, or indirectly by conducting heat from the blades to an internally cooled turbine rotor (Fig. 2–9).   The indirect method, which we shall examine here in brief detail, is known appropriately as *conduction cooling*.

The effectiveness of conduction cooling is judged in part by the conditions under which the actual temperature at any point x along the blade (Fig. 2–10) is just equal to the maximum *allowable* temperature for the particular blade material in question.   To find this distribution of allowable temperature along the spanwise axis of the blade, $t_a(x)$, we first determine the centrifugal-load stress distribution as a function of turbine-rotor and blade dimensions and the turbine rotative speed or blade tip speed.   This information is then related to experimental stress-rupture data, which give the maximum allowable stress for a given temperature and expected blade life.   The maximum permissible blade temperature can then be evaluated for a given assumed blade life as a function of x/L and the blade tip speed.

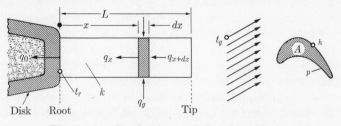

Fig. 2–10.   Conduction-cooled turbine blade.

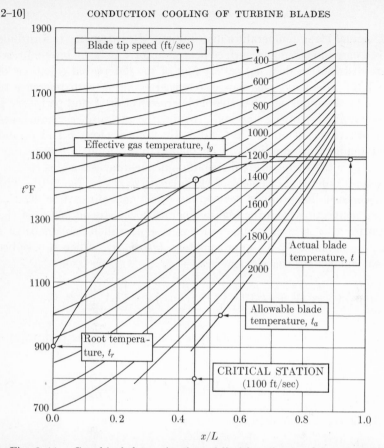

Fig. 2–11. Graphical determination of limiting tip speed from actual blade temperature distribution and allowable temperature based on a blade life of 1000 hours.

A family of allowable temperature curves is shown in Fig. 2–11 for a turbine with a blade-length to blade-tip radius ratio of 0.26, the blades being constructed of a forged ferrous alloy and having an assumed life of 1000 hours (2). The limiting tip speed for the turbine is found by superimposing the actual blade temperature distribution on the family of allowable distributions, the blade being expected to fail at the "critical station," where allowable and actual temperatures are just equal. Figure 2–11 illustrates such a critical station at $x/L = 0.45$ for a blade operating in an effective gas temperature of $t_g = 1500°F$ and having its root $x = 0$ maintained at a uniform temperature of $t_r = 900°F$. If a blade tip speed of 1200 ft/sec were allowed (i.e., 100 ft/sec above the limiting tip speed for these conditions), then it should be expected that the blade would become overstressed and subject to failure somewhere between stations $x/L = 0.25$ and 0.62.

2–11 Actual blade temperature distribution. Heat transfer to a turbine blade is a case of continuous surface heat gain for which the internal temperature distribution does not satisfy any of the differential equations of Article 1–3. We derive this new differential equation with reference to Fig. 2–10 by assuming (a) that the blade cross section A and periphery p are the same at all spanwise stations x, (b) that the unit surface conductance h and effective gas temperature t_g are both uniform along p and L, and (c) that temperature gradients in all blade cross sections are negligible. In such a case the temperature distribution is one-dimensional, as $t(x)$.

Consider a differential element of blade length dx, as in Fig. 2–10. The element conducts longitudinal heat q_x and q_{x+dx}, and gains lateral heat q_g by forced convection from the high-temperature gas stream at t_g. If the temperature at x is t, the temperature at $x + dx$ will be greater than t (Articles 1–3 and 2–7) by approximately $(dt/dx)dx$. Then a steady-state heat balance for this element is $q_g + q_{x+dx} - q_x = 0$, or

$$[hpdx(t_g - t)] + \left[kA \frac{d}{dx}\left(t + \frac{dt}{dx} dx\right)\right] - \left[kA \frac{dt}{dx}\right] = 0,$$

and this gives the characteristic differential equation for the temperature distribution $t(x)$ as

$$\frac{d^2t}{dx^2} - N^2(t - t_g) = 0, \qquad\qquad (2\text{–}28)$$

in which the constant N reads

$$N = \sqrt{hp/kA}. \qquad\qquad (2\text{–}29)$$

If this constant is put into the form

$$NL = \sqrt{(hpL)/(kA/L)} = \sqrt{K_s/K_i},$$

we can see that the dimensionless parameter NL has a physical interpretation as the square-root ratio of surface conductance to internal conductance.

By defining a new dependent variable as $T = t - t_g$, we can linearly transform (2–28) into the familiar differential equation

$$\frac{d^2T}{dx^2} - N^2T = 0,$$

whose general solution has the well-known form

$$T = t - t_g = C_1 e^{Nx} + C_2 e^{-Nx}.$$

The two integration constants C_1 and C_2 are to be evaluated by the particular boundary conditions

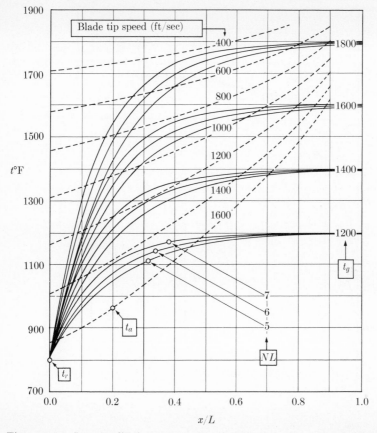

Fig. 2–12. Longitudinal temperature distribution in a conduction-cooled turbine blade as a function of the effective gas temperature t_g and the blade parameter NL.

$$\left\{ \begin{array}{l} t = t_r \quad \text{at} \quad x = 0, \\ \dfrac{dt}{dx} = 0 \quad \text{at} \quad x = L \end{array} \right\}, \qquad (2\text{--}30)$$

where the second condition implies that the blade tip $x = L$ is impervious to heat; i.e., insulated so that $q_L = -kA\,(dt/dx)_L = 0$. Thus from the first condition of a constant root temperature t_r, we have $C_1 + C_2 = t_r - t_g$, and by the second condition we get $C_1 N e^{NL} = C_2 N e^{-NL}$. Then, by simultaneous solution, the constants themselves are

$$C_1 = (t_r - t_g)e^{-NL}/2 \cosh NL,$$

$$C_2 = (t_r - t_g)e^{NL}/2 \cosh NL.$$

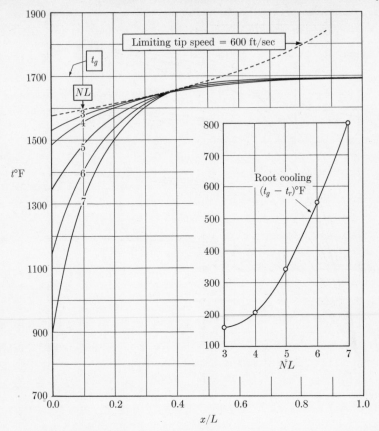

Fig. 2–13. Effect of blade parameter NL on required root cooling for limiting tip speed of 600 ft/sec.

This serves to complete the particular solution which satisfies both (2–28) and (2–30) as

$$\frac{t - t_g}{t_r - t_g} = \frac{\cosh NL(1 - x/L)}{\cosh NL} . \qquad (2\text{--}31)$$

Note again that for a given gas and root temperature, the blade temperature itself depends only on the dimensionless parameter NL, which in turn depends only on the ratio of surface to internal blade conductance.*

Typical blade temperature profiles for a constant root temperature and a number of selected gas temperatures are shown in Fig. 2–12, where limiting profiles are evidently t_r for $NL = 0$ and t_g for $NL = \infty$. Low values of the blade parameter NL required to increase the effectiveness of

---

*Values of the *hyperbolic functions* can be computed from exponential functions listed in Table A–2 of the Appendix.

conduction cooling can be obtained by either decreasing the blade surface conductance $K_s = hpL$ or increasing the blade internal conductance $K_i = kA/L$. For a given mass flow of gas, the value of the unit surface conductance h depends on the flow velocity, whose magnitude and distribution are essentially fixed by proper aerodynamic design. These design conditions also fix the shape of the blade and hence its p/A ratio. A given mass flow of gas requires, in addition, a certain blade length L; if L is reduced, then NL is decreased at the expense of a larger turbine diameter. Practical reductions in the operating value of NL therefore depend to a large extent on either decreasing the surface conductance by coating blades with some form of insulation or increasing the thermal conductivity of the blade itself. In either event NL can be halved only if h is reduced to a quarter of its value or if k is quadrupled.

The amount of "root cooling" $(t_g - t_r)$ for critical operation at a given tip speed and effective gas temperature can be determined from critical blade temperature distributions as in Fig. 2–13, which illustrates this for the special conditions of $t_g = 1700°F$ and a limiting tip speed of 600 ft/sec. Here we see that the required root cooling increases sharply for higher values of the blade parameter NL.

The turbine-blade problem considered here is an introduction to a more general class of structures commonly known as *extended surfaces*. In Chapter 4 we examine such extended surfaces in the familiar form of fins.

REFERENCES

1. T N. Çetinkale and M. Fishenden, "Thermal Conductance of Metal Surfaces in Contact," *General Discussion on Heat Transfer*. London, *IME* and New York, *ASME*, 1951, pp. 271–275.

2. L. Wolfenstein, G. L. Meyer, and J. S. McCarthy, "Cooling of Gas Turbines; II—Effectiveness of Rim Cooling of Blades," *NACA RM* No. E7B11b. Washington: March, 1947.

PROBLEMS

2–1. A large composite wall is built up of the following materials: $3''$ marble ($k = 0.75$ Btu/hr-ft-°F), $3''$ brick ($k = 0.37$), $1''$ pine ($k = 0.06$ across grain), and $\frac{3}{4}''$ inside plaster ($k = 0.04$). The outside unit surface conductance is 6.00 Btu/hr-ft²-°F based on a 15 mph wind and an outside air temperature of $-10°F$, and the inside unit surface conductance is 1.65, based on an inside air temperature of 72°F. (a) Neglecting the thermal resistance of a $\frac{1}{4}''$ mortar joint between marble and brick, show that the over-all transmittance for the wall is 0.212 Btu/hr-ft²-°F. (b) Show that the heat loss through the wall is 17.4 Btu/hr per square foot of face surface. (c) Show that the temperature of the brick-pine interface is 10.2°F. (d) A thermocouple embedded in the mortar-brick interface registers $-1.4°F$. Show that the thermal conductivity of the mortar is 0.42 Btu/hr-ft-°F if it can be assumed that the heat loss would be reduced 10% when the thermal resistance of the mortar is considered.

2–2. Determine graphically the temperature distribution through the wall in problem 2–1, neglecting the thermal resistance of the mortar joint.

2–3. A plane wall with isothermal faces t_1 at $x = 0$ and t_2 at $x = L$ has a linear thermal conductivity $k_t = k_0(1 + \beta_0 t)$. (a) Show directly by (1–2) that heat is conducted through this wall (Example 1–2) in amount

$$q = k_0 \frac{A}{L}\left[1 + \frac{\beta_0}{2}(t_1 + t_2) \right](t_1 - t_2),$$

and that the temperature profile in the wall is (footnote, p. 31)

$$t = \frac{1}{\beta_0}\left\{ (1 + \beta_0 t_1)^2 - [(1 + \beta_0 t_1)^2 - (1 + \beta_0 t_2)^2]\frac{x}{L} \right\}^{\frac{1}{2}} - \frac{1}{\beta_0}.$$

(b) Reproduce the solution $t = t(x)$ in (a) by using the general Kirchhoff method of Article 2–7.

2–4. Plot to scale the temperature profile in a plane wall with boundary conditions $t = 212°F$ at $x = 0$ and $t = 32°F$ at $x = L$ for wall materials of brass for which $k_t = 59 + 0.052t$, aluminum for which $k_t = k = 116.8$, and mild steel for which $k_t = 36.7 - 0.017t$ Btu/hr-ft-°F.

2–5. A rectangular building with inside dimensions 16′ long, 16′ wide, and 10′ high has 6″ marble sides and a ceiling built up of 1″ pine and 3″ brick. If inside and outside unit surface conductances are 1.65 and 6.00 Btu/hr-ft²-°F, show that the total air-to-air conductance based on the inside surface area is 535 Btu/hr-°F.

2–6. Air at 193°F flows in a copper tube of 1.5″ inner diameter and with $\frac{1}{4}$″ thick walls which are heated from the outside by water at 260°F. The thermal conductivity of a $\frac{1}{16}$″ thick scale deposit is 1 Btu/hr-ft-°F, and air and water-side unit surface conductances are known to be 38 and 620 Btu/hr-ft²-°F respectively. (a) Show that the over-all water-to-air transmittance is 22.6 Btu/hr-ft²-°F. (b) Show that the water-to-air heat exchange is 840 Btu/hr per foot length of tube. (c) Show that the temperature drop across the scale deposit is approximately 8°F.

2–7. An electrical company is using $\frac{1}{8}$″ diameter copper wires covered with insulation $\frac{1}{32}$″ thick and of thermal conductivity 0.092 Btu/hr-ft-°F. The unit surface conductance between insulation and ambient air is estimated for the particular installation in question to be 5.9 Btu/hr-ft²-°F. Show by reference to Fig. 2–6 that the dissipation of *Joulean* heat generated in these wires could be increased, at most, by approximately 18.5% if the electrical insulation thickness were increased by $\frac{3}{32}$″.

2–8. The inside surface of a spherical iron shell having an inner radius of 6″ is at a uniform temperature of 120°F. Show that 31,850 Btu/hr is the maximum amount of heat which could be transferred to such a sphere from ambient water at 212°F and under the condition that the water-side unit surface conductance is 100 Btu/hr-ft²-°F.

2–9. The integrated form of the one-dimensional Fourier law leads to a mean conducting area for a plane wall of $A_{m_w} = A$. (a) Show that the mean conducting area for a cylindrical shell is

$$A_{m_c} = \frac{2\pi L(r_2 - r_1)}{\ln (r_2/r_1)} = \frac{S_2 - S_1}{\ln (S_2/S_1)}.$$

This is to say that A_{m_c} is the *log mean* of the inner and outer cylindrical surface areas S. (b) Show that the mean conducting area for a spherical shell is

$$A_{m_s} = 4\pi r_1 r_2 = \sqrt{S_1 S_2}.$$

This is to say that A_{m_s} is the *geometric mean* of the inner and outer spherical surface areas S. (c) Plot a graph of percent error vs. radius ratio r_2/r_1 from 1 to 10 if (1) the *arithmetic mean* conducting area $\pi(r_2 + r_1)$ for a cylindrical shell is used in place of the true log mean area, and if (2) the arithmetic mean conducting area $2\pi(r_2^2 + r_1^2)$ for a spherical shell is used in place of the true geometric mean area.

2–10. The inside of a small refractory furnace constructed of Alfrax BI whose mean conductivity is 0.583 Btu/hr-ft-°F is 12″ long, 12″ wide, and 2″ high. Show that the heat loss through this furnace is 926 Btu/hr if all of its uniform walls are 1′ thick and all inside and outside face surfaces are at a uniform temperature of 380 and 130°F respectively.

2–11. Show that the temperature profile $t(x)$ in a "very long" rod protruding from a heat source which maintains its root $x = 0$ at t_r is given by

$$(t - t_g)/(t_r - t_g) = e^{-Nx}.$$

This result can be used to experimentally determine the unknown thermal conductivity of a rod A from the known conductivity of a second rod B by having rods A and B both protruding from the same heat source, so that $t_{r_A} = t_{r_B} = t_r$ and also $h_A = h_B$. If both rods are long and of the same cross section, then by (2–29) $N_A/N_B = (k_B/k_A)^{\frac{1}{2}}$. (a) Show that k_A can be found by recording the temperature at the same point $x = x_1$ in each rod as t_{Ax_1} and t_{Bx_1} and then substituting in

$$k_A = \left\{\frac{\ln [(t_r - t_g)/(t_{Bx_1} - t_g)]}{\ln [(t_r - t_g)/(t_{Ax_1} - t_g)]}\right\}^2 k_B.$$

(b) Show that if the temperature at $x = x_1$ on B is t_{Bx_1} and this same temperature is recorded at $x = x_2$ on A as t_{Ax_2}, then

$$k_A = \left(\frac{x_2}{x_1}\right)^2 k_B.$$

Another method for obtaining k_A from k_B is to have rods A and B both of the same length L, and the heat sources, now at both ends of each rod, maintaining both $x = 0$ and $x = L$ at t_r. Show that the longitudinal temperature in each rod is given in this case by

$$\frac{t - t_g}{t_r - t_g} = \frac{e^{Nx} + e^{NL(1-x/L)}}{1 + e^{NL}},$$

and if the mid-length temperature is recorded as $t_{A\frac{1}{2}}$ on A and $t_{B\frac{1}{2}}$ on B, then

$$k_A = \left\{\frac{\cosh^{-1}[(t_r - t_g)/(t_{B\frac{1}{2}} - t_g)]}{\cosh^{-1}[(t_r - t_g)/(t_{A\frac{1}{2}} - t_g)]}\right\}^2 k_B.$$

2–12. Show that the amount of heat which must be conducted from each blade in a conduction-cooled turbine is

$$q_0 = (t_r - t_g)\sqrt{hpkA}\ \tanh NL,$$

and plot dimensionless graphs of this and the longitudinal temperature as functions of the blade parameter NL.

2–13. Consider a turbine blade losing heat by *radiation* from its tip $x = L$ to a cooler turbine casing at t_c. If the radiation unit surface conductance between blade tip and turbine casing is known to be h_R, then show that the arbitrary integration constants for the blade-temperature solution are

$$C_1 = (t_r - t_g) - \frac{(t_g - t_c) + (t_r - t_g)(kN/h_R + 1)e^{NL}}{2\sinh NL + (2kN/h_R)\cosh NL} = (t_r - t_g) - C_2.$$

Show that blade-tip heat loss has a negligible effect on the limiting tip speed by plotting $t(x)$ for blade dimensions $L = 0.313$ ft, $p = 0.377$ ft, $A = 0.00415$ ft^2, a blade conductivity of $k = 15$ Btu/hr-ft-°F, and operating conditions of $t_r = 1000$, $t_g = 1500$, $t_c = 1000$°F, $h_g = 100$, and $h_R = 0$, 25, and 50 Btu/hr-ft^2-°F.

2–14. Consider a turbine blade whose tip is impervious to heat but whose longitudinal surface receives heat by radiation from high-temperature upstream nozzle surfaces at t_n as well as principal convective heat from the main gas stream. If the radiation unit surface conductance between the blade and upstream nozzles is h_R, then show that the longitudinal temperature profile in the blade is

$$t = \frac{1}{\bar{N}^2}\,(N^2 t_g + R^2 t_n) + \left[t_r - \frac{1}{\bar{N}^2}\,(N^2 t_g + R^2 t_n)\right]\frac{\cosh \bar{N}L(1 - x/L)}{\cosh \bar{N}L},$$

in which $R^2 = h_R p/kA$ and $\bar{N}^2 = N^2 + R^2$. Show also that nozzle heat gain has a substantial effect on the limiting tip speed by plotting $t(x)$ for the particular blade in problem 2–13 with $t_n = 1500$°F and $h_R = 0$, 50, 100, and 150 Btu/hr-ft^2-°F, and show that this effect is much like that of decreasing k.

2–15. Consider a turbine blade operating in an ambient gas stream whose temperature is not uniform but varies parabolically with x as

$$t_g(x) = t'_g - \mu L^2 (x/L - \tfrac{1}{2})^2,$$

where t'_g is the maximum effective gas temperature at midspan $x = L/2$. Then the average effective gas temperature would be

$$t_{g\mathrm{av}} = \frac{1}{L}\int_0^L t_g(x)dx = t'_g - \mu L^2/12.$$

Show that in this case the blade temperature must satisfy the differential equation

$$\frac{d^2 t}{dx^2} - N^2 t = N^2 L^2 \mu (x/L - \tfrac{1}{2})^2 - N^2 t'_g,$$

and if the blade tip is impervious to heat that the blade temperature itself must read

$$t = t_g' + \left(t_r - t_g' + \mu \frac{L^2}{4} + \frac{2\mu}{N^2}\right) \frac{\cosh NL(1 - x/L)}{\cosh NL} + \frac{\mu L}{N} \frac{\sinh NL(x/L)}{\cosh NL}$$

$$- \mu L^2 (x/L - \tfrac{1}{2})^2 - \frac{2\mu}{N^2}.$$

Plot temperature distributions $t(x)$ for the particular blade in problem 2–13 and a parabolic gas-temperature profile in which t_g' is the minimum effective gas temperature ($\mu = -\mu$). Consider two gas profiles for which $t_g' = 1400$ and 1450°F, both of average temperature 1500°F.

CHAPTER 3

DIFFERENTIAL EQUATIONS OF BESSEL AND LEGENDRE

This chapter reviews a number of higher mathematical functions for which we shall find frequent use in later work. In particular, we consider solutions of the Bessel and Legendre differential equations, and indicate briefly the expansion of arbitrary functions in a series of Bessel functions and a series of Legendre polynomials.

BESSEL FUNCTIONS

3–1 The Bessel differential equation. Up to this point our study of heat conduction has required that we obtain general solutions of only the most familiar second-order differential equations with constant coefficients, such as $d^2y/dx^2 + cy = 0$. Solutions of these homogeneous differential equations have appeared in terms of the elementary trigonometric, exponential, and hyperbolic functions. However, when the coefficients c are not constant but related to the independent variable x, then general solutions cannot be found in terms of these elementary functions. A frequently occurring example is

$$x^2 \frac{d^2y}{dx^2} + x \frac{dy}{dx} + (x^2 - n^2)y = 0, \tag{3-1}$$

which is known as *Bessel's differential equation*, in honor of the German mathematician Friedrich Bessel (1784–1846) who first formulated the fundamental solutions of this equation. These solutions are called *Bessel functions* or, technically, *cylindrical harmonics*. Since (3–1) is of second order, its general solution will necessarily contain two arbitrary integration constants. As we shall later see, this general solution will be the sum of two linearly independent Bessel functions each multiplied by an integration constant. The form of these two functions of *order n* depends on the value of n, which may be positive or negative, integral or fractional, or complex. The first solution is spoken of as a *Bessel function of the first kind*, and the second solution as a *Bessel function of the second kind*. We write the general solution of (3–1) in the standard form

$$y = C_1 y_{\mathrm{I}} + C_2 y_{\mathrm{II}}, \tag{3-2}$$

where y_{I} and y_{II} are the first- and second-kind Bessel functions constituting independent solutions of (3–1).

3–2 The Bessel functions. By a process of development in power series, we first consider the special case of Bessel's zero-order differential equation obtained by taking $n = 0$,

$$\frac{d^2y}{dx^2} + \frac{1}{x}\frac{dy}{dx} + y = 0. \tag{3-3}$$

Now assume that the *first* solution y_I is given by the infinite power series

$$y_I = a + a_1x^2 + a_2x^3 + \cdots,$$

in which the a's are undetermined constants. Then by differentiating this twice and substituting therewith in (3–3), we have

$$(a + 4a_1) + (9a_2)x + (a_1 + 16a_3)x^2 + \cdots = 0.$$

But, since $f(x) = 0$, this last equation holds only if the coefficients x^0, x^1, x^2, $\cdots$ vanish. Therefore, to satisfy this equation identically, we find that

$$a_1 = -a/4,$$
$$a_2 = 0,$$
$$a_3 = -a_1/16 = a/4 \cdot 16,$$
$$a_4 = 0,$$
$$\vdots$$

and so for y_I,

$$y_I = a\left(1 - \frac{x^2}{2^2} + \frac{x^4}{2^2 \cdot 4^2} - \frac{x^6}{2^2 \cdot 4^2 \cdot 6^2} + \cdots\right). \tag{3-4}$$

The series (3–4) is a solution of (3–3) provided it is absolutely *convergent* for all x. To establish this convergence we apply the well-known *Cauchy test* by forming the ratio of the $(m + 1)$ Mth term to the (m) Mth term of the series as $M_{m+1}/M_m = R$. Then if, as m increases indefinitely, the limit of the absolute value of R, $|R|$, exists and is less than unity, the given series converges absolutely. In the case of (3–4),

$$M_{m+1} = (-1)^{m+1}x^{2(m+1)}/2^{2(m+1)}[(m+1)!]^2,$$
$$M_m = (-1)^m x^{2m}/2^{2m}(m!)^2,$$

$$\lim_{m\to\infty} |R| = \lim_{m\to\infty}\left|\frac{x^2}{4(m+1)^2}\right| = 0.$$

Hence the infinite series (3–4) for y_I converges uniformly in any interval as well as at $x = 0$.

Using the common notation $J_n(x)$ for y_I, we can now write *Bessel function of the first kind* as

$$J_0(x) = 1 - \frac{x^2}{2^2} + \frac{x^4}{2^2 \cdot 4^2} - \frac{x^6}{2^2 \cdot 4^2 \cdot 6^2} + \cdots, \tag{3-5}$$

which is easily verified as a solution of (3–3) by straightforward differentiation. Recalling that a convergent power series can be differentiated term by term, we have

$$\frac{d}{dx} J_0(x) = -\frac{x}{2} + \frac{x^3}{2^2 \cdot 4} - \cdots,$$

$$\frac{d^2}{dx^2} J_0(x) = -\frac{1}{2} + \frac{3x^2}{2^2 \cdot 4} - \cdots,$$

and by this it is clear that

$$\frac{d^2}{dx^2} J_0(x) + \frac{1}{x} \frac{d}{dx} J_0(x) + J_0(x) = 0,$$

so that in view of its convergence also, $J_0(x)$ must be a solution of (3–3).

It remains now to find the *second* independent solution of (3–3). This second solution can be obtained from the first solution by the method of undetermined functions,* and without presenting the method itself we simply indicate that y_{II} for $n = 0$ has the particular form

$$y_{II} = Y_0(x) = J_0(x) \ln x + \frac{x^2}{2^2} - \frac{x^4}{2^2 \cdot 4^2}\left(1 + \frac{1}{2}\right)$$

$$+ \frac{x^6}{2^2 \cdot 4^2 \cdot 6^2}\left(1 + \frac{1}{2} + \frac{1}{3}\right) - \cdots. \tag{3-6}$$

This second solution is called the *zero-order Bessel function of the second kind*, and is commonly referred to as *Neumann's second solution*. That $Y_0(x)$ is independent of $J_0(x)$ is suggested on examining the behavior at the origin, for here $Y_0 \to -\infty$, while $J_0 \to 1$.

With the two independent solutions (3–5) and (3–6), the general solution of (3–3) takes the more realistic form

$$y = C_1 J_0(x) + C_2 Y_0(x). \tag{3-7}$$

Essentially the same power-series method as above is used to obtain the corresponding Bessel functions for n other than zero. For example, if n is either zero or a positive integer, then

$$J_n(x) = \frac{(x/2)^n}{n!}\left[1 - \frac{x^2}{2(2n+2)} + \frac{x^4}{2 \cdot 4(2n+2)(2n+4)} - \cdots\right];$$

$$n = 0, 1, 2, \cdots, \tag{3-8}$$

which, on recalling that $0! = 1$, is seen to reduce to $J_0(x)$ for $n = 0$, as in

---

*See, for example, Kármán and Biot (1), p. 32.

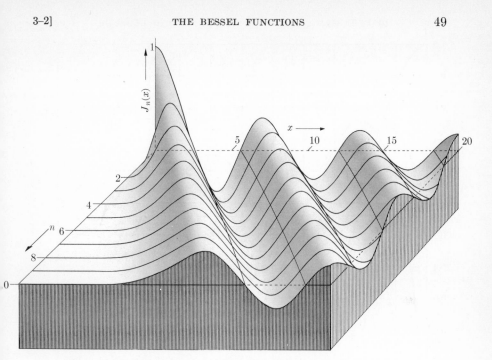

Fig. 3–1.   Relief of nth-order Bessel functions of the first kind.

(3–5).   Thus for $n = 1$, we have the important series

$$J_1(x) = \frac{x}{2}\left(1 - \frac{x^2}{2 \cdot 4} + \frac{x^4}{2 \cdot 4^2 \cdot 6} - \frac{x^6}{2 \cdot 4^2 \cdot 6^2 \cdot 8} + \cdots\right).$$

The ordinates of the positive-order Bessel functions of the first kind are represented in Fig. 3–1 as a surface determined by the argument x and order n of the $J_n(x)$ functions. The solid lines in the wave direction x represent the first-kind Bessel functions of positive integral order, the surfaces in between these lines containing the functions of positive non-integral order to be considered in Article 3–4. The six transverse lines on the relief are intersections of the wave surface with the particular horizontal plane $J_n(x) = 0$, and therefore they represent the loci of what are called the *zeros* of the Bessel functions.

The second kind of Bessel function for zero or positive integral n is given by the more elaborate expression

$$Y_n(x) = J_n(x) \ln x - \frac{1}{2} \sum_{p=0}^{n-1} \frac{(n-p-1)!}{p!}\left(\frac{x}{2}\right)^{2p-n}$$

$$- \frac{1}{2} \sum_{p=0}^{\infty} \frac{(-1)^r}{p!(n+p)!}\left(\frac{x}{2}\right)^{2p+n} [f(p) + f(n+p)], \quad (3\text{–}9)$$

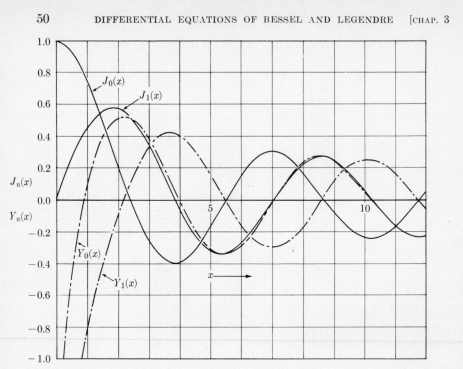

Fig. 3–2.   Zero and first-order Bessel functions of the first and second kind.

wherein

$$[f(p) + f(n + p)] = \frac{1}{1} + \frac{1}{2} + \cdots + \frac{1}{p} + \frac{1}{1} + \frac{1}{2} + \cdots + \frac{1}{n + p};$$

$$= f(0) = 0. \qquad\qquad [n = 0, 1, 2, \cdots]$$

Note again that this reduces to $Y_0(x)$, as in (3–6), for $n = 0$, while for $n = 1$,

$$Y_1(x) = J_1(x) \ln x - \frac{1}{2}\left(\frac{x}{2}\right)^{-1} - \frac{1}{2}\left(\frac{x}{2}\right) + \frac{1}{2}\frac{(x/2)^3}{2!}\left(1 + 1 + \frac{1}{2}\right)$$

$$- \frac{1}{2}\frac{(x/2)^5}{2!3!}\left(1 + \frac{1}{2} + 1 + \frac{1}{2} + \frac{1}{3}\right)$$

$$+ \frac{1}{2}\frac{(x/2)^7}{3!4!}\left(1 + \frac{1}{2} + \frac{1}{3} + 1 + \frac{1}{2} + \frac{1}{3} + \frac{1}{4}\right) - \cdots.$$

Since the solutions (3–8) and (3–9) independently satisfy (3–1), the corresponding general solution of (3–1) for the positive integral n is

$$y = C_1 J_n(x) + C_2 Y_n(x); \quad n = 0, 1, 2, \cdots. \qquad (3\text{–}10)$$

Several useful *recurrence formulas* for the derivatives of the Bessel functions can be obtained at once. Thus by (3–5)

$$\frac{d}{dx} J_0(x) = -\frac{x}{2}\left(1 - \frac{x^2}{2 \cdot 4} + \frac{x^4}{2 \cdot 4^2 \cdot 6} - \cdots\right) = -J_1(x),$$

or, in general,*

$$\frac{d}{dx} J_n(x) = \frac{n}{x} J_n(x) - J_{n+1}(x). \tag{3–11}$$

A similar recurrence formula can be derived for the second kind of Bessel function. Thus, by (3–6),

$$\frac{d}{dx} Y_0(x) = \ln x \frac{d}{dx} J_0(x) + \frac{1}{x} J_0(x) + \frac{x}{2} - \frac{x^3}{2^2 \cdot 4}\left(1 + \frac{1}{2}\right) + \cdots$$

$$= -J_1(x) \ln x + \frac{1}{x} - \frac{x^2}{2^2} - \frac{5x^3}{2^2 \cdot 4^2} + \cdots = -Y_1(x).$$

Computed values of $J_0(x)$, $J_1(x)$, $Y_0(x)$, and $Y_1(x)$ are given in Tables A–3 and A–4 of the Appendix, and Fig. 3–2 indicates their essential differences in behavior. All of these functions are seen to have an infinite number of real and distinct roots (zeros). Except for the damping characteristic, the functions $J_0(x)$ and $J_1(x)$ behave much like the elementary trigonometric functions, particularly for large x, where the period is seen to be nearly 2π. The $J_0(x)$ being an *even* function, as $J_0(-x) = J_0(x)$, resembles $\cos x$, while $J_1(x)$, being an *odd* function as $J_1(-x) = -J_1(x)$, resembles $\sin x$.

3–3 The gamma function. To extend the Bessel functions to cases where n is not an integer, we need to consider the definition and most elementary properties of the transcendental *gamma function*, $\Gamma(n)$, or what is frequently referred to as the *Eulerian integral*, in honor of its discoverer.

For all real values of n other than zero or negative integers, we have as Euler's definition of the gamma function the convergent integral

$$\Gamma(n) = \int_0^\infty e^{-x} x^{n-1} dx; \quad n > 0, \tag{3–12}$$

or

$$\Gamma(n + 1) = \int_0^\infty e^{-x} x^n dx.$$

The latter of these two integrals can be integrated by parts. Choosing $u = x^n$ and $dv = e^{-x} dx$, then $du = nx^{n-1} dx$ and $v = -e^{-x}$, wherewith

$$\int_0^\infty e^{-x} x^n dx = -x^n e^{-x}\Big]_0^\infty + n \int_0^\infty e^{-x} x^{n-1} dx = n \int_0^\infty e^{-x} x^{n-1} dx.$$

_____

*See problem 3–6.

A comparison of this result with (3–12) gives the important *difference equation*

$$\Gamma(n+1) = n\Gamma(n); \quad 0 > n \neq -1, -2, \cdots. \tag{3–13}$$

Using (3–13), we find that

$$\Gamma(2) \quad = 1\Gamma(1) = \int_0^\infty e^{-x}dx = 1 = 1!,$$

$$\Gamma(3) \quad = 2\Gamma(2) = 2 = 2!,$$

$$\Gamma(4) \quad = 3\Gamma(3) = 6 = 3!,$$

$$\vdots$$

$$\Gamma(n+1) = (n+1-1)! = n!,$$

which suggests that $n\Gamma(n)$ is a generalized definition of the factorial n as $n!$, commonly defined only for positive integers according to $n! = n(n-1)(n-2)\cdots 1$.

The fundamental importance of the difference formula (3–13) lies in the fact that it will give us the value of the gamma function $\Gamma(n)$ for any negative nonintegral n which cannot be found from (3–12) defined for positive n. To demonstrate this, consider the case of $n = -\frac{5}{2}$; for $n = \frac{1}{2}$,

$$\Gamma(\tfrac{1}{2}) = \int_0^\infty x^{-\frac{1}{2}}e^{-x}dx = \sqrt{\pi},$$

so that by successive application of (3–13)

$$\Gamma(n) \quad = \frac{\Gamma(n+1)}{n},$$

$$\Gamma(-\tfrac{1}{2}) = \frac{\Gamma(\tfrac{1}{2})}{-\tfrac{1}{2}} = -2\sqrt{\pi},$$

$$\Gamma(-\tfrac{3}{2}) = \frac{\Gamma(-\tfrac{1}{2})}{-\tfrac{3}{2}} = \tfrac{4}{3}\sqrt{\pi},$$

$$\Gamma(-\tfrac{5}{2}) = \frac{\Gamma(-\tfrac{3}{2})}{-\tfrac{5}{2}} = -\tfrac{8}{15}\sqrt{\pi},$$

$$\vdots$$

Numerical values of the gamma function are tabulated in a number of familiar sources.* The reader should be aware that the function is frequently represented as $\Pi(n) = \Gamma(n+1)$, in which case $\Pi(n) = n\Gamma(n)$ is called the *Gauss* Π-*function*.

---

*See, for example, Peirce (2).

3–4 Bessel functions of nonintegral order. The general definition of Bessel's nth-order function of the first kind is given by*

$$J_n(x) = \sum_{p=0}^{\infty} \frac{(-1)^p}{\Gamma(p+1)\Gamma(n+p+1)} \left(\frac{x}{2}\right)^{n+2p} . \qquad (3\text{–}14)$$

For positive integral n, $\Gamma(n+p+1) = (n+p)!$, so that (3–14) takes the special form

$$J_n(x) = \sum_{p=0}^{\infty} \frac{(-1)^p}{p!(n+p)!} \left(\frac{x}{2}\right)^{n+2p} ; \quad n = 0, 1, 2, \cdots ,$$

which is seen to agree formally with (3–8) if we expand this as

$$J_n(x) = \frac{(x/2)^n}{n!} \left[1 - \frac{n!(x/2)^2}{(n+1)!} + \frac{n!(x/2)^4}{2!(n+2)!} - \cdots \right].$$

Now if n is replaced by $-n$, we have by (3–14) the J series

$$J_n(x) = \sum_{p=0}^{\infty} \frac{(-1)^p}{\Gamma(p+1)\Gamma(p-n+1)} \left(\frac{x}{2}\right)^{2p-n} ,$$

in which the factor $\Gamma(p-n+1)$ is infinite when $p = n-1$, and finite when $p = n$ (a positive integer). This implies that all terms of this series are zero up to and including the $(n-1)$ term, and finite for the nth term and all terms thereafter. Then for negative integral order

$$J_{-n}(x) = \sum_{p=n}^{\infty} \frac{(-1)^p}{\Gamma(p+1)\Gamma(p-n+1)} \left(\frac{x}{2}\right)^{2p-n} = \sum_{p=n}^{\infty} \frac{(-1)^p}{p!(n+p)!} \left(\frac{x}{2}\right)^{n+2p} ,$$

which in expanded form reads

$$J_{-n}(x) = \frac{(-1)^n}{n!} \left(\frac{x}{2}\right)^n + \frac{(-1)^{n+1}}{1!(n+1)!} \left(\frac{x}{2}\right)^{n+2} + \cdots$$

$$= (-1)^n \sum_{p=0}^{\infty} \frac{(-1)^p}{p!(n+p)!} \left(\frac{x}{2}\right)^{n+2p} .$$

This gives the important recurrence formula

$$J_{-n}(x) = (-1)^n J_n(x); \quad n = 0, 1, 2, \cdots . \qquad (3\text{–}15)$$

Evidently both $J_n(x)$ and $J_{-n}(x)$ cannot represent independent solutions of (3–1) when n is integral (problem 3–3), although these functions do enter the general solution when n is fractional, in which case (3–15) no longer holds true. It can also be shown that the Bessel function of the second kind satisfies this same form of recurrence formula such that

$$Y_{-n}(x) = (-1)^n Y_n(x); \quad n = 0, 1, 2, \cdots . \qquad (3\text{–}16)$$

---

*See Gray and Mathews (3), p. 14, or Relton (4), p. 47.

Then by virtue of (3–15) and (3–16), the general solution of (3–1) for negative integral order is

$$y = C_1(-1)^n J_n(x) + C_2(-1)^n Y_n(x). \tag{3–17}$$

When n is half an odd integer $\frac{1}{2}, \frac{3}{2}, \cdots$, it is found that the independent Bessel functions satisfying (3–1) are expressible in closed form.* If $n = N + \frac{1}{2}$, then for the first case of $N = 0$

$$J_{\frac{1}{2}}(x) = \sum_{p=0}^{\infty} \frac{(-1)^p}{\Gamma(p+1)\Gamma(\frac{3}{2}+p)} \left(\frac{x}{2}\right)^{\frac{1}{2}+2p} = \sqrt{\frac{2x}{\pi}}\left(1 - \frac{x^2}{6} + \frac{x^4}{120} - \cdots\right).$$

Using the formal Taylor expansion of $\sin x$ as

$$\sin x = x - \frac{x^3}{3!} + \frac{x^5}{5!} - \cdots,$$

we find that

$$J_{\frac{1}{2}}(x) = \sqrt{\frac{2}{\pi x}} \sin x,$$

and, in like manner, for $N = -1$

$$J_{-\frac{1}{2}}(x) = \sqrt{\frac{2}{\pi x}} \cos x.$$

Since these two results are odd and even functions, they must represent independent solutions of the Bessel equation for $n = \frac{1}{2}$. This assures us that the recurrence formula (3–15) does not hold for fractional n, and that, in general,

$$y = C_1 J_{N+\frac{1}{2}}(x) + C_2 Y_{N+\frac{1}{2}}(x); \quad N = n - \frac{1}{2} = 0, 1, 2, \cdots. \tag{3–18}$$

3–5 The modified Bessel functions. A form of second-order differential equation which resembles the general Bessel equation (3–1) except for the third term is

$$x^2 \frac{d^2 y}{dx^2} + x \frac{dy}{dx} + m^2 x^2 y = 0.$$

Here m is a constant coefficient, and on taking $\eta = mx$ as the independent variable, we obtain

$$\eta^2 \frac{d^2 y}{d\eta^2} + \eta \frac{dy}{d\eta} + \eta^2 y = 0.$$

This is recognized as Bessel's equation of zero order, its general solution being given by (3–7) as

---

*The reader can verify this by examining Bessel's equation for, say, $n = \frac{1}{2}$. In this case the equation is directly integrable by substitution, for if we let $u = y\sqrt{x}$, then $y = (C_1 \cos x + C_2 \sin x)/\sqrt{x}$.

$$y = C_1 J_0(mx) + C_2 Y_0(mx).$$

In not all cases will the substitution of a real variable reduce a given differential equation to a recognized Bessel form. This is exemplified by the frequently occurring differential equation

$$x^2 \frac{d^2y}{dx^2} + x \frac{dy}{dx} - (x^2 + n^2)y = 0, \tag{3–19}$$

which can be transformed to a standard Bessel form only if an imaginary variable $i\eta$ is substituted for x, as

$$\eta^2 \frac{d^2y}{d\eta^2} + \eta \frac{dy}{d\eta} + (\eta^2 - n^2)y = 0.$$

The general solution of (3–19) requires the use of two new Bessel functions with imaginary arguments corresponding to the substitution of ix for x, i.e., $J_n(ix)$ and $Y_n(ix)$. In the usual notation of $I_n(x)$ and $K_n(x)$, these *modified Bessel functions* are defined for integral n as

$$I_n(x) = i^{-n} J_n(ix), \tag{3–20}$$

and

$$K_n(x) = i^{n+1} \frac{\pi}{2} [J_n(ix) + iY_n(ix)]. \tag{3–21}$$

As in the case of Bessel functions with real arguments, if n is either zero or a positive integer we can write the general solution of (3–19) as

$$y = C_1 I_n(x) + C_2 K_n(x); \quad n = 0, 1, 2, \cdots, \tag{3–22}$$

where again, since $I_{-n}(x) = i^n J_{-n}(ix) = i^n(-1)^n J_n(ix) = i^{-n} J_n(ix)$,

$$I_{-n}(x) = I_n(x); \quad n = 0, 1, 2, \cdots,$$

and, in like fashion,

$$K_{-n}(x) = K_n(x); \quad n = 0, 1, 2, \cdots.$$

Also, for n not an integer but a fraction, the general solution of (3–19) reads

$$y = C_1 I_n(x) + C_2 I_{-n}(x); \quad n = 0, 1, 2, \cdots. \tag{3–23}$$

Computed values of $I_0(x)$, $I_1(x)$, $K_0(x)$, and $K_1(x)$ are listed in Tables A–5 and A–6 of the Appendix, and Fig. 3–3 illustrates the behavior of these four modified functions.

3–6 Generalized Bessel solution. It is sometimes difficult to determine the change of independent variable that will reduce a given differential equation to either a recognized Bessel form (if possible) or an equation whose general solution must contain a linear combination of Bessel functions. The usual trial-and-error procedure may be reduced to a problem of

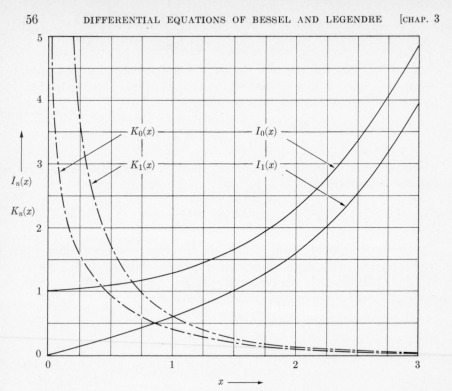

Fig. 3–3. Zero and first-order modified Bessel functions of the first and second kind.

mere inspection by simply comparing the differential equation with the following *generalized Bessel equation* as developed by Douglass:*

$$x^2 \frac{d^2y}{dx^2} + [(1 - 2A)x - 2Bx^2] \frac{dy}{dx}$$

$$+ [C^2D^2x^{2C} + B^2x^2 - B(1 - 2A)x + A^2 - C^2n^2]y = 0, \quad (3\text{--}24)$$

where again n is the order of Bessel's equation. The *generalized solution* of (3–24) is given by Douglass as

$$y = x^A e^{Bx} [C_1 J_n(Dx^C) + C_2 Y_n(Dx^C)]. \tag{3--25}$$

EXAMPLE 3–1. Determine the general solution of (3–19) from the generalized Bessel equation (3–24) and corresponding solution (3–25).

Solution. By comparing (3–19) with (3–24), we find that for equivalent coefficients of the second term $A = 0 = B$, and for equivalent coefficients of the third term $C = 1$ and $D = i$. Then by (3–25), the general solution of (3–19) must read

$$y = C_1 J_n(ix) + C_2 Y_n(ix) = C_3 I_n(x) + C_4 K_n(x),$$

as in (3–22).

---

*See Sherwood and Reed (5), p. 210.

3–7 Expansion in a series of Bessel functions. In later work we shall be forced to consider the possibility of the following *series expansion:*

$$f(x) = \sum_{i=1}^{\infty} C_i J_n(R_i x) = C_1 J_n(R_1 x) + C_2 J_n(R_2 x) + \cdots. \quad (3\text{–}26)$$

Here $f(x)$ is an arbitrary function in which the values of x are restricted to the interval from $x = 0$ to $x = 1$, and the R_i are the *consecutive* positive roots of the equation $J_n(R_i) = 0$.* The problem is to find the general coefficients C_i which make this expansion possible.

To determine the constant coefficients C_i, we multiply both sides of (3–26) by $x J_n(R_i x)$ and then integrate the result over the convergent interval from $x = 0$ to $x = 1$ as

$$\int_0^1 x J_n(R_i x) f(x) dx = C_1 \int_0^1 x J_n(R_i x) J_n(R_1 x) dx$$

$$+ C_2 \int_0^1 x J_n(R_i x) J_n(R_2 x) dx + \cdots + C_i \int_0^1 x J_n^2(R_i x) dx + \cdots. \quad (3\text{–}27)$$

Now there are two well-known integrals that stem from the "orthogonality" property of the Bessel functions which are useful here, namely, that†

$$\int_0^1 x J_n(R_i x) J_n(R_j x) dx = 0 \quad (3\text{–}28)$$

if $i \neq j$, and

$$\int_0^1 x J_n^2(R_i x) dx = \tfrac{1}{2} J_{n+1}^2(R_i) \quad (3\text{–}29)$$

if $i = j$. According to (3–28), all the integrals on the right side of (3–27) not containing like roots R must vanish, and therefore the only integral which enters the evaluation of (3–27) is that for which $i = j$, as

$$\int_0^1 x J_n(R_i x) f(x) dx = C_i \int_0^1 x J_n^2(R_i x) dx.$$

Then, by virtue of (3–29),

$$C_i = \frac{2}{J_{n+1}^2(R_i)} \int_0^1 x J_n(R_i x) f(x) dx. \quad (3\text{–}30)$$

These are the consecutive coefficients which are to be used in expanding the arbitrary function $f(x)$ in a series of nth-order Bessel functions of the first kind, as in (3–26).

---

*The first five consecutive roots ($i = 1, 2, 3, 4, 5$) for the first-kind Bessel functions of orders $n = 0, 1, 2, 3, 4$ are tabulated in Table A–11 of the Appendix.
†See, for example, Pipes (6), p. 320.

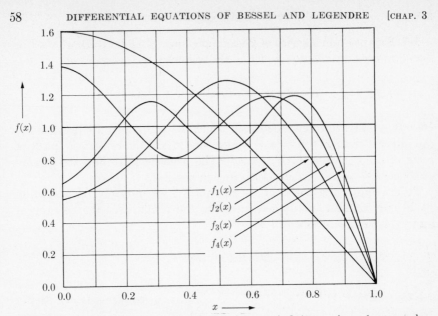

Fig. 3–4. Approximation of $f(x) = 1$ by an infinite series of zero-order Bessel functions of the first kind. The first term in the series is represented by $f_1(x)$, sum of the first and second terms by $f_2(x)$, and so on.

EXAMPLE 3–2. Expand the function $f(x) = 1$, $0 \leq x \leq 1$, in an infinite series of zero-order Bessel functions of the first kind, and illustrate graphically how this series builds up termwise to represent the given function.

Solution. The zero-order Bessel series which will represent unity in the interval $x = 0$–1 is

$$1 = C_1 J_0(R_1 x) + C_2 J_0(R_2 x) + \cdots + C_i J_0(R_i x) + \cdots,$$

provided the coefficients C_i are evaluated according to (3–30) as

$$C_i = \frac{2}{J_1^2(R_i)} \int_0^1 x J_0(R_i x) dx.$$

The integration can be performed by reference to (3–5) as

$$\int_0^1 x J_0(R_i x) dx = \frac{x}{R_i} \left(\frac{R_i x}{2} - \frac{R_i^3 x^3}{2^2 \cdot 4} + \frac{R_i^5 x^5}{2^2 \cdot 4^2 \cdot 6} - \cdots \right) \Big]_0^1,$$

and by recalling the expansion of $J_1(R_i x)$ according to (3–8), we find that

$$\int_0^1 x J_0(R_i x) dx = \frac{J_1(R_i)}{R_i}.$$

This serves to complete the evaluation of the coefficients as $C_i = 2/R_i J_1(R_i)$, so that the required series reads

$$f(x) = 1 = \frac{2}{R_1 J_1(R_1)} J_0(R_1 x) + \frac{2}{R_2 J_1(R_2)} J_0(R_2 x) + \cdots,$$

where the R_i are consecutive positive roots of $J_0(R_i) = 0$. This series also holds for the double interval from $x = -1$ to $x = 1$, the reason for this being that $J_0(x)$ is an even function. It should also be noted here that similar expansions can be developed for the general interval from $x = 0$ to $x = a$.

By referring to Table A–3 for computed values of $J_1(R_i)$, and to Table A–11 for the consecutive roots of $J_0(R_i) = 0$, the series takes the form

$$f(x) = 1 = 1.602\, J_0(2.405x) - 1.065\, J_0(5.520x) + 0.851\, J_0(8.654x)$$

$$-0.729\, J_0(11.792x) + \cdots = F_1(x) + F_2(x) + F_3(x) + F_4(x) + \cdots.$$

Figure 3–4 illustrates how the series builds up. The curve $f_1(x)$ representing the first term $F_1(x)$ is a crude approximation to $f(x) = 1$, while the curve $f_2(x)$ representing the sum of the first two terms as $F_1(x) + F_2(x)$ is somewhat improved. The representation is markedly improved when four terms are used, as in $f_4(x) = F_1(x) + F_2(x) + F_3(x) + F_4(x)$, the curve oscillating four times about $f(x) = 1$. The addition of still more terms will always improve the approximation, although it is clear that the series will not converge to unity at the end points regardless of the number of terms used.

LEGENDRE POLYNOMIALS

3–8 The Legendre differential equation. A second-order differential equation which arises in the solution of Laplace's equation in spherical coordinates is

$$(1 - x^2)\frac{d^2 y}{dx^2} - 2x\frac{dy}{dx} + n(n + 1)y = 0, \tag{3–31}$$

which is known as *Legendre's differential equation* in honor of the French mathematician Adrien Legendre (1752–1833), who first obtained its fundamental solutions. These general solutions are known as *Legendre functions*. When n is equal to zero or a positive integer (the only cases to be considered here), the Legendre functions take the form of polynomials and are then called *Legendre polynomials*.

The general solution of (3–31) is written in a form analogous to the general solution of the Bessel equation, namely,

$$y = C_1 P_n(x) + C_2 Q_n(x), \tag{3–32}$$

where again C_1 and C_2 are integration constants, and $y_I = P_n(x)$ and $y_{II} = Q_n(x)$ are *first-* and *second-kind* Legendre functions constituting independent solutions of (3–31). Only the $P_n(x)$ functions will have application in later work, so we restrict our attention to these polynomials in particular.

3-9 The Legendre polynomials.   Here again a power-series solution is obtained by first assuming that the first solution y_I of (3-31) is given by the infinite power series

$$y = a_0 + a_1 x + a_2 x^2 + \cdots . \tag{3-33}$$

Then by differentiating this twice and substituting in (3-31), we have

$$[a_0 n(n+1) + 2a_2] + [a_1(n-1)(n+2) + 6a_3]x$$
$$+ [a_2(n-2)(n+3) + 12a_4]x^2 + \cdots = 0,$$

which evidently is satisfied only if the coefficients of x^0, x^1, x^2, $\cdots$ vanish. This results in the system of linear equations

$$a_2 = -\frac{a_0}{2} n(n+1),$$

$$a_3 = -\frac{a_1}{6} (n-1)(n+2),$$

$$a_4 = -\frac{a_2}{12} (n-2)(n+3) = \frac{a_0}{24} n(n+1)(n-2)(n+3),$$
$$\vdots$$

whereby the infinite series solution (3-33) reappears in the form

$$y = a_0 \left[1 - \frac{n(n-1)}{2!} x^2 + \frac{n(n-2)(n+1)(n+3)}{4!} x^3 - \cdots \right]$$
$$+ a_1 \left[x - \frac{(n-1)(n+2)}{3!} x^3 + \frac{(n-1)(n-3)(n+2)(n+4)}{5!} x^5 \right]$$
$$= a_0 y_I + a_1 y_{II}. \tag{3-34}$$

Since (3-34) has two arbitrary constants a_0 and a_1, we can consider it as being a general solution of Legendre's equation (3-31).* For n either zero or a positive integer, we obtain a solution of the first kind, $y_I = P_n(x)$, by taking a_0 or a_1 as zero.   It is to be noted that when n is an even integer, then the y_I solution is a polynomial in x of degree n and not an infinite series, because of the terminating terms such as $(n-2)$ for $n = 2$.   In such a case $y_I = P_n(x)$, a polynomial, and y_{II} is an infinite series.   Likewise, if n is an odd integer, then y_I is an infinite series and y_{II} a polynomial. With these two possibilities, we have the Legendre functions

$$P_n(x) = \sum_{p=0}^{n/2} (-1)^p \frac{(2n-2p)!}{2^n p!(n-p)!(n-2p)!} x^{n-2p};$$

$$n = 0, 2, 4, \cdots , \tag{3-35}$$

---

*The reader should verify that this series is convergent in the interval -1 to 1.

and

$$P_n(x) = \sum_{p=0}^{(n-1)/2} (-1)^p \frac{(2n-2p)!}{2^n p!(n-p)!(n-2p)!} x^{n-2p};$$

$$n = 1, 3, 5, \cdots. \quad (3\text{–}36)$$

As mentioned previously, only the first-kind Legendre functions in the form of polynomials need be considered here, and these are obtained directly from (3–35) and (3–36) for $n = 0, 1, 2, \cdots$ as

$$P_0(x) = 1,$$
$$P_1(x) = x,$$
$$P_2(x) = \tfrac{1}{2}(3x^2 - 1), \qquad\qquad (3\text{–}37)$$
$$P_3(x) = \tfrac{1}{2}(5x^3 - 3x),$$
$$P_4(x) = \tfrac{1}{8}(35x^4 - 30x^2 + 3),$$

$$\cdot$$
$$\cdot$$
$$\cdot$$

A useful recurrence formula can be established at once by observing that each of these polynomials is a function of the polynomial preceding and succeeding it. Thus

$$P_0(x) = \frac{1}{x} P_1(x),$$

$$P_1(x) = \frac{1}{3x} [P_0(x) + 2P_2(x)],$$

$$P_2(x) = \frac{1}{5x} [2P_1(x) + 3P_3(x)],$$

$$\cdot$$
$$\cdot$$
$$\cdot$$

or, in general,

$$P_n(x) = \frac{nP_{n-1}(x) + (n+1)P_{n+1}(x)}{(2n+1)x}. \qquad (3\text{–}38)$$

The first five Legendre polynomials of the first kind, $P_1(x)$, $P_2(x)$, $P_3(x)$, $P_4(x)$, and $P_5(x)$, are tabulated in Table A–7 of the Appendix. Such tabulations are frequently listed as *Legendre coefficients*, where x is replaced by the trigonometric substitution $\cos \varphi$, such listings being useful when (3–31) is expressed in spherical coordinates. In this case the polynomials (3–37) reappear as

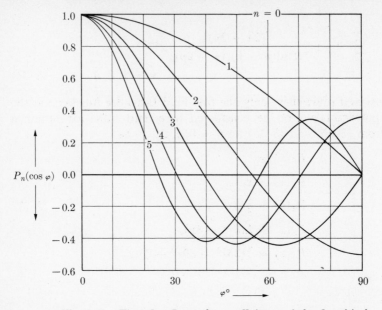

Fig. 3–5. First five Legendre coefficients of the first kind.

$$P_0(\cos \varphi) = 1,$$

$$P_1(\cos \varphi) = \cos \varphi,$$

$$P_2(\cos \varphi) = \tfrac{1}{4}(3 \cos 2\varphi + 1),$$

$$P_3(\cos \varphi) = \tfrac{1}{8}(5 \cos 3\varphi + 3 \cos 3\varphi),$$

$$P_4(\cos \varphi) = \tfrac{1}{64}(35 \cos 4\varphi + 20 \cos 2\varphi + 9),$$

$$\vdots$$

or, in general (Fig. 3–5),

$$P_n(\cos \varphi) = \frac{nP_{n-1}(\cos \varphi) + (n + 1)P_{n+1}(\cos \varphi)}{(2n + 1) \cos \varphi} . \tag{3–39}$$

3–10 Expansion in a series of Legendre polynomials. Consider the expansion of an arbitrary but restricted function $f(x)$ into a series of Legendre polynomials according to

$$f(x) = \sum_{n=0}^{\infty} C_n P_n(x) = C_0 P_0(x) + C_1 P_1(x) + \cdots, \tag{3–40}$$

which is generally valid if $f(x)$ and its derivatives are continuous in the required interval of convergence of the Legendre polynomials, namely, from $x = -1$ to $x = 1$. Multiplying both sides of (3–40) by $P_n(x)$ and integrating over this interval of convergence, we have

$$\int_{-1}^{1} P_n(x)f(x)dx = C_0 \int_{-1}^{1} P_n(x)P_0(x)dx$$

$$+ C_1 \int_{-1}^{1} P_n(x)P_1(x)dx + \cdots + C_n \int_{-1}^{1} P_n^2(x)dx + \cdots . \quad (3\text{–}41)$$

Again, as with the Bessel functions, the orthogonality property of the Legendre functions leads to the integral relations*

$$\int_{-1}^{1} P_n(x)P_m(x)dx = 0 \qquad (3\text{–}42)$$

if $m \neq n$, and

$$\int_{-1}^{1} P_n^2(x)dx = \frac{2}{2n+1} \qquad (3\text{–}43)$$

if $m = n$. Then, according to (3–42), all the integrals on the right side of (3–41) vanish except the integral whose coefficient is C_n. By virtue of (3–43), the general coefficients C_n in the expansion of $f(x)$ in a series of Legendre polynomials become

$$C_n = \frac{2n+1}{2} \int_{-1}^{1} P_n(x)f(x)dx, \qquad (3\text{–}44)$$

which holds only in the interval $-1 \leq x \leq 1$.

When $\cos \varphi$ replaces x, the expansion is to be carried out according to

$$f(\varphi) = \sum_{n=0}^{\infty} C_n P_n(\cos \varphi) = f(\cos \varphi).$$

Since the interval of convergence for $\cos \varphi$ is from π (corresponding to -1 for x) to 0 (corresponding to 1 for x), the general coefficients for the expansion of $f(\varphi)$ read

$$C_n = \frac{2n+1}{2} \int_{0}^{\pi} P_n(\cos \varphi)f(\varphi) \sin \varphi \, d\varphi. \qquad (3\text{–}45)$$

The expansion of an arbitrary function into a series of Legendre polynomials is seen to be closely related to expanding such a function into a series of Bessel functions. In Chapter 5 we shall consider the expansion of arbitrary functions in a series of trigonometric functions, and the reader will recall that such expansions are known as *Fourier series*.

REFERENCES

1. T. von Kármán and M. A. Biot, *Mathematical Methods in Engineering.* New York: McGraw-Hill, 1940.
2. B. O. Peirce, *A Short Table of Integrals.* Boston: Ginn and Company, 1929.

*See Reference (6), pp. 329–330.

3. A. Gray and G. B. Mathews, *A Treatise on Bessel Functions and Their Application to Physics.* London: Macmillan, 1922.

4. F. E. Relton, *Applied Bessel Functions.* London: Blackie & Son, 1946.

5. T. K. Sherwood and C. E. Reed, *Applied Mathematics in Chemical Engineering.* New York: McGraw-Hill, 1939.

6. L. A. Pipes, *Applied Mathematics for Engineers and Physicists.* New York: McGraw-Hill, 1946.

PROBLEMS

3-1. Find the general solution of the following differential equations:

(a) $x\dfrac{d^2y}{dx^2} + \dfrac{dy}{dx} - ay = 0,$ (b) $\dfrac{d^2y}{dx^2} - a^2xy = 0,$

(c) $\dfrac{d^2y}{dx^2} + \dfrac{A}{x}\dfrac{dy}{dx} + ay = 0.$

3-2. Does the differential equation

$$x\frac{d^2y}{dx^2} + (1 - ax)\frac{dy}{dx} - ay = 0$$

have a general solution in terms of Bessel functions?

3-3. Prove that the following general solutions of (3-1) and (3-19) are incorrect:

$$\left.\begin{aligned}(3\text{-}1)\!: \quad y &= C_1J_n(x) + C_2J_{-n}(x) \\ (3\text{-}19)\!: \quad y &= C_1I_n(x) + C_2I_{-n}(x)\end{aligned}\right\} n = 0, 1, 2, \cdots.$$

3-4. Using (3-20), show that since

$$J_{1/2}(x) = \sqrt{2/\pi x}\,\sin x, \qquad J_{-1/2}(x) = \sqrt{2/\pi x}\,\cos x,$$

then

$$I_{1/2}(x) = \sqrt{2/\pi x}\,\sinh x, \qquad I_{-1/2}(x) = \sqrt{2/\pi x}\,\cosh x.$$

3-5. Evaluate $\Gamma(7/2)$, and verify that $\Gamma(n)\Gamma(1 - n) = \pi/\sin n\pi$ for $0 < n < 1$.

3-6. An important recurrence formula is derived from (3-14) as follows:

$$\frac{d}{dx}J_n(x) = \sum_{p=0}^{\infty} \frac{(-1)^p(n + 2p)/2}{\Gamma(p + 1)\Gamma(n + p + 1)}\left(\frac{x}{2}\right)^{n+2p-1},$$

$$x\frac{d}{dx}J_n(x) = n\sum_{p=0}^{\infty} \frac{(-1)^p}{\Gamma(p + 1)\Gamma(n + p + 1)}\left(\frac{x}{2}\right)^{n+2p}$$

$$+ x\sum_{p=0}^{\infty} \frac{(-1)^p(2/x)}{\dfrac{\Gamma(p + 1)}{p}\Gamma(n + p + 1)}\left(\frac{x}{2}\right)^{n+2p}$$

$$= nJ_n(x) + x\sum_{p=1}^{\infty} \frac{(-1)^p}{\Gamma(p)\Gamma(n + p + 1)}\left(\frac{x}{2}\right)^{n+2p-1}.$$

Setting $p' = p - 1$, we have

$$x \frac{d}{dx} J_n(x) = n J_n(x) + x \sum_{p'=0}^{\infty} \frac{-(-1)^{p'}}{\Gamma(p'+1)\Gamma(n+p'+2)} \left(\frac{x}{2}\right)^{n+2p'+1},$$

or

$$\frac{d}{dx} J_n(x) = \frac{n}{x} J_n(x) - J_{n+1}(x).$$

Using the difference formula for the gamma function, and by replacing $n + 2p$ by $2(n + p) - n$, show that

$$\frac{d}{dx} J_n(x) = -\frac{n}{x} J_n(x) + J_{n-1}(x),$$

and from these last two relations establish the identities

(a) $\quad \dfrac{2n}{x} J_n(x) = J_{n-1}(x) + J_{n+1}(x),$ \qquad (b) $\quad \dfrac{d}{dx} x^n J_n(x) = x^n J_{n-1}(x),$

(c) $\quad \dfrac{d}{dx} x^{-n} J_n(x) = -x^{-n} J_{n+1}(x).$

3–7. Verify that $Y_n(x)$ satisfies identities of the form in (a), (b), and (c) of problem 3–6.

3–8. Using the results of problems 3–4 and 3–6, show that

$$J_{3/2}(x) = \sqrt{\frac{2}{\pi x}} \left(\frac{\sin x}{x} - \cos x\right),$$

$$J_{-3/2}(x) = \sqrt{\frac{2}{\pi x}} \left(-\sin x - \frac{\cos x}{x}\right),$$

$$J_{5/2}(x) = \sqrt{\frac{2}{\pi x}} \left(\frac{3 - x^2}{x^2} \sin x - \frac{3}{x} \cos x\right),$$

$$J_{-5/2}(x) = \sqrt{\frac{2}{\pi x}} \left(\frac{3}{x} \sin x - \frac{3 - x^2}{x^2} \cos x\right).$$
$\vdots$

3–9. Using (3–14) and (3–20), show that

$$I_n(x) = \sum_{p=0}^{\infty} \frac{1}{\Gamma(p+1)\Gamma(n+p+1)} \left(\frac{x}{2}\right)^{n+2p},$$

and therefore that

(a) $\quad \dfrac{2n}{x} I_n(x) = I_{n-1}(x) - I_{n+1}(x),$ \qquad (b) $\quad \dfrac{d}{dx} x^n I_n(x) = x^n I_{n-1}(x),$

(c) $\quad \dfrac{d}{dx} x^{-n} I_n(x) = x^{-n} I_{n+1}(x).$

3–10. Verify that $K_n(x)$ satisfies identities of the form in (a), (b), and (c) of problem 3–9.

3–11. Using (3–14), establish the indefinite integrals

$$\int x^{n+1}J_n(x)dx = x^{n+1}J_{n+1}(x), \qquad \int x^{1-n}J_n(x)dx = x^{1-n}J_{n-1}(x),$$

and show that these also hold for the $I_n(x)$.

3–12. Compute the general coefficients C_i in a Bessel-function expansion of x^2 in the interval $0 \le x \le 1$ according to

$$x^2 = \sum_{i=0}^{\infty} C_i J_2(R_i x).$$

3–13. Show that in the general interval $0 \le x \le a$, the coefficients C_i in a Bessel-function expansion of $f(x)$ are given by

$$C_i = \frac{2}{a^2 J_{n+1}^2(R_i a)} \int_0^a x J_n(R_i x)f(x)dx,$$

and verify that this reduces to (3–30) for the particular interval $0 \le x \le 1$.

3–14. Show first by (3–35) and (3–36), and then by (3–38), that

$$P_5(x) = \tfrac{1}{8}(63x^5 - 70x^3 + 15x),$$

$$P_6(x) = \tfrac{1}{16}(231x^6 - 315x^4 + 105x^2 - 5).$$

3–15. Verify the following general derivative for the Legendre polynomials:

$$\frac{d}{dx} P_n(x) = \frac{nP_{n-1}(x) - xnP_n(x)}{1 - x^2}.$$

3–16. Verify the definite integral

$$\int_0^1 x^p P_n(x)dx = \frac{p(p-1)\cdots(p-n+2)}{(p+n+1)(p+n-1)\cdots(p-n+3)};$$

$$n = 2, 3, 4, \cdots, \quad p > -1.$$

3–17. Compute the general coefficients C_n in a Legendre-coefficient expansion of the function $f(\varphi) = \cos^2\varphi$ in the interval $0 \le \varphi \le \pi$ according to

$$\cos^2\varphi = \sum_{n=0}^{\infty} C_n P_n(\cos \varphi).$$

3–18. Develop the following functions in a series of Legendre polynomials, and illustrate graphically how each series builds up to represent the given function:

$$f(x) = 1; \quad -1 \le x \le 0, \qquad f(x) = -1; \quad 0 \le x \le 1.$$

CHAPTER 4

EXTENDED SURFACE

In this chapter we examine the method of increasing the efficiency of heat removal from a structure by means of extended surfaces in the form of straight and circumferential fins and spines of various profile shapes.

4–1 Introduction. *Extended surfaces* are commonly found in the form of *fins* attached to the surface of a structure for the express purpose of increasing the heat transfer between the structure and an ambient fluid. According to Article 2–2, the use of fins on one side of a wall separating two heat-exchanging fluids is exploited most if the fins are attached to or made an integral part of that face on which the thermal surface resistivity is greatest. In such a case the fins serve the purpose of artificially increasing the surface transmittance. It is on this principle that fins find numerous applications in electrical apparatus in which generated heat must be efficiently dissipated, and in such specialized installations as single and double-tube heat exchangers for boilers and radiators, on cylinders of air-cooled internal-combustion engines, and so on.

The general disposition of fins on the *primary surface* is usually either longitudinal, as in Fig. 4–1(a), or circumferential, as in Fig. 4–1(b). Fins may also be disposed in the form of a continuous spiral on the primary surface, or in the form of individual rods known as *pin-fins* or *spines*. The cross-section shape of the extended surface in a plane normal to the primary surface is to be referred to as the *profile* of the fin or spine.

For any one particular installation, the problem is to choose a fin or spine which will give maximum cooling efficiency, minimum material for cost, weight, and space considerations, minimum resistance to the flow of

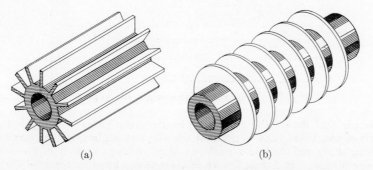

(a)   (b)

Fig. 4–1. Straight and circular fins of rectangular profile.

ambient cooling medium, adequate strength, and ease of manufacture. In the consideration of this problem we again assume, as in Chapter 2, that the conduction process is both steady and linear.

4–2 Straight fin of rectangular profile. Among the very first inquiries in connection with extended surfaces is the examination of those conditions under which one might expect the addition of fins to increase the heat flow through an otherwise plain wall. When fins are placed on a surface with a high thermal resistance, we should expect the rate of heat flow to be proportional to the extension of the primary wall surface, other things being equal. In some cases, however, the thermal resistance of the primary surface may be of such proportion to the other partial resistances of the wall that the addition of surface fins of a certain minimum width w will not only fail to increase the heat transferred but in extreme cases may actually decrease the heat exchange. We are therefore interested in finding these minimal conditions under which the finned surface will have advantage over the plain wall.

Consider the straight fin of rectangular *profile area* $A = 2\delta w$ and of uniform thermal conductivity k, as in Fig. 4–2. Both the unit surface conductance h and ambient gas temperature t_g are assumed uniform. In addition, we consider the fin to be long enough longitudinally so that the effects of heat loss at the terminating profile edges $z = \pm L/2$ are negligible. This is to say that no heat flows in the z-direction, since the thermal resistance in this direction far exceeds the resistance in the x-direction if w/L is small. Then for a comparatively wide fin, i.e., small δ/w, all yz-planes in the fin can be taken as isothermal, including the base plane at $x = 0$.*

The general solution for $t(x)$ in the straight fin of rectangular profile is evidently the same as that derived for the turbine blade in Chapter 2.

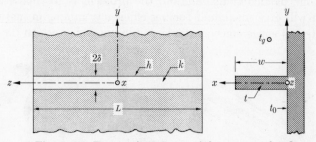

Fig. 4–2.   Denotations for straight rectangular fin.

---

*Harper and Brown (1) have analytically investigated this assumption of one-dimensional flow, and found that the effect of neglecting the temperature gradients dt/dy and dt/dz in a relatively thick rectangular fin is of the order of only one percent. In Article 7–8 we shall examine a fin of exaggerated thickness for which the temperature gradient dt/dy cannot be neglected.

Thus, by Article 2–11,

$$T = t - t_g = C_1 e^{Nx} + C_2 e^{-Nx}, \tag{4-1}$$

where the parameter N, originally defined by (2–29), is now given by

$$N = \sqrt{h/k\delta}, \tag{4-2}$$

$(p/A = 2/2\delta = 1/\delta)$ in which δ is the semithickness of the rectangular profile (Fig. 4–2). The general solution (4–1) is to satisfy the boundary conditions expressed in T as

$$T = T_0 \text{ at } x = 0,$$

$$-k \frac{dT}{dx} = hT \text{ at } x = w,$$

the second of these two conditions describing the heat loss at the fin tip. Then at $x = w$

$$-kN(C_1 e^{Nw} - C_2 e^{-Nw}) = h(C_1 e^{Nw} + C_2 e^{-Nw}),$$

and on solving this simultaneously with the result obtained by applying the first boundary condition, $T_0 = C_1 + C_2$, we determine the integration constants as $C_1 = T_0/(1 - \sigma e^{2Nw})$ and $C_2 = T_0\sigma/(\sigma - e^{-2Nw})$, wherein $\sigma = (h + Nk)/(h - Nk)$. The temperature distribution follows as

$$\frac{t - t_g}{t_0 - t_g} = \frac{e^{Nw(x/w)} - \sigma e^{-Nw(x/w-2)}}{1 - \sigma e^{2Nw}}, \tag{4-3}$$

and the heat conducted through the fin base at $x = 0$ must therefore be

$$q_0 = -k(2\delta) \left(\frac{dT}{dx}\right)_0 = 2\delta k N T_0 \left(\frac{\sigma e^{2Nw} + 1}{\sigma e^{2Nw} - 1}\right),$$

or, by reintroducing the parameter σ,

$$q_0 = 2\delta k N T_0 \left[\frac{(h/Nk) + \tanh Nw}{1 + (h/Nk)\tanh Nw}\right]. \tag{4-4}$$

The form of the solution (4–4) suggests that for a fixed δ there exists a value of fin width w above which q_0 will decrease and below which q_0 will increase. The limiting condition where it is no longer of advantage to increase the fin width to increase q_0 must therefore correspond to the point of vanishing slope dq_0/dw. Thus, by differentiating (4–4), considering δ, k, N, and T_0 as constant, we find the *optimum Nusselt number*

$$(N_u)_{opt} = \left(\frac{h\delta}{k}\right)_{opt} = 1, \tag{4-5}$$

which indicates that for a value of N_u less than unity the fin will have a cooling effect, and for N_u greater than unity the fin will have an unfavorable insulating effect. Equation (4–5), if written as $h \leq k/\delta$, suggests more clearly that when the unit surface conductance for the fin is just equal to or less than the unit internal conductance, then the fin is just becoming useful. When the converse is true, then the addition of fins will decrease the heat transfer and so defeat the purpose of the extended surface.

It is easily shown by (4–5) that straight rectangular fins are generally advantageous for surface heat-exchange with gases, less effective for forced convection heat-exchange to liquids, and of no advantage for surface condensers and the like. The differences in these three cases show up in the relative magnitude of h. Thus for a typical $\frac{1}{8}''$ thick aluminum fin, $N_u = 25(0.0625/12)/117 = 0.0011$, which indicates that such a fin should have a pronounced effect, since $N_u \ll 1$. But for liquids the effect would be much smaller, with say $N_u = 0.0011(2,500/25) = 0.11$. Finally, for condensing liquids or vapors with h increased tenfold, $N_u = 1.1$, which suggests that the primary surface would be more effective without fins at all.

4–3 Simplified solution. In Article 4–2 the integration constants C_1 and C_2 for the general solution (4–1) were determined by a consideration of the fin-tip heat loss as a second boundary condition. Since this method of accounting for tip heat loss will prove much too tedious for the more complicated profiles, we now consider a simplified approach using the concept of a *corrected fin width* w_c, as first used by Harper and Brown (1).

A particular solution of (4–1) satisfying the boundary conditions

$$T = T_0 \quad \text{at } x = 0,$$

$$\frac{dT}{dx} = 0 \quad \text{at } x = w,$$

is [see (2–31)]

$$\frac{T}{T_0} = \frac{\cosh N(1 - x/w)}{\cosh Nw}, \tag{4–6}$$

so that for the case of neglected fin-tip heat loss, the heat conducted through a unit length of rectangular fin base becomes

$$q_0 = 2\delta k N T_0 \tanh Nw, \tag{4–7}$$

as compared with the exact solution (4–4).

Now the prototype situation is not that of an adiabatic tip surface, since all of the heat conducted through the fin base is not dissipated to the ambient gas up to the exposed edge $x = w$ ($t_w \neq t_g$). To correct for this,

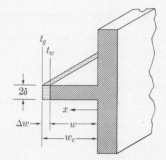

Fig. 4–3. Fictitious extension of fin width w to corrected adiabatic tip at w_c.

we imagine an extension of the fin width, as in Fig. 4–3. The added length Δw is to absorb the excess heat left at $x = w$, whereby the fictitious tip at $x = w_c$ will take on the ambient gas temperature t_g ($T = 0$) as in the second boundary condition, which leads to (4–6) and (4–7).

Without the extended tip, the heat rate at $x = w$ is

$$q_w = h(2\delta)(t_w - t_g), \tag{4–8}$$

and under the condition that $dt/dx = 0$ at $x = w_c$, Δw must be such that (4–8) is all dissipated on the fictitious surface $2\Delta w$, or

$$h(2\delta)(t_w - t_g) = h(2\Delta w)(t_w - t_g).$$

This assumes that all of the added surface $2\Delta w$ is at a temperature t_w. With such an approximation $\Delta w \doteq \delta$, whereby

$$w_c = w + \delta = w + h/N^2 k.$$

The simplified solution for q_0 which approximately accounts for fin-tip heat loss is therefore

$$q_0 = 2\delta k N T_0 \tanh (Nw + \sqrt{N_u}). \tag{4–9}$$

The two solutions (4–4) and (4–9) are compared in Fig. 4–4. The

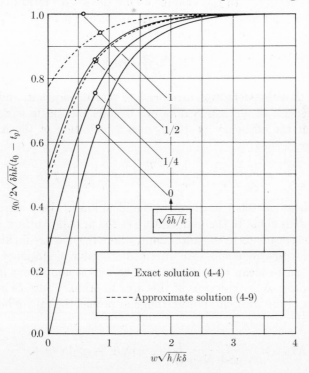

Fig. 4–4. Heat flow through straight rectangular fin by solutions which exactly and approximately account for fin-tip heat loss.

maximum deviation of the approximate solution (4–9) is seen to occur for $w(h/k\delta)^{1/2} = 0$ and a square-root Nusselt number of $(h\delta/k)^{1/2} = 1$. Under these conditions the approximate solution gives a value of heat flow $(1 - 0.764) = 23.6\%$ too small. For $(h\delta/k)^{1/2} = \frac{1}{2}$ the maximum error is reduced to $(0.5 - 0.462)/0.5 = 7.6\%$, and for $(h\delta/k)^{1/2} = \frac{1}{4}$ the solutions (4–4) and (4–9) are nearly identical [as they are officially for $(h\delta/k)^{1/2} = 0$]. In the solutions which follow, we use the corrected length $w_c = w + \delta$, keeping in mind that such an approximation is reasonable only if $\sqrt{N_u} \leq \frac{1}{2}$.

4–4 Efficiency of the straight rectangular fin. There are several criteria used for judging the relative performance of extended surface. The first of these is the ratio of the heat conducted through the fin root to that which would be transferred from the same root area if the fin were not present and if the root temperature t_0 remained the same. As pointed out by Gardner (2), the *effectiveness* is not a true indication of fin performance, since t_0 cannot be expected to remain constant if the fin is removed. A second and more realistic measure of fin performance is the *ratio of the total heat dissipated by the fin to that which would be dissipated if the entire fin surface were at t_0*. In this chapter we use the second ratio as an index of performance, and consistently refer to it as the *fin efficiency*. If S is the fin surface area, then the fin efficiency e is defined by

$$e = \frac{1}{T_0 S} \int_0^S T dS. \tag{4–10}$$

Note first that this definition assumes h to remain constant, and that if w_c is used in place of w, then S does not include the fin-tip surface. Note finally that the efficiency (4–10) is also a definition of the *mean profile temperature*, $\bar{t}$, since

$$\frac{\bar{T}}{T_0} = \frac{(\bar{t} - t_g)}{(t_0 - t_g)} = \frac{1}{w} \int_0^w \frac{T}{T_0} dx = \frac{1}{T_0 S} \int_0^S T dS = e.$$

A fin efficiency of 100% is therefore the ideal limit, where the average fin temperature is equal to the temperature of the primary surface, and a zero efficiency corresponds to the lower limit, where the average fin and ambient gas temperatures are equal. An intermediate value of efficiency, say 70%, is then taken to mean that the fin surface area is equivalent in heat dissipating power to seven-tenths of this area in primary surface at t_0.*

In terms of the straight fin of rectangular profile, the rate of heat dissipation from its surfaces at T is

$$q = 2 \int_0^{w_c} hT dx = \frac{2T_0 h}{N \cosh N w_c} \int_0^{w_c} \cosh [N(x - w_c)] N dx = \frac{2T_0 h}{N} \tanh N w_c,$$

*It is shown in the Harper and Brown paper (1) that e is independent of any variation in t_0 in the z-direction (Fig. 4–2).

and if the entire fin surface is at T_0, then the larger rate of heat dissipation is

$$q^0 = 2whT_0.$$

The approximate efficiency $e = q/q^0$ is thus

$$e_s = \frac{1}{Nw_c} \tanh Nw_c,$$

or, in terms of the rectangular profile area $A = 2\delta w_c$,

$$e_s = \frac{1}{\sqrt{2\xi}} \tanh \sqrt{2}\xi, \tag{4-11}$$

in which

$$\xi = w_c^{3/2}\sqrt{h/kA}. \tag{4-12}$$

The efficiency function (4-11) is useful for predicting the influence of changes in the various parameters involved, namely, the unit surface conductance, the fin conductivity, and fin thickness and width dimensions. For example, if $\xi = 1.0$ and thus $e_s = 63\%$, then doubling the thermal conductivity of the fin would increase its efficiency to 76%, corresponding to $\xi = 1/\sqrt{2} = 0.7$. In other words, the higher-conductivity fin has the effect of increasing the heat-transfer area of the primary surface at t_0 by approximately 76% of the total fin area S, while the lower-conductivity fin increases this area by only 63% of S. It is also clear that a lower unit surface conductance h, a decrease in fin width w, and an increase in fin thickness 2δ all contribute to a higher fin efficiency.

EXAMPLE 4-1. The outer surface of an aircraft oil heater at a uniform temperature of 300°F is to be fitted with straight fins of rectangular profile having a uniform thermal conductivity of 15 Btu/hr-ft-°F. The design ambient air temperature is 66°F and the unit surface conductance is estimated to be 100 Btu/hr-ft²-°F. Determine the thickness and efficiency of these fins if each is restricted in width to $\frac{3}{8}''$, and each is to remove 1000 Btu/hr per foot length of primary surface.

Solution. By (4-5) we first check to see that $h < k/\delta$ or $\delta < k/h = 15/100 = 1.8''$, and therefore the proposed fin would not be too thin to manufacture and maintain. Then, according to (4-9),

$$q_0 = 2\sqrt{100 \times 15\delta}\,(300 - 66)\tanh\,[\sqrt{100/15\delta}\,(3/8 \times 12) + \sqrt{100\delta/15}],$$

or

$$1000 = 18{,}130\sqrt{\delta}\tanh\,(0.0806/\sqrt{\delta} + 2.58\sqrt{\delta}),$$

and by trial and error we find this equation to be satisfied by $2\delta = 0.09''$ With these data, $Nw_c = (h/k\delta)^{1/2}(w + \delta) = 1.475$, and the fin efficiency becomes

$$e_s = \frac{1}{Nw_c} \tanh Nw_c = 61.0\%.$$

4–5 Optimum dimensions for straight rectangular fin. For any given rectangular profile area $A = 2\delta w_c$, the best dimensions of width and thickness are those for which the fin dissipates the maximum quantity of heat. To find these optimum dimensions, we express q_0 as a function of only one of these dimensions, say the thickness 2δ, and then determine that particular value of δ for which q_0 is a maximum. Thus by (4–9) and the definition of N given by (4–2),

$$q_0 = 2T_0\sqrt{kh\delta}\tanh\left(w_c\sqrt{h/k\delta}\right) = 2T_0\sqrt{kh\delta}\tanh\left(\frac{1}{2}\frac{A}{\delta^{3/2}}\sqrt{h/k}\right),$$

and on forming the derivative $dq_0/d\delta = 0$, we obtain

$$3\lambda\,\mathrm{sech}^2\,\lambda = \tanh\lambda,$$

wherein $\lambda = (A/2)\delta^{-3/2}(h/k)^{1/2}$. This result can be rearranged by hyperbolic identities to read

$$\lambda = \tfrac{1}{6}\sinh 2\lambda,$$

and from this we obtain by trial and error the real root

$$\lambda_{opt} = 1.4192.$$

The optimum semithickness for fixed rectangular area A is therefore

$$\delta_{opt} = (A^2h/4\lambda_{opt}^2 k)^{1/3}, \tag{4–13}$$

whence the optimum width becomes $w_{c\,opt} = A/2\delta_{opt}$.

EXAMPLE 4–2.   The base and tip temperatures of a straight fin of rectangular profile are measured during operation in 80°F ambient air and found to be 211°F and 140°F respectively. Does this fin have the most favorable dimensions?

Solution. If the fin has optimum dimensions, then $\lambda = \lambda_{opt}$, and by (4–6),

$$\frac{T_w}{T_0} = 1/\cosh\,(Nw_c)_{opt} = 1/\cosh\lambda_{opt} = 0.4571.$$

With the given data, $(t_w - t_g)/(t_0 - t_g) = (140 - 80)/(211 - 80) = 0.458$, and therefore the fin must have been constructed with the most favorable thickness and width dimensions for maximum heat dissipation.

4–6 Straight fin of triangular profile. Rather than formally derive the differential equation for $t(x)$ in each profile, we can develop a general differential equation in which y (Fig. 4–2) is treated as a variable dependent on x as $y_x = y(x)$.* Then for unit length of fin, the difference between the heat conducted in the x-direction into a differential slice at x and out at $x + dx$ is

---

*See also Gardner (2) or Jakob (3), p. 217.

$$\frac{d}{dx}\left(2ky_x\frac{dT}{dx}\right)dx =$$

$$2ky_x\frac{d^2T}{dx^2}dx + 2k\frac{dT}{dx}\frac{dy_x}{dx}dx,$$

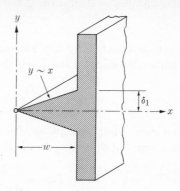

and in the steady state the general heat balance requires that this be equal to the heat dissipated on the two differential elements of fin surface between x and $x + dx$. If we assume that dx on the arbitrary surface is equivalent to dx on the x-axis, then this surface heat dissipation is $2hTdx$, and the generalized differential equation for T reads

Fig. 4–5.   Straight triangular fin.

$$y_x\frac{d^2T}{dx^2} + \frac{dy_x}{dx}\frac{dT}{dx} - \frac{h}{k}T = 0. \tag{4–14}$$

Consider now the straight fin of triangular profile, as in Fig. 4–5. Since $x = 0$ is chosen at the fin tip and the maximum thickness at the base $x = w$ is $2\delta_1$, then $y_x = \delta_1(x/w)$, and the general differential equation (4–14) reduces to

$$x\frac{d^2T}{dx^2} + \frac{dT}{dx} - N^2wT = 0. \tag{4–15}$$

This is a disguised form of Bessel's differential equation (3–1), and on comparing it with the generalized Bessel equation (3–24) and solution (3–25) we determine its general solution as

$$T = C_1J_0(2iN\sqrt{wx}) + C_2Y_0(2iN\sqrt{wx}), \tag{4–16}$$

where the J_0 and Y_0 are zero-order Bessel functions of the first and second kind respectively (Article 3–2).

As before, the integration constants C_1 and C_2 are to be determined such that T satisfies the required boundary conditions

$$T = T_0 \quad \text{at } x = w,$$

$$\frac{dT}{dx} = 0 \quad \text{at } x = 0.$$

Now by reference to Fig. 3–2, it is seen that $J_1(0) = 0$ and $Y_1(0) = -\infty$, so on applying the second boundary condition as

$$\left(\frac{dT}{dx}\right)_0 = 0$$

$$= -C_1iN\sqrt{w/x}\,J_1(2iN\sqrt{wx})\Big]_0 -C_2iN\sqrt{w/x}\,Y_1(2iN\sqrt{wx})\Big]_0,$$

we find that $C_2 = 0$, and the general solution must then be represented by

$$T = C_1 J_0(2iN\sqrt{wx}).$$

The evaluation of C_1 by application of the first boundary condition leads to the particular solution for T which reads

$$\frac{t - t_g}{t_0 - t_g} = \frac{J_0(2iN\sqrt{wx})}{J_0(2iNw)}. \tag{4–17}$$

The rate of heat dissipation from the surfaces of the straight triangular fin is computed according to (4–17) as

$$q = 2h \int_0^w T\,dx = \frac{2hT_0}{J_0(2iNw)} \int_0^w J_0(2iN\sqrt{wx})\,dx.$$

To perform this integration, we expand the J_0 function according to the Bessel series (3–5) and then integrate term by term, as

$$\int_0^w J_0(2iN\sqrt{wx})\,dx = \int_0^w \left(1 + N^2 wx + \frac{N^4 w^2 x^2}{2^2} + \cdots\right)dx$$

$$= w\left(1 + \frac{N^2 w^2}{2} + \frac{N^4 w^4}{2^2 \cdot 3} + \cdots\right),$$

and on comparing this with the J_1 series given by (3–8) as

$$J_1(2iNw) = iNw\left(1 + \frac{N^2 w^2}{2} + \frac{N^4 w^4}{2^2 \cdot 3} + \cdots\right),$$

we have

$$\int_0^w J_0(2iN\sqrt{wx})\,dx = \frac{-i}{N} J_1(2iNw),$$

wherewith

$$q = \frac{-2ihT_0}{N} \frac{J_1(2iNw)}{J_0(2iNw)}. \tag{4–18}$$

If the entire fin surface were at the base temperature t_0, then the ideal rate of heat dissipation would be $q^0 = 2whT_0$. The efficiency of the straight triangular fin, $e_{s'} = q/q^0$, is therefore

$$e_{s'} = \frac{-i}{Nw} \frac{J_1(2iNw)}{J_0(2iNw)},$$

in which both $J_0(2iNw)$ and $-iJ_1(2iNw)$ are real and positive for real and positive Nw. A more concise form for the efficiency is written in terms of the modified Bessel functions (Article 3–5) as $e_{s'} = I_1(2Nw)/NwI_0(2Nw)$, and for comparison with other profiles we introduce the triangular profile area $A = \delta_1 w$, giving

$$e_{s'} = (1/\xi)I_1(2\xi)/I_0(2\xi). \tag{4–19}$$

4–7 Optimum dimensions for straight triangular fin. Again we want to find the particular dimensions δ_1 and w for a fixed triangular profile area which make the heat dissipation from a unit length of fin a maximum. To express $q_0 = q_0(\delta_1)$, the profile area $A = \delta_1 w$ is substituted in (4–18) and the result rearranged to read in terms of the modified Bessel functions as

$$q_0 = (2kAh^2/\lambda')^{1/2}T_0 I_1(\lambda')/I_0(\lambda'),$$

where $\lambda' = (2A)\delta_1^{-3/2}(h/k)^{1/2}$. In computing the δ_1 for which this expression is a maximum, we find that

$$\frac{d}{d\lambda'}\left[\lambda'^{-1/3}I_1(\lambda')/I_0(\lambda')\right] = 0,$$

or

$$I_0(\lambda')\frac{d}{d\lambda'}\left[\lambda'^{-1/3}I_1(\lambda')\right] - \lambda'^{-1/3}I_1(\lambda')\frac{d}{d\lambda'}\left[I_0(\lambda')\right] = 0.$$

Carrying out the differentiation as

$$I_0(\lambda')\left\{\lambda'^{-1/3}\left[\frac{1}{\lambda'}I_1(\lambda') + I_2(\lambda')\right] - I_1(\lambda')\frac{\lambda'^{-4/3}}{3}\right\}$$
$$- \lambda'^{-1/3}I_1(\lambda')\{I_1(\lambda')\} = 0,$$

we find that $\lambda'_{\rm opt}$ must satisfy

$$\tfrac{2}{3}I_0(\lambda')I_1(\lambda') + I_2(\lambda')I_0(\lambda') = I_1^2(\lambda'),$$

which has a real root determined by trial and error equal to

$$\lambda'_{\rm opt} = 2.6188.$$

This value of $\lambda'_{\rm opt}$ fixes the optimum semithickness of the triangular profile as

$$\delta_{1{\rm opt}} = (4A^2h/\lambda'^2_{\rm opt}k)^{1/3}, \tag{4–20}$$

and thus the optimum width $w_{\rm opt} = A/\delta_{1{\rm opt}}$.

EXAMPLE 4–3. A plain surface is to be fitted with straight triangular fins of specific weight 0.1 lb/in.^{3} and thermal conductivity 48 Btu/hr-ft-°F. Determine the optimum dimensions and efficiency of these fins if the unit surface conductance is estimated to be 196 Btu/hr-ft^2-°F, and if the maximum weight of each unit length of fin is restricted to 0.02 lb.

Solution. The maximum permissible profile area of each fin is computed as $A = 0.02/12 \times 0.1 = 0.0167$ in.^{2}, so that by (4–20) the optimum semithickness at the base is

$$\delta_{1{\rm opt}} = [4(0.0167)^2(196)/(144)^2(2.6188)^2(48)]^{1/3} = 0.0032 = 0.038''.$$

The optimum fin width is then $w_{\rm opt} = 0.0167/0.038 = 0.44''$. With these data the value of ξ becomes

$$\xi = (0.44/12)^{3/2}(196 \times 144/48 \times 0.0167)^{1/2} = 1.317,$$

so that by (4–19) the efficiency of this triangular fin is

$$e_{s'} = \frac{1}{1.317} \frac{I_1(2.634)}{I_0(2.634)} = \frac{1}{1.317} \frac{2.844}{3.651} = 59.3\%,$$

where the modified Bessel functions are linearly interpolated from the values listed in Table A–5 of the Appendix.

4–8 Straight fins of parabolic profile. In this case we consider two possible profiles, the first bounded by the parabolic contour $y \sim x^2$ and the second bounded by the parabolic contour $y \sim x^{\frac{1}{2}}$, as in Fig. 4–6.

Considering the first case for which the profile equation $y_x = \delta_1(x/w)^2$ and its first derivative $dy_x/dx = 2\delta_1 x/w^2$ is substituted in (4–14), we have the characteristic differential equation

$$x^2 \frac{d^2T}{dx^2} + 2x \frac{dT}{dx} - N^2 w^2 T = 0. \qquad (4\text{–}21)$$

Comparing (4–21) with (3–24) shows that this is not a Bessel equation. In fact, it may be shown that no straight fin whose thickness is described by the square of its x-coordinate can have a solution in terms of Bessel functions. Equation (4–21) is, rather, an Euler differential equation whose general solution is obtained by first assuming a solution of the form $T = x^P$. Substituting this in (4–21), we have

$$x^2 P(P - 1)x^{(P-2)} + 2xPx^{(P-1)} - N^2 w^2 x^P = 0,$$

which is satisfied by the dual roots $P_1 = -\frac{1}{2} + (1 + 4N^2w^2)^{\frac{1}{2}}/2$ and $P_2 = -\frac{1}{2} - (1 + 4N^2w^2)^{\frac{1}{2}}/2$, wherewith the general solution of (4–21) reads

$$T = C_1 x^{P_1} + C_2 x^{P_2}. \qquad (4\text{–}22)$$

The particular solution satisfying both (4–22) and the usual set of boundary conditions is

$$\frac{T}{T_0} = \left(\frac{x}{w}\right)^{P_1}. \qquad (4\text{–}23)$$

The efficiency of the straight fin of inverse parabolic profile is then

$$\frac{q}{q^0} = \frac{1}{w} \int (x/w)^{P_1} dx$$

$$= \frac{2}{1 + \sqrt{1 + 4N^2 w^2}},$$

or, in terms of the profile area $A = (\frac{2}{3})\delta_1 w$,

$$e_{s''} = \frac{2}{1 + \sqrt{1 + \frac{8}{3}\xi^2}}. \qquad (4\text{–}24)$$

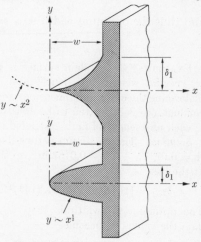

Fig. 4–6. Straight parabolic fins.

An interesting result is contained in (4–23), since if $P_1 = 1$ then the profile temperature must be linear. To visualize the significance of a linear profile temperature, imagine a rod perfectly insulated on its surfaces and conducting heat q along its longitudinal axis. If the rod is of constant cross section, then the specific rate of heat flow will be the same at each station i, as $q/A_1 = q/A_2 = \cdots = q/A_i = \cdots$. This implies that each element of rod is equally effective in conducting the heat q between any two stations, and that no element has an excess or deficiency of material. However, if we allow heat to escape from the rod surfaces, then a constant cross section will not represent the optimum contour, since q will now differ at each station. To regain a constant specific rate of heat flow with surface losses, the contour of the rod must be changed such that $A_1 > A_2 > \cdots$. If the contour is such that the condition $q/A_i = $ constant is satisfied, then the temperature distribution along the rod will be linear, and the rod will contain a minimum of material to conduct the given heat rate q.

The inverse parabolic fin $y \sim x^2$ is therefore, according to the above discussion, a fin of *least material* only under the condition that $P_1 = 1$, or

$$\frac{hw^2}{k\delta_1} = 2. \tag{4–25}$$

This value of $N^2w^2 = 2$ corresponds to $\xi = \sqrt{3}$ and therefore an efficiency of $e_{s''} = 50\%$.

The optimum dimensions are again found by determining that particular value of δ_1 for which q_0 is a maximum. The calculation for an inverse parabolic profile area $A = 2w\delta_1/3$ leads to

$$27\lambda''^2 - 15\lambda'' + 1 = 0,$$

in which $\lambda'' = hA^2/k\delta_1^3$. A positive root of this quadratic is

$$\lambda''_{opt} = 0.9111,$$

and this fixes the optimum semithickness as

$$\delta_{1opt} = (hA^2/\lambda''_{opt}k)^{1/3}. \tag{4–26}$$

The optimum width is then $w_{opt} = 3A/2\delta_{1opt}$.

The fin efficiency for the second parabolic profile $y_x = \delta_1(x/w)^{1/2}$ is derived in problem 4–6. In this case,

$$e_{s'''} = \frac{1}{\sqrt{\frac{4}{3}}\xi} \frac{I_{2/3}[(\frac{4}{3})^{3/2}\xi]}{I_{-1/3}[(\frac{4}{3})^{3/2}\xi]}. \tag{4–27}$$

Equations (4–11), (4–19), (4–24), and (4–27) give a comparison of the efficiency for straight fins, the comparison being on the basis of equal width w and equal profile area A. As shown in Fig. 4–7, for values of ξ exceeding roughly 1.25, the approximate efficiency (or average profile

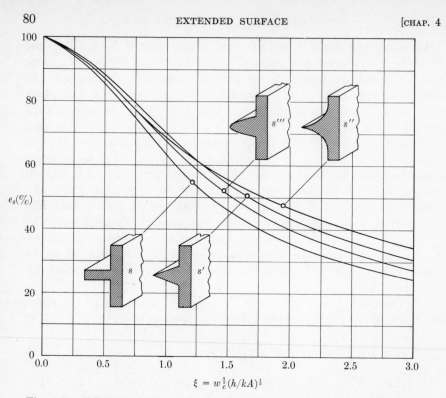

Fig. 4–7.   Efficiency of four straight fins of equal width w and profile area A.

temperature) is highest for the inverse parabolic profile. This follows naturally by recognizing that to maintain equal fin width and equal profile area, a higher proportion of the fin material must be concentrated near the base region where the temperature head is highest. Even though Fig. 4–7 suggests that the inverse parabolic profile is most efficient in the higher range of ξ, one keeps in mind that practical applications will nearly always favor the less effective rectangular and triangular profiles which are not only easier to manufacture but easier to maintain as well.*

4–9 Design of straight fins. As mentioned previously, the selection of a particular fin profile depends not only on the efficiency, manufacture, and maintenance characteristics of each profile, but on considerations of weight and space limits as well. We consider first the question of which profile requires the least cross-sectional area to dissipate a given heat rate. Substituting optimum dimensions (4–13), (4–20), and (4–26) in q_0 for the rectangular, triangular, and parabolic profiles, we have

$$A = \frac{0.252}{h^2 k}\left(\frac{q_0}{T_0}\right)^3 , \tag{4–28}$$

---

*The straight fin of trapezoidal profile is considered in problem 4–7.

$$A' = \frac{0.174}{h^2 k}\left(\frac{q_0}{T_0}\right)^3, \qquad\qquad (4\text{–}29)$$

$$A'' = \frac{0.167}{h^2 k}\left(\frac{q_0}{T_0}\right)^3. \qquad\qquad (4\text{–}30)$$

According to these results, the optimum rectangular fin with profile area (4–28) requires nearly 51% more material to dissipate the same heat rate as the optimum parabolic fin having the least profile area (4–30), whereas the optimum triangular fin with profile area (4–29) requires only about 4% more material. These equations also show that the required profile area is inversely proportional to the thermal conductivity, $A \sim 1/k$. Since, however, the total weight W of the fin is proportional to the specific weight γ of the material used, then $W \sim A\gamma \sim \gamma/k$.

Consider the change in fin material from iron to aluminum as used, for instance, on cylinder heads in aircraft engines where weight is at a premium. In this case (Table 1–2),

$$\frac{W_{\text{AL}}}{W_{\text{FE}}} = \frac{(\gamma/k)_{\text{AL}}}{(\gamma/k)_{\text{FE}}} = \frac{(169/117)}{(492/36)} = 0.106,$$

so that approximately 90% of the weight for fins is saved by changing from iron to aluminum. A similar calculation for copper shows that while the conductivity of copper is higher than aluminum, its specific weight is so much higher that only 42% of the fin weight can be saved by substituting copper for iron.

According to (4–28), (4–29), and (4–30), the volume of material is seen to increase as the cube of q_0. It is therefore best to design the fins as small as possible, since to double the heat rate requires a fin eight times as large instead of two fins of the same size. There is a limit, however, to spacing fins closer and closer together which is imposed by permissible fluid pressure drops and changes in the unit surface conductance, the latter occurring from mutual interference of the developed boundary layers on each fin surface. The boundary-layer thickness δ_b (Fig. 4–8) can be calculated to range in the neighborhood of one-tenth of an inch for forced convection to one-half an inch for free convection. If no interference should be allowed between adjacent boundary layers, then the fin spacing d should be just

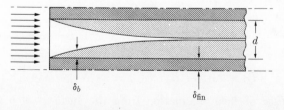

Fig. 4–8. Boundary-layer development on surfaces of adjacent fins.

twice as large as the fully developed boundary-layer thickness as $d = 2\delta_{b\max}$. On the other hand, tests have shown that mutual interference in the outer regions of the boundary layers is only slight, and that the optimum fin spacing can be as small as approximately $d = 1.12\delta_{b\max}$.

4–10 Circular fin of rectangular profile. A generalized differential equation for $t(r)$ in a circular fin of arbitrary profile follows directly by the procedure used in connection with straight fins. According to Fig. 4–9, the radial heat flow by conduction through a differential element dr is

$$\frac{d}{dr}\left(4k\pi r y_r \frac{dT}{dr}\right)dr = 4\pi k\left[y_r\left(r\frac{d^2T}{dr^2} + \frac{dT}{dr}\right) + r\frac{dT}{dr}\frac{dy_r}{dr}\right]dr,$$

and the heat dissipated from the two surface elements between r and $r + dr$ is approximately $2h(2\pi r)T dr$ if we neglect second-degree differentials $(dr)^2$. Thus the generalized differential equation

$$y_r\frac{d^2T}{dr^2} + \frac{y_r}{r}\frac{dT}{dr} + \frac{dy_r}{dr}\frac{dT}{dr} - \frac{h}{k}T = 0. \qquad (4\text{--}31)$$

With a rectangular profile for which $y_r = \delta$ and $dy_r/dr = 0$, (4–31) reduces to the particular differential equation

$$r^2\frac{d^2T}{dr^2} + r\frac{dT}{dr} - N^2r^2T = 0, \qquad (4\text{--}32)$$

whose general solution is of the form

$$T = C_1 J_0(iNr) + C_2 Y_0(iNr). \qquad (4\text{--}33)$$

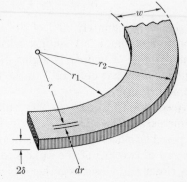

Fig. 4–9.   Circular rectangular fin.

Then the particular solution which satisfies (4–33) and the boundary conditions

$$T = T_0 \quad \text{at } r = r_1,$$

$$\frac{dT}{dr} = 0 \quad \text{at } r = r_{2c} = r_2 + \delta,$$

is given by

$$\frac{T}{T_0} = \frac{I_0(Nr)K_1(Nr_{2c}) + I_1(Nr_{2c})K_0(Nr)}{I_0(Nr_1)K_1(Nr_{2c}) + I_1(Nr_{2c})K_0(Nr_1)}. \qquad (4\text{--}34)$$

In the case of heat dissipation from the surfaces of a circular fin of rectangular profile, we have

$$q = 2\int_{r_1}^{r_{2c}} h(2\pi r)T\,dr = 2\pi h\int_{r_1}^{r_{2c}} Tr\,dr, \tag{4-35}$$

in which the integration of $Tr\,dr$ can best be effected by noting from (4–32) that

$$\frac{d}{dr}\left(r\,\frac{dT}{dr}\right) = r\,\frac{d^2T}{dr^2} + \frac{dT}{dr} = N^2 rT,$$

whence

$$\int_{r_1}^{r_{2c}} Tr\,dr = \frac{1}{N^2}\int_{r_1}^{r_{2c}} \frac{d}{dr}\left(r\,\frac{dT}{dr}\right)dr = \frac{-r_1}{N^2}\left(\frac{dT}{dr}\right)_{r_1}.$$

Here the second integration limit does not enter in the evaluation of the integral, since $dt/dr = 0$ at $r = r_{2c}$. With $(dT/dr)_{r_1}$ evaluated as

$$\frac{1}{T_0}\left(\frac{dT}{dr}\right)_{r_1} = \frac{NI_1(Nr_1)K_1(Nr_{2c}) - NI_1(Nr_{2c})K_1(Nr_1)}{I_0(Nr_1)K_1(Nr_{2c}) + I_1(Nr_{2c})K_0(Nr_1)} = N\Lambda,$$

(4–35) takes the form

$$q = -4\pi hr_1 T_0\Lambda/N,$$

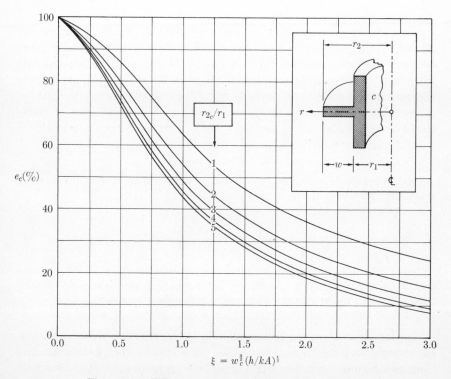

Fig. 4–10. Efficiency of the circular rectangular fin.

and this gives the efficiency $e_c = q/q^0$ if we divide by the ideal heat dissipation $q^0 = 2\pi h(r_{2c}^2 - r_1^2)T_0$ as $-2r_1\Lambda/N(r_{2c}^2 - r_1^2)$ or, in terms of the parameter ξ defined by (4–12), in which $A = 2\delta(r_{2c} - r_1)$,

$$e_c = \frac{\sqrt{2}/\xi}{(1 + r_{2c}/r_1)}\left[\frac{I_1(R_a\xi)K_1(R_b\xi) - I_1(R_b\xi)K_1(R_a\xi)}{I_1(R_a\xi)K_0(R_b\xi) + I_0(R_b\xi)K_1(R_a\xi)}\right], \quad (4\text{–}36)$$

where $R_a = \sqrt{2}/(1 - r_1/r_{2c})$ and $R_b = (r_1/r_{2c})R_a$. Here we see that the efficiency of a circular fin is a function of the radius ratio r_1/r_2 as well as of ξ. This additional dependence is illustrated in Fig. 4–10.

EXAMPLE 4–4. A $1''$ OD pipe of thermal conductivity 15 Btu/hr-ft-°F is fitted with circular fins of rectangular profile $\frac{1}{4}''$ wide and $\frac{1}{16}''$ thick. Compute the efficiency of these fins if they are made of the same material as the pipe, and if the unit surface conductance is estimated to be 100 Btu/hr-ft²-°F.

Solution. In this case $N = (100 \times 32 \times 12/15 \times 1)^{1/2} = 50.55$, $r_{2c} = \frac{3}{4} + \frac{1}{32} = \frac{25}{32}''$, $Nr_1 = 50.55/24 = 2.107$, and $Nr_{2c} = 3.290$. With these data (Tables A-5 and A-6),

$$e_c = \frac{2 \times 144}{24 \times 50.55[(\frac{25}{32})^2 - (\frac{1}{2})^2]}\left(\frac{5.137 \times 0.243 - 1.757 \times 0.057}{2.459 \times 0.057 + 5.137 \times 0.200}\right) = 64.8\%.$$

Since (4–36) does not lend itself to repeated computation, Harper and Brown (1) suggest the less accurate procedure of determining the difference between the exact solution for e_c given by (4–36) and the approximate efficiency for the straight rectangular fin given by (4–11), the latter being the much easier solution to compute by. The negative correction $-\Delta e_c = e_s - e_c$ is to be computed for a number of conditions and a set of corresponding correction curves plotted. Such a set of curves is reproduced from the Harper and Brown paper (1) in Fig. 4–11.

EXAMPLE 4–5. Recompute the efficiency of the fin in Example 4–4, using the correction curves of Fig. 4–11.

Solution. By (4–11),

$$e_s = \frac{1}{Nw_c}\tanh Nw_c = \frac{0.8256}{1.1860} = 69.7\%.$$

Entering Fig. 4–11 with a radius ratio $r_1/r_{2c} = 0.64$ and $e_s = 69.7\%$, we find that $\Delta e_c = -5.0\%$. Then $e_c = 69.7 - 5.0 = 64.7\%$, and this is in substantial agreement with the exact value obtained in Example 4–4 as 64.8%.

The fact that a curved rectangular fin is less effective than its analog, the straight rectangular fin, can best be visualized by noting the geometric changes which occur in bending a straight fin into an arc. It is clear that any redistribution of material which adds either conducting area or dis-

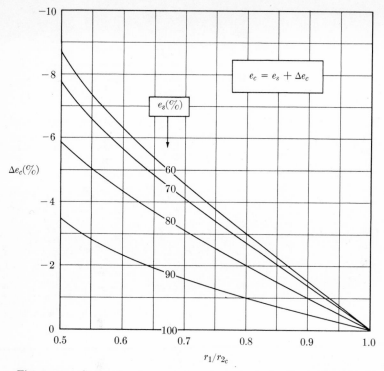

$e_c = e_s + \Delta e_c$

$e_s(\%)$

$\Delta e_c(\%)$

60

70

80

90

100

0.5   0.6   0.7   0.8   0.9   1.0

r_1/r_{2_c}

Fig. 4–11.   Correction for curvature in rectangular fin.   [*Data by Harper and Brown* (1).]

sipating surface at or near the fin root will increase the fin efficiency, since the dissipation of heat from an extended surface is a function of both the surface area and the temperature excess.   With a curved rectangular fin, both the conducting and surface areas are reduced in the vicinity of the fin root and increased in the less effective tip region.   Consequently the redistribution of conducting area and dissipating surface which accompanies the bending of a rectangular fin, as in Fig. 4–9, both contribute to the loss in fin efficiency as illustrated in Fig. 4–10.   Obviously, the more one shrinks r_1 or expands r_2, the more pronounced this effect becomes.

4–11 Circular fin of hyperbolic profile.   A profile for a circular fin which is reasonably close to a trapezoid is one bounded by hyperbolas, as in Fig. 4–12.   Here, as in the straight rectangular fin, the conducting area normal to the heat-flow path is constant, since $ry = $ constant.   The appropriate profile equation for this case is given by $y_r = \delta_1(r_1/r)$, so that with the aid of (4–31) the particular characteristic differential equation for T is

$$r^2 \frac{d^2T}{dr^2} - H^2 r^3 T = 0, \qquad (4\text{–}37)$$

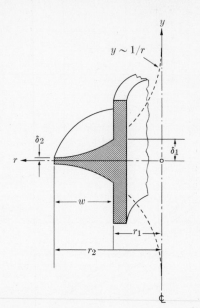

Fig. 4–12.   Circular hyperbolic fin.

wherein

$$H^2 = h/k\delta_1 r_1 = N^2/r_1.$$

Using the generalized Bessel equation and solutions (3–24) and (3–25), we find the general solution of (4–37) to be

$$T = \sqrt{r}[C_1 J_{1/3}(\tfrac{2}{3}iHr^{3/2}) + C_2 Y_{1/3}(\tfrac{2}{3}iHr^{3/2})]. \qquad (4\text{–}38)$$

The particular solution satisfying both (4–38) and the usual boundary conditions is

$$\frac{T}{T_0} = \sqrt{\frac{r}{r_1}}\left[\frac{I_{1/3}(\tfrac{2}{3}Hr^{3/2})I_{2/3}(\tfrac{2}{3}Hr_{2_c}^{3/2}) - I_{-1/3}(\tfrac{2}{3}Hr^{3/2})I_{-2/3}(\tfrac{2}{3}Hr_{2_c}^{3/2})}{I_{1/3}(\tfrac{2}{3}Hr_1^{3/2})I_{2/3}(\tfrac{2}{3}Hr_{2_c}^{3/2}) - I_{-1/3}(\tfrac{2}{3}Hr_1^{3/2})I_{-2/3}(\tfrac{2}{3}Hr_{2_c}^{3/2})}\right], \quad (4\text{–}39)$$

and from the temperature distribution we derive the efficiency

$$e_{c'} = \frac{2r_1}{N(r_{2_c}^2 - r_1^2)}\left[\frac{I_{-2/3}(\tfrac{2}{3}Hr_1^{3/2})I_{2/3}(\tfrac{2}{3}Hr_{2_c}^{3/2}) - I_{2/3}(\tfrac{2}{3}Hr_1^{3/2})I_{-2/3}(\tfrac{2}{3}Hr_{2_c}^{3/2})}{I_{-1/3}(\tfrac{2}{3}Hr_1^{3/2})I_{-2/3}(\tfrac{2}{3}Hr_{2_c}^{3/2}) - I_{1/3}(\tfrac{2}{3}Hr_1^{3/2})I_{2/3}(\tfrac{2}{3}Hr_{2_c}^{3/2})}\right].$$
$$(4\text{–}40)$$

The total profile area for the hyperbolic contour reads

$$A = 2\int_{r_1}^{r_{2_c}} \delta_1 \frac{r_1}{r}\, dr = 2\delta_1 r_1 \ln\left(\frac{r_{2_c}}{r_1}\right),$$

so that δ_1 in N is to be replaced by $A/2r_1 \ln (r_{2_c}/r_1)$. This reduces (4–40) to the desired expression in terms of the parameter ξ and the radius ratio r_1/r_{2_c} as

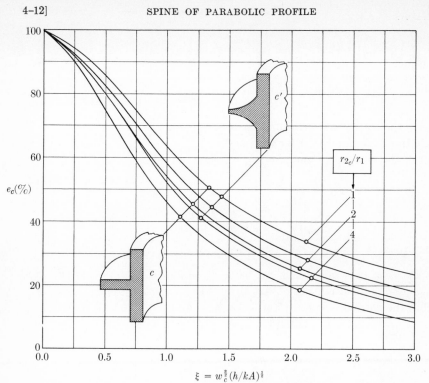

Fig. 4–13.   Efficiency of two circular fins of equal width w and profile area A.

$$e_{c'} = \frac{\sqrt{2\rho(1 - \rho^3 + 3\rho^2 - 3\rho)/\ln\,(1/\rho)}}{\xi(1 - \rho^2)} \left[\frac{I_{2/3}(u)I_{-2/3}(v) - I_{-2/3}(u)I_{2/3}(v)}{I_{-2/3}(u)I_{-1/3}(v) - I_{2/3}(u)I_{1/3}(v)}\right],$$

$$(4\text{--}41)$$

where $\rho = r_1/r_{2c}$, and where u and v are abbreviations for

$$u = \tfrac{2}{3}\xi\sqrt{[2\ln\,(1/\rho)]/(1 - \rho^3 + 3\rho^2 - 3\rho)},$$

$$v = \tfrac{2}{3}\xi\sqrt{[2\rho^3 \ln\,(1/\rho)]/(1 - \rho^3 + 3\rho^2 - 3\rho)}.$$

The performance of the circular hyperbolic fin is compared with that of an equivalent circular rectangular fin in Fig. 4–13.

4–12 Spine of parabolic profile. The analysis of extended surface in the form of pin fins or spines is a simple extension of the methods employed for straight and circular fins, and for convenience we again set up a general differential equation in T for treating a large number of possible cases.

Consider a spine of circular cross section and arbitrary profile contour. The heat conducted through an element of the spine is identified in general terms as

$$\frac{d}{dx}\left(kA_x\frac{dT}{dx}\right)dx =$$

$$kA_x\frac{d^2T}{dx^2}dx + k\frac{dA_x}{dx}\frac{dT}{dx},$$

and in the steady state this must balance the heat dissipated on the surface of the element in amount

$$h(dS_x/dx)T\,dx,$$

or

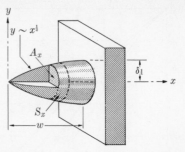

Fig. 4–14. Denotations for spine of parabolic profile.

$$A_x\frac{d^2T}{dx^2} + \frac{dA_x}{dx}\frac{dT}{dx} - \frac{h}{k}\frac{dS_x}{dx}T = 0. \qquad (4\text{--}42)$$

In the case of straight fins we have $A_x = 2y_x$, $dA_x/dx = 2dy_x/dx$, and $dS_x = 2dx$, which reduces (4–42) to (4–14).

For the parabolic spine in Fig. 4–14, $y_x = \delta_1(x/w)^{1/2}$, so that $A_x = \pi y_x^2 = \pi\delta_1^2 x/w$, $dA_x/dx = \pi\delta_1^2/w$, and $dS_x/dx = 2\pi y_x = 2\pi\delta_1(x/w)^{1/2}$, wherewith, by (4–42),

$$x^2\frac{d^2T}{dx^2} + x\frac{dT}{dx} - 2N^2\sqrt{w}x^{3/2}T = 0. \qquad (4\text{--}43)$$

The general solution of the particular differential equation (4–43) is

$$T = C_1 J_0(\tfrac{4}{3}\sqrt{2}iNw^{1/4}x^{3/4}) + C_2 Y_0(\tfrac{4}{3}\sqrt{2}iNw^{1/4}x^{3/4}),$$

and if this is to be satisfied by $dT/dx = 0$ at $x = 0$, then Y_0 cannot enter the solution because $Y_1(0) = -\infty$ (see problems 3–6 and 3–7, and Fig. 3–2). Thus $C_2 = 0$, and by the first boundary condition that $T = T_0$ at $x = w$, we have $C_1 = T_0/J_0(\tfrac{4}{3}\sqrt{2}iNw)$, whereby

$$\frac{T}{T_0} = \frac{I_0(\tfrac{4}{3}\sqrt{2}Nw^{1/4}x^{3/4})}{I_0(\tfrac{4}{3}\sqrt{2}Nw)}. \qquad (4\text{--}44)$$

With the temperature distribution T, we determine the heat dissipation from the spine surface as $dq = h[2\pi\delta_1(x/w)^{1/2}]T\,dx$, or

$$q = \frac{2\pi h\delta_1 T_0}{\sqrt{w}J_0(\tfrac{4}{3}\sqrt{2}iNw)}\int_0^w \sqrt{x}J_0(\tfrac{4}{3}\sqrt{2}iNw^{1/4}x^{3/4})dx.$$

Then with the integral evaluated as

$$\int_0^w \sqrt{x}J_0(\tfrac{4}{3}\sqrt{2}iNw^{1/4}x^{3/4})dx = \frac{w}{i\sqrt{2}N}J_1(\tfrac{4}{3}\sqrt{2}iNw),$$

q takes the final form

$$q = \frac{-i\sqrt{2}\pi h\delta_1 T_0}{N} \frac{J_1(\frac{4}{3}\sqrt{2iN}w)}{J_0(\frac{4}{3}\sqrt{2iN}w)}.$$

Finally, if the spine were at a uniform temperature t_0, then it would dissipate heat in amount

$$q^0 = \int_0^w h[2\pi\delta_1(x/w)^{1/2}]T_0 dx = \tfrac{4}{3}\pi h\delta_1 w T_0,$$

and therefore its efficiency $e = q/q^0$ is

$$e_{p'} = \frac{2}{(\frac{4}{3}\sqrt{2}Nw)} \frac{I_1(\frac{4}{3}\sqrt{2}Nw)}{I_0(\frac{4}{3}\sqrt{2}Nw)} = \frac{2}{\nu_{p'}} \frac{I_1(\nu_{p'})}{I_0(\nu_{p'})}, \qquad (4\text{--}45)$$

where $\nu_{p'} = (\frac{4}{3}\sqrt{2}Nw)$.

The efficiency of spines is not directly comparable with corresponding fins, since for equal profile areas the surface of a spine is not the same as the unit-length surface of a fin. However, we can compare the efficiency of spines which differ in profile contour, choosing to compare the parabolic spine with, for example, a rectangular spine for which the efficiency is easily derived from the turbine-blade temperature distribution (2–31) as (problem 4–10)

$$e_p = \frac{1}{\sqrt{2}Nw_c} \tanh \sqrt{2}Nw_c = \frac{1}{\nu_p} \tanh \nu_p, \qquad (4\text{--}46)$$

where $\nu_p = \sqrt{2}Nw_c$.

The efficiency of rectangular and parabolic spines is shown in Fig. 4–15. The calculation is illustrated for spines of (a) equal width and base area A_0, for which

$$\nu_{p_{A_0}} = \sqrt{2}w_c\sqrt{\left(\frac{\pi}{A_0}\right)^{1/2}\frac{h}{k}}, \quad \nu_{p'_{A_0}} = \tfrac{4}{3}\sqrt{2}w_c\sqrt{\left(\frac{\pi}{A_0}\right)^{1/2}\frac{h}{k}},$$

(b) equal width and volume V, for which

$$\nu_{p_V} = \sqrt{2}w_c^{5/4}\sqrt{\left(\frac{\pi}{V}\right)^{1/2}\frac{h}{k}}, \quad \nu_{p'_V} = \tfrac{4}{3}(2)^{1/4}w_c^{5/4}\sqrt{\left(\frac{\pi}{V}\right)^{1/2}\frac{h}{k}},$$

and (c) equal width and surface area S, for which

$$\nu_{p_S} = 2w_c^{3/2}\sqrt{\left(\frac{\pi}{S}\right)\frac{h}{k}}, \quad \nu_{p'_S} = \tfrac{8}{3}\sqrt{\tfrac{2}{3}}w_c^{3/2}\sqrt{\left(\frac{\pi}{S}\right)\frac{h}{k}}.$$

These results show that, regardless of the comparative basis, the efficiency of parabolic spine is always substantially higher than that of rectangular spine.

In problem 4–11 we determine the optimum dimensions of a rectangular spine, and in problems 4–12 and 4–13 we derive the efficiency for spines of inverse parabolic and triangular profile.

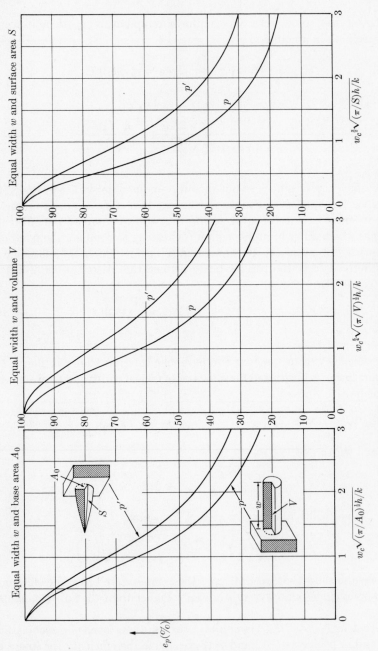

Fig. 4–15. Efficiency of rectangular and parabolic spines.

4–13 Closure. The following comments and short bibliography will interest the reader who wishes more detailed information on the general problem of extended surface.

As mentioned previously, Harper and Brown's paper (1) is to be referred to for the first comprehensive treatment of the temperature gradient and efficiency for straight fins of rectangular, triangular, and trapezoidal profile, and circular fins of rectangular profile. These authors were the first to introduce the method of a corrected fin width to approximately compensate for fin-tip heat loss, and were the first to develop exact equations for illustrating the effects of neglecting the temperature gradient dt/dy at any spanwise station, and dt/dz at the fin base.

Some years later Schmidt (4) investigated straight and circular fins from the standpoint of least-material requirements for which the temperature gradient is linear. Among the more practical results of this paper, we find the optimum dimensions for straight rectangular and triangular fins. Schmidt also finds the optimum dimensions for the impractical straight and circular fins of least material, and recommends using the least-material circular fin for approximating the behavior of the circular triangular fin, for which there is no exact solution in terms of common functions. If the fin curvature is small, it is recommended that the straight fin be used for this approximation, while for large curvatures Schmidt suggests a compromise between the circular rectangular fin and the circular fin of least material.*

Avrami and Little (5) have studied the temperature gradients dt/dy and dt/dx in thick fins of rectangular profile, and have also established the critical Nusselt number below which straight rectangular fins are useful.

Carrier and Anderson (6) have presented open solutions in terms of infinite series for circular fins of rectangular and hyperbolic profile. Many of these authors refer to the efficiency index as the fin effectiveness.

Gardner (2) has generalized the extended-surface problem by deriving general equations for the efficiency from the generalized Bessel equation (3–24) and solution (3–25). The results are perfectly general for both fins and spines; substituting the order n of the appropriate differential equation identifies the equations of previous investigators and several more less important ones, except of course those profiles generated by a thickness varying as the square of x. Curves presented for fin efficiency are not comparable, since they are given in terms of equal fin base thickness and equal fin width.

Zabronsky (7) has presented an exact solution for the efficiency of square fins on round tubes. All four rectangular fin edges are considered adiabatic, as would occur in a heat exchanger, where a large single fin sheet is penetrated by a symmetrically spaced bank of normal tubes. The efficiency of

---

*For the profile equation of a least-material circular fin, see (b) of problem 4–9.

such fins is found to be nearly identical with that of a circular fin of the
same surface area.

REFERENCES

1. W. B. Harper and D. R. Brown, "Mathematical Equations for Heat
Conduction in the Fins of Air-Cooled Engines," *NACA Report* No. 158. Washington: 1922, pp. 679–708.
2. K. A. Gardner, "Efficiency of Extended Surface," *Trans. ASME*, Vol. 67,
No. 8, 1945, pp. 621–631.
3. M. Jakob, *Heat Transfer*, Vol. I. New York: John Wiley, 1949.
4. E. Schmidt, "Die Warmeubertragung durch Rippen," *Zeit, VDI*, Vol. 70,
1926, pp. 885–889, 947–951.
5. M. Avrami and J. B. Little, "Diffusion of Heat Through a Rectangular
Bar and the Cooling and Insulating Effect of Fins," *Journal of Applied Physics*,
Vol. 13, 1942, pp. 255–264.
6. W. H. Carrier and S. W. Anderson, "The Resistance to Heat Flow Through
Finned Tubing," *Heating, Piping, and Air Conditioning*, Vol. 10, 1944, pp. 304–
320.
7. H. Zabronsky, "Efficiency of a Heat Exchanger Using Square Fins on
Round Tubes," *USAEC*, K-929. Oak Ridge Technical Information Service,
August, 1952 (see also *ASME* Reprint No. 54-A-12).

PROBLEMS

4–1. Plot a family of dimensionless temperature curves for various Nw in
a straight rectangular fin. Use both the exact solution (4–3), which takes into
account fin-tip heat loss, and the approximate solution (4–6), which neglects
fin-tip heat loss. Choose several different values of the parameter σ in the
exact solution (4–3).

4–2. A plane surface is fitted with rectangular cooling fins $\frac{1}{2}''$ wide and $\frac{1}{8}''$
thick. The fin material is of thermal conductivity 15 Btu/hr-ft-°F, and the unit
surface conductance, based on an ambient air temperature of 0°F, is estimated
to be 60 Btu/hr-ft²-°F. Show (a) that the effect of neglecting fin-tip heat loss is
to overestimate the fin temperature at $x = w/2$ by 4.0% and underestimate the
heat dissipated from the primary surface by 4.1%, and (b) that the efficiency of
these fins, based on a corrected width, is 66.4%.

4–3. A plane wall is fitted with rectangular fins of thermal conductivity
30 Btu/hr-ft-°F, and profile area 0.0004 ft². The fins operate in an 80°F fluid,
and the unit surface conductance is estimated to be 100 Btu/hr-ft²-°F. If the
fin base temperature is measured as 332°F, then show that 188 Btu/hr is the
maximum possible rate at which heat is being dissipated from each unit length
of fin.

4–4. A straight triangular fin of profile area 0.0005 ft² is constructed with
best dimensions and of a material having a thermal conductivity 30 Btu/hr-
ft-°F. Under the condition that the unit surface conductance is 30 Btu/hr-ft²-°F,
(a) show that the efficiency of this fin is 59.4%, (b) show that the ratio of tip
to base temperature excess is 0.277.

4–5. A straight inverse parabolic fin is to dissipate the same quantity of heat and have the same total profile area as the straight triangular fin in problem 4–4. Show that for the same unit surface conductance and base temperature, the thermal conductivity of this fin must be 28.8 Btu/hr-ft-°F.

4–6. The profile contour of a straight fin varies as $y_x = \delta_1(x/w)^{1/2}$. Show that its efficiency is given by

$$e_{s'''} = \frac{1}{Nw} \frac{I_{2/3}(\tfrac{4}{3}Nw)}{I_{-1/3}(\tfrac{4}{3}Nw)} ,$$

as in (4–27).

4–7. Consider the straight trapezoidal fin shown in Fig. 4–16. In this case $y_x = \delta_1 + (\delta_2 - \delta_1)(x - \delta_1)/w = \delta_1 + 2(x - \delta_1)\tan \epsilon$, so that by (4–14),

$$\frac{d^2T}{dx^2} + \frac{2\tan \epsilon}{\delta_1 + 2(x - \delta_1)\tan \epsilon} \frac{dT}{dx} - \frac{h}{k[\delta_1 + 2(x - \delta_1)\tan \epsilon]} T = 0.$$

An involved substitution for the independent variable x according to (1),

$$\eta^2 = 4c^2[x + \delta_1(1 - 2\tan \epsilon)/2\tan \epsilon],$$

where $c = (h/k\sin \epsilon)^{1/2}$, reduces this to the familiar form of Bessel's zero-order equation,

$$\frac{d^2T}{d\eta^2} + \frac{1}{\eta}\frac{dT}{d\eta} - T = 0,$$

whose general solution is

$$T = C_1 J_0(i\eta) + C_2 Y_0(i\eta).$$

The particular solution satisfying this general solution and the usual boundary conditions is found to be

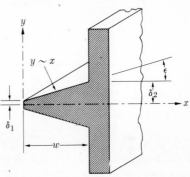

Fig. 4–16. Straight trapezoidal fin.

$$\frac{T}{T_0} = \frac{I_0(\eta)K_1(\eta_1) - I_1(\eta_1)K_0(\eta)}{I_0(\eta_2)K_1(\eta_1) - I_1(\eta_1)K_0(\eta_2)} , \qquad \eta_1 = \eta_{x=0}, \ \eta_2 = \eta_{x=w_c},$$

and the fin efficiency is derived from this as

$$e_{s''''} = \frac{\pi k\eta_2 \tan \epsilon}{4hw_c} \left[\frac{I_1(\eta_2)K_1(\eta_1) - I_1(\eta_1)K_1(\eta_2)}{I_0(\eta_2)K_1(\eta_1) - I_1(\eta_1)K_0(\eta_2)}\right].$$

This result reduces, as it should, to the case of the straight fin of triangular profile considered in Article 4–6, for then $\eta_1 = 0$ and $\eta_2 = 2c\sqrt{w}$ (since w and w_c are coincident). The solution then reduces to $e_{s'} = I_1(2c\sqrt{w})/c\sqrt{w}I_0(2c\sqrt{w})$, which is in formal agreement with (4–19), since for small taper $\sin \epsilon = \epsilon = \tan \epsilon = \delta_2/w$.

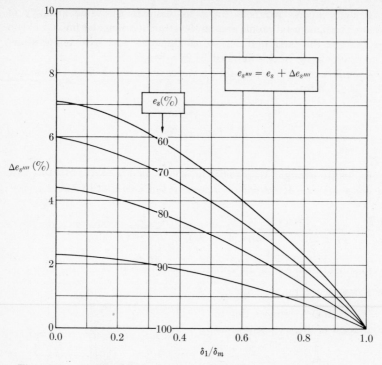

Fig. 4–17. Correction for taper in straight fin. [*Data by Harper and Brown* (1).]

As in Article 4–10, these awkward results expressed in linear combinations of Bessel functions may be used to compute a set of correction curves for the simply computed efficiency e_s. In this case the correction is positive because material at the fin tip is now redistributed near the fin base. Figure 4–17 shows such a set of correction curves as computed by Harper and Brown (1). Note that the abscissa of each curve is expressed as a taper ratio δ_1/δ_m, where δ_m is the arithmetic mean of δ_1 and δ_2. This value of δ_m is also used in computing N in e_s.

A plane surface is fitted with $\frac{3}{4}''$ wide fins of trapezoidal profile having $\frac{1}{4}''$ and $\frac{1}{16}''$ base and tip thicknesses. The conductivity of the fin material is 15 Btu/hr-ft-°F, and the unit surface conductance is estimated to be 10 Btu/hr-ft²-°F. (a) Show by the exact solution that the efficiency of these fins is approximately 90% (Tables A-5 and A-6).   (b) Recompute the efficiency in (a) by using the approximate correction curves of Fig. 4–17.

4–8. The profile contour of a straight fin varies as $y_x = \delta_1(x/w)^{3/2}$. (a) Show that the efficiency of this fin is given by

$$e_s''''' = \frac{1}{Nw_c}\frac{I_2(4Nw_c)}{I_1(4Nw_c)}.$$

(b) Express this efficiency in terms of the parameter ξ, and then plot e_s''''' vs. ξ on Fig. 4–7.

4–9. Consider a circular fin requiring the least material. (a) Show that the profile equation for this fin must satisfy the differential equation

$$\frac{dy_r}{dr} + \frac{y_r}{r} - \frac{h}{k}(r - r_2) = 0.$$

(b) Show that this result is directly integrable, since it contains the integrable combination $r\,dy_r + y_r\,dr$, and that if the profile is to be peaked at $r = r_2$, then

$$y_r = \frac{h}{6k}(2r^2 - 3r_2r + r_2^3/r).$$

(c) Show that the base semithickness of the least-material circular fin is

$$\delta = (hr_1^2/6k)(r_2/r_1 + 2)(r_2/r_1 - 1)^2.$$

4–10. The profile contour of a spine of circular cross section varies as $y_x = \delta$. Show that its efficiency is given by

$$e_p = \frac{1}{2\xi}\tanh 2\xi,$$

as in (4–46).

4–11. Show that if the spine in problem 4–10 is to have optimum dimensions, then

$$\lambda_{\text{opt}} = \tfrac{1}{2}\sinh 2\lambda_{\text{opt}},$$

where $\lambda = A(h/2k\delta^3)^{1/2}$, and from this show that the optimum semithickness of the spine is

$$\delta_{\text{opt}} = 4(2A^2h/k)^{1/3}.$$

4–12. The profile contour of a spine of circular cross section varies as $y_x = \delta_1(x/w)^2$. (a) Show that its efficiency is given by

$$e_{p''} = \frac{2}{1 + (1 + \tfrac{8}{9}N^2w^2)^{1/2}}.$$

(b) Show that this inverse parabolic spine requires the least material when $N^2w^2 = 2$. (c) Plot the efficiency in (a) on the second graph of Fig. 4–15.

4–13. The profile contour of a spine of circular cross section varies as $y_x = \delta_1(x/w)$. (a) Show that its efficiency is given by

$$e_{p'''} = \frac{4}{\tfrac{2}{3}\sqrt{2}Nw}\frac{I_2(\tfrac{2}{3}\sqrt{2}Nw)}{I_1(\tfrac{2}{3}\sqrt{2}Nw)}.$$

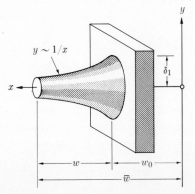

Fig. 4–18. Turbine blade of hyperbolic profile.

(b) Plot the efficiency in (a) on the second graph of Fig. 4–15.

4–14. It is of interest to examine the temperature gradient in a turbine blade whose contour varies hyperbolically as $y_x = \delta_1(w_0/x)$, as in Fig. 4–18. Show that the temperature distribution along the blade axis is given by

$$\frac{T}{T_0} = \left(\frac{x}{w_0}\right)^{3/2} \left[\frac{I_1(Wx^{3/2})K_0(W\bar{w}_c^{3/2}) + I_0(W\bar{w}_{ci}^{3/2})K_1(Wx^{3/2})}{I_1(Ww_0^{3/2})K_0(W\bar{w}_c^{3/2}) + I_0(W\bar{w}_c^{3/2})K_1(Ww_0^{3/2})}\right],$$

where W is defined by $W = N/(w_0/2)^{1/2}$.

4-15. Plot the one-dimensional temperature distribution in two turbine blades, one of uniform circular cross section and the other of circular cross section whose radius varies hyperbolically, as in problem 4–14. If a graphical comparison is to be made on the basis of equal surface area S and equal blade length w, then the parameters N and W must be expressed in terms of S and w. Show that these parameters take the form

$$N^2 = 4\pi wh/kS, \qquad W^2 = 4\pi h[\ln(1 + w/w_0)]/kS,$$

and then plot the temperature distributions for several particular values of w_0.

CHAPTER 5

FOURIER SERIES AND INTEGRATION OF PARTIAL-DIFFERENTIAL EQUATIONS

In this chapter we review the important problem of expanding an arbitrary function by means of an infinite trigonometric series. In particular, we develop the Fourier sine and cosine series for expansions over a finite range, and the Fourier sine and cosine integrals for expansions over an infinite range. A brief outline is also given for the separation-of-variable and Laplace-transform methods used in the integration of partial-differential equations.

FOURIER SERIES AND INTEGRALS

5–1 The Fourier theorem. In the process of obtaining solutions of the Laplace equation in two rectangular coordinates, we ultimately arrive at the form

$$t(x,y) = \frac{a_0}{2} + \sum_{n=1}^{\infty} f(y)(A_n \cos nx + B_n \sin nx)$$

as a primitive solution for the temperature field $t(x,y)$. If $t(x,y)$ is to finally satisfy a particular temperature function $f(x)$ along, say, $y = c$, then

$$f(x) = \frac{a_0}{2} + \sum_{n=1}^{\infty} (a_n \cos nx + b_n \sin nx), \qquad (5\text{–}1)$$

which means that in order to complete the solution for $t(x,y)$, $f(x)$ must be expanded in an infinite series of trigonometric sine and cosine terms as in (5–1). An expansion of this sort is called a *Fourier series*, and the *constant* coefficients a_n and b_n are known as the *amplitudes* of the series. The immediate problem is to determine the a_n and b_n under the simplest condition that the n are consecutive positive integers, $n = 1, 2, 3, \cdots.$*

The possibility of representing a given arbitrary function $f(x)$ by a special type of infinite trigonometric series, namely, a linear combination of sines and cosines, was a question which originally arose in connection with the now classical problem of the vibrating string. This question was

---

*In later work we shall be forced to reconsider both the Fourier and Bessel series under the condition where the n are not simple integers but consecutive roots of trigonometric and Bessel equations.

under strong debate among such mid-eighteenth century mathematicians as Euler, d'Alembert, Bernoulli, Lagrange, and Fourier, until finally, in the early part of the nineteenth century, the work of Fourier in connection with problems of heat diffusion led to the formal statement of his famous theorem.

The *Fourier theorem* states that any single-valued function $f(x)$ defined in the interval $-\pi < x < \pi$ can be represented over this interval by a linear series of sines and cosines according to (5–1) if the coefficients a_n and b_n are those computed from the given function $f(x)$ by the relations

$$a_n = \frac{1}{\pi} \int_{-\pi}^{\pi} f(x) \cos nx dx; \quad n = 1, 2, 3, \cdots, \tag{5–2}$$

and

$$b_n = \frac{1}{\pi} \int_{-\pi}^{\pi} f(x) \sin nx dx; \quad n = 1, 2, 3, \cdots, \tag{5–3}$$

where, if the interval is $0 < x < \pi$, then either sines or cosines alone suffice for the series representation, the series in the one case being

$$f(x) = \sum_{n=1}^{\infty} b_n \sin nx, \tag{5–4}$$

where the amplitudes b_n are given by

$$b_n = \frac{2}{\pi} \int_{0}^{\pi} f(x) \sin nx dx, \tag{5–5}$$

and in the other case

$$f(x) = \sum_{n=1}^{\infty} a_n \cos nx, \tag{5–6}$$

where the amplitudes a_n are given by (1)

$$a_n = \frac{2}{\pi} \int_{0}^{\pi} f(x) \cos nx dx. \tag{5–7}$$

The formal proof of the general Fourier theorem for all restricted but arbitrary functions is due to Dirichlet (1829). The principal restrictions that Dirichlet imposed on Fourier's theorem are that $f(x)$ must be sectionally continuous, single-valued, finite, and possess a finite number of maxima and minima. In short, the function $f(x)$ must be what mathematicians call "piecewise regular." This is to say that its graph must be either continuous and finite or made up of a finite number of pieces each of which is a continuous arc or an isolated point. Fortunately, this includes nearly all of the functions which arise in the study of physical systems, and certainly any function which we need deal with in the present work.

5–2 The Fourier coefficients. To obtain the Fourier coefficients a_n and b_n in the series (5–1), we first assume that the series converges to $f(x)$ as

$$f(x) = \frac{a_0}{2} + a_1 \cos x + a_2 \cos 2x + \cdots + b_1 \sin x$$

$$+ \, b_2 \sin 2x + \cdots, \quad (5\text{--}1a)$$

and then apply the simple artifice originally used by Fourier and Euler (and in Articles 3–7 and 3–10 in connection with Bessel and Legendre series), namely, that of multiplying both sides of (5–1) by $\sin nx$ and integrating over the 2π interval $-\pi < x < \pi$.* The termwise integration is allowable since (5–1) is uniformly convergent, i.e., the limit of both $|\cos (n + 1)x/\cos nx|$ and $|\sin (n + 1)x/\sin nx|$ exists and is less than or equal to zero for $j\pi < x < (j\pi + 2\pi)$. Thus

$$\int_{-\pi}^{\pi} f(x) \sin nx dx = \frac{a_0}{2} \int_{-\pi}^{\pi} \sin nx dx + a_1 \int_{-\pi}^{\pi} \sin nx \cos x dx + \cdots$$

$$+ \, a_n \int_{-\pi}^{\pi} \sin nx \cos nx dx + b_1 \int_{-\pi}^{\pi} \sin nx \sin x dx$$

$$+ \, b_2 \int_{-\pi}^{\pi} \sin nx \sin 2x dx + \cdots + b_n \int_{-\pi}^{\pi} \sin^2 nx dx,$$

in which all the integrals on the right side vanish except the last integral, whose value is π. Herewith

$$b_n = \frac{1}{\pi} \int_{-\pi}^{\pi} f(x) \sin nx dx; \quad n = 1, 2, 3, \cdots,$$

which is seen to formally agree with (5–3). Multiplying (5–1) by $\cos nx$ and integrating over the same interval leads to

$$\int_{-\pi}^{\pi} f(x) \cos nx dx = a_n \int_{-\pi}^{\pi} \cos^2 nx dx = \pi; \quad n = 1, 2, 3, \cdots,$$

$$= 2\pi; \quad n = 0,$$

from which

$$a_n = \frac{1}{\pi} \int_{-\pi}^{\pi} f(x) \cos nx dx; \quad n = 1, 2, 3, \cdots,$$

---

*Because of the periodicity of the sine and cosine functions, this interval could also be the 2π range $0 < x < 2\pi$, $\pi < x < 3\pi$, $\cdots$. Hence only the interval $-\pi < x < \pi$ need be considered, since the behavior of the series is identical in all the remaining 2π intervals.

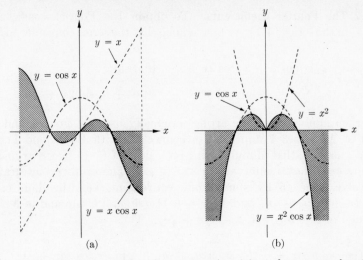

Fig. 5-1. Product of an odd and even function (a), and two even functions (b).

as in (5–2). Then the complete Fourier series equivalent to $f(x)$ reads

$$f(x) = \frac{1}{\pi}\left\{\frac{1}{2}\int_{-\pi}^{\pi} f(x)dx + \left[\int_{-\pi}^{\pi} f(x)\cos x dx\right]\cos x\right.$$

$$+ \left[\int_{-\pi}^{\pi} f(x)\cos 2x dx\right]\cos 2x + \cdots + \left[\int_{-\pi}^{\pi} f(x)\sin x dx\right]\sin x$$

$$\left. + \left[\int_{-\pi}^{\pi} f(x)\sin 2x dx\right]\sin 2x + \cdots\right\}. \quad (5\text{–}8)$$

Depending on whether $f(x)$ is an *odd function*, $f(-x) = -f(x)$, or an *even function*, $f(-x) = f(x)$, the series is represented by sines alone or cosines alone. The reasons why the a_n or b_n vanish according as to whether $f(x)$ is odd or even is easily seen by reference to Fig. 5–1. In Fig. 5–1(a), $f(x)$ is odd, so that $f(x)\cos x$ is odd also. The integration of this product then gives a zero value, since the positive and negative areas are precisely equal. This leaves the sine series alone as the only remaining possible representation of the odd function $f(x) = x$. In Fig. 5–1(b), $f(x)$ is even, so that $f(x)\cos x$ is even also. In this case the integration between $-\pi$ and π gives -4π, so that the cosines alone remain to represent the even function $f(x) = x^2$.

Verification that the sines alone remain for the odd $f(x)$ and vanish for the even $f(x)$ can also be seen by investigating the actual integrals involved.

One first recalls that for the general integral $\int_{u_1}^{0} f(u)du$ we get a sign change on changing either the order of the integration limits or the sign of any one integration limit. Moreover, this sign change can be effected by changing the sign of the integration variable in the integrand and differential, such as

$$\int_{-u_1}^{0} f(u)du = \int_{u_1}^{0} f(-u)d(-u) = \int_{0}^{u_1} f(-u)du.$$

It then follows that if $f(u)$ is even, that is, $f(-u) = f(u)$,

$$\int_{-u_1}^{0} f_e(u)du = \int_{0}^{u_1} f_e(u)du,$$

and if $f(u)$ is odd, that is, $f(-u) = -f(u)$,

$$\int_{-u_1}^{0} f_0(u)du = -\int_{0}^{u_1} f_0(u)du.$$

Thus for the symmetric range $-u_1$ to u_1,

$$\int_{-u_1}^{u_1} f_e(u)du = \int_{-u_1}^{0} f_e(u)du + \int_{0}^{u_1} f_e(u)du = 2\int_{0}^{u_1} f_e(u)du,$$

and

$$\int_{-u_1}^{u} f_0(u)du = \int_{-u_1}^{0} f_0(u)du + \int_{0}^{u_1} f_0(u)du = 0.$$

This assures us that in computing the amplitudes of a Fourier series we need consider *only the sine series if the given function to be expanded is odd,* or *only the cosine series if the function is even.* For functions $f(x)$ neither odd nor even, both series are required and the amplitudes are then given by both (5–2) and (5–3).

5–3 Extension of the interval. In nearly all applications of the infinite trigonometric series, a given function is to be expanded over the general interval $-L < x < L$ rather than over the specific interval $-\pi < x < \pi$. To obtain the Fourier amplitudes for the interval from $x = -L$ to L, we introduce the transformation variable

$$u = \frac{\pi}{L}x; \qquad \begin{array}{l} x \to -L, u \to -\pi, \\[1mm] x \to L, u \to \pi, \end{array}$$

which has the effect of shrinking or expanding the 2π interval according as L is less than or exceeds π. The Fourier series for the variable u is then

$$f(x) = f\left(\frac{L}{\pi}u\right) = \frac{a_0}{2} + \sum_{n=1}^{\infty} (a_n \cos nu + b_n \sin nu),$$

where

$$a_n = \frac{1}{\pi} \int_{-\pi}^{\pi} f\left(\frac{L}{\pi} u\right) \cos nu \, du; \quad -\pi < u < \pi,$$

$$b_n = \frac{1}{\pi} \int_{-\pi}^{\pi} f\left(\frac{L}{\pi} u\right) \sin nu \, du; \quad -\pi < u < \pi.$$

The amplitudes a_n and b_n can be returned to the original variable x by observing that the limit $-L$ corresponds to the limit $-\pi$ and the limit L to π, and that $du = (\pi/L)dx$. Thus

$$a_n = \frac{1}{L} \int_{-L}^{L} f(x) \cos \frac{n\pi}{L} x \, dx; \quad -L < x < L, \tag{5-9}$$

and

$$b_n = \frac{1}{L} \int_{-L}^{L} f(x) \sin \frac{n\pi}{L} x \, dx; \quad -L < x < L. \tag{5-10}$$

With these coefficients we are no longer restricted to a 2π range of x, but may now develop Fourier expansions of a given function defined over the arbitrary interval $-L < x < L$, where L is finite.

5–4 Illustrated Fourier expansions. We can now develop the Fourier series for a few simple piecewise-differentiable functions.

EXAMPLE 5–1. Obtain the Fourier series expansion of the function $f(x) = 1$ defined in the interval $0 < x < \pi$.

Solution. Since the given function is odd, we need only the sine series (5–4) and the amplitudes (5–5). Then

$$b_n = \frac{2}{\pi} \int_0^{\pi} \sin nx \, dx = \frac{-2}{n\pi} \cos nx \Big]_0^{\pi}$$

$$= \frac{2}{n\pi} (1 - \cos n\pi) = 0; \quad n = 0, 2, 4, \cdots, \quad = \frac{4}{n\pi}; \quad n = 1, 3, 5, \cdots,$$

wherewith, according to (5–4),

$$f(x) = 1 = \frac{4}{\pi} \left(\sin x + \tfrac{1}{3} \sin 3x + \tfrac{1}{5} \sin 5x + \cdots \right).$$

The validity of this expansion is easily checked by reference to the formal Taylor or Maclaurin expansion of $\tan^{-1} x$ as

$$\tan^{-1} x = x - \tfrac{1}{3} x^3 + \tfrac{1}{5} x^5 - \cdots$$

for $x^2 \leq 1$. Choosing $x = \pi/2$ in the Fourier expansion gives $1 = (4/\pi)(1 - \tfrac{1}{3} + \tfrac{1}{5} - \cdots)$ or, in terms of the above series, $1 = (4/\pi)\tan^{-1} 1 = 1$.

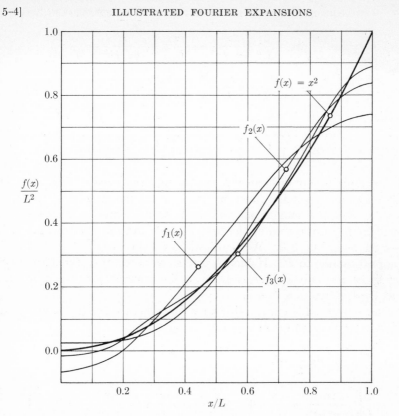

Fig. 5–2. Fourier cosine-series approximation to the even function

$$f(x) = x^2, \quad -L < x < L.$$

In Example 5–1 we note that the sine series represents $f(x) = 1$ only in the interval $0 < x < \pi$ (exclusive of the end points, where the representation vanishes), and does not represent unity in the remaining half-range $-\pi < x < 0$. In general, an odd function can be expanded in sines over the entire 2π interval only if the function is also odd over this entire interval, as would be the case if $f(x) = -1$, $-\pi < x < 0$, and $f(x) = 1$, $0 < x < \pi$.

EXAMPLE 5–2. Obtain the Fourier series expansion of the function $f(x) = x^2$ defined in the interval $-L < x < L$.

Solution. This is an even function, so we first compute the a_0 as

$$a_0 = \frac{2}{L} \int_0^L x^2 dx = \tfrac{2}{3}L^2,$$

and then the a_n cosine amplitudes as

$$a_n = \frac{2}{L} \int_0^L x^2 \cos \frac{n\pi}{L} x\, dx = \frac{2}{L} \left[\frac{2x}{(n\pi/L)^2} \cos \frac{n\pi}{L} x - \frac{2}{(n\pi/L)^3} \sin \frac{n\pi}{L} x \right.$$

$$\left. + \frac{x^2}{(n\pi/L)} \sin \frac{n\pi}{L} x \right]_0^L = \left(\frac{2L}{n\pi} \right)^2 (-1)^n \,; \quad n = 1, 2, 3, \cdots.$$

Herewith

$$f(x) = x^2 = \frac{L^2}{3} - \frac{4L^2}{\pi^2} \left(\cos \frac{\pi}{L} x - \frac{1}{4} \cos \frac{2\pi}{L} x + \frac{1}{9} \cos \frac{3\pi}{L} x - \cdots \right).$$

By a composition of ordinates we can see how the series in Example 5–2 builds up to approach the function $f(x) = x^2$ as the number of terms is increased. Let the sum of the first and second terms in the series be denoted by $f_1(x)$, the sum of the first, second, and third terms by $f_2(x)$, and so on, as in Fig. 5–2. We see that the third curve $f_3(x)$ is already a fair approximation to x^2. If enough terms are taken, then this particular cosine series not only converges to x^2 in the interval $-L < x < L$, but also at the end points $x = \pm L$.

If it were required to expand this same function in a sine series, we could do so only for the half range $0 < x < L$. In this case,

$$b_n = \frac{2}{L} \int_0^L x^2 \sin \frac{n\pi}{L} x\, dx$$

$$= \frac{2}{L} \left[\frac{2x}{(n\pi/L)^2} \sin \frac{n\pi}{L} x + \frac{2}{(n\pi/L)^3} \cos \frac{n\pi}{L} x - \frac{x^2}{(n\pi/L)} \cos \frac{n\pi}{L} x \right]_0^L$$

$$= \frac{2L^2}{\pi^3} \left(\frac{\pi^2}{n} - \frac{4}{n^3} \right); \quad n = 1, 3, 5, \cdots$$

$$= \frac{2L^2}{\pi^3} \left(-\frac{\pi^2}{n} \right); \quad n = 2, 4, 6, \cdots,$$

whereby

$$f(x) = x^2 = \frac{2L^2}{\pi^3} \left[(\pi^2 - 4) \sin \frac{\pi}{L} x - \frac{\pi^2}{2} \sin \frac{2\pi}{L} x \right.$$

$$\left. + \left(\frac{\pi^2}{3} - \frac{4}{3^3} \right) \sin \frac{3\pi}{L} x - \frac{\pi^2}{2^2} \sin \frac{4\pi}{L} x + \cdots \right].$$

That this sine series represents x^2 only for $0 < x < L$ is easily seen by replacing x by $-x$, for then the series represents $-x^2$ for $-L < x < 0$. We therefore have two series (cosine and sine), both of which represent $f(x) = x^2$ in the interval $x = 0$ to L, $2L$ to $3L$, $\cdots$, and only one of which represents $f(x) = x^2$ in the complete periodic interval $x = -L$ to L, L to $3L$, $\cdots$.

EXAMPLE 5–3. Obtain the Fourier series expansion of the following step function:

$$\begin{cases} f(x) = 0; & 0 < x < L/2, \\ f(x) = L/2; & L/2 < x < L. \end{cases}$$

Solution. This is an example of a function which is not continuous over the defined range, but one which has a finite discontinuity at $x = L/2$.

Consider first an expansion in sines. For the b_n coefficients we integrate each piece of the function as

$$b_n = \frac{2}{L} \int_0^L f(x) \sin \frac{n\pi}{L} x \, dx = \frac{2}{L} \int_0^{L/2} (0) \sin \frac{n\pi}{L} x \, dx + \frac{2}{L} \int_{L/2}^L \frac{L}{2} \sin \frac{n\pi}{L} x \, dx$$

$$= \frac{L}{n\pi} \left(\cos \frac{n\pi}{2} - \cos n\pi \right),$$

which shows that b_n vanishes for $n = 4, 8, 12, \cdots$, but has distinct values for all other integral n. The sine series is then

$$f(x) = \frac{L}{\pi} \left(\sin \frac{\pi}{L} x - \sin \frac{2\pi}{L} x + \frac{1}{3} \sin \frac{3\pi}{L} x + \frac{1}{5} \sin \frac{5\pi}{L} x + \cdots \right).$$

Consider now an expansion in cosines. For the a_0, we have

$$a_0 = \frac{2}{L} \int_0^L f(x) dx = \frac{2}{L} \int_0^{L/2} (0) dx + \frac{2}{L} \int_{L/2}^L \frac{L}{2} dx = \frac{L}{2},$$

and for the a_n,

$$a_n = \frac{2}{L} \int_0^L f(x) \cos \frac{n\pi}{L} x \, dx$$

$$= \frac{2}{L} \int_0^{L/2} (0) \cos \frac{n\pi}{L} x \, dx + \frac{2}{L} \int_{L/2}^L \frac{L}{2} \cos \frac{n\pi}{L} x \, dx = \frac{-L}{n\pi} \sin \frac{n\pi}{2}.$$

Here the a_n vanish for even n and alternate sign for the remaining odd n, beginning with $-L/n\pi$ for a_1. Thus for the cosine series,

$$f(x) = \frac{L}{\pi} \left(\frac{\pi}{4} - \cos \frac{\pi}{L} x + \frac{1}{3} \cos \frac{3\pi}{L} x - \frac{1}{5} \cos \frac{5\pi}{L} x + \cdots \right).$$

Again the cosine series converges to $f(x)$ over the entire interval $0 < x < L$, as well as at the end points $x = 0$, L. On the other hand, while the sine series also converges to the given function over the range $0 < x < L$, its sum does not converge to the value $L/4$ at the discontinuity at $x = L/2$. The cosine series reveals this by mere inspection, and for the sine series at $x = L/2$,

$$f(x) = \frac{L}{\pi} \left(1 - \frac{1}{3} + \frac{1}{5} - \cdots \right) = \frac{L}{\pi} \tan^{-1} 1 = \frac{L}{4}.$$

Note that this value is the mean of the given function, i.e., the constant term $a_0/2$.

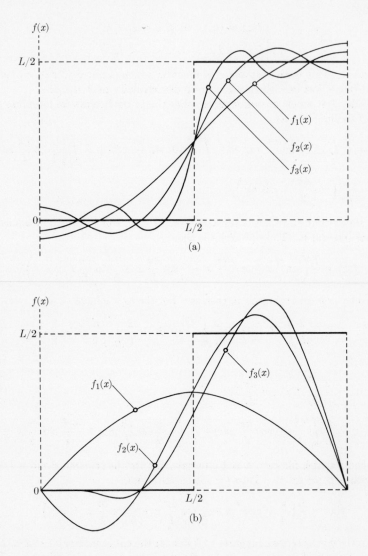

Fig. 5–3. Fourier cosine-series (a) and sine-series (b) approximation to the step function $f(x) = 0$, $0 < x < L/2$, $f(x) = L/2$, $L/2 < x < L$.

Figure 5-3 illustrates how both the sine and cosine series of Example 5–3 build up to represent $f(x) = 0$, $0 < x < L/2$, and $f(x) = L/2$, $L/2 < x < L$. The convergence to this discontinuous function appears to be much slower than that shown in Fig. 5–2 (Example 5–2) for the comparatively simple function $f(x) = x^2$, $-L < x < L$.

5–5 Double Fourier series. As an extension of the expansion (5–1), we now examine expansions of the type

$$f(x,y) = \sum_{n=1}^{\infty} \sum_{m=1}^{\infty} c_{nm} \sin \frac{n\pi}{L} x \sin \frac{m\pi}{l} y, \tag{5–11}$$

in which a given function of two variables, $f(x,y)$, is to be expanded in a *double Fourier series*.

The formal theory of double Fourier series follows the same lines as the development in trigonometric series for a single-variable function (2). To illustrate this similarity, we consider the special case already introduced, namely, the expansion of $f(x,y)$ in a sine series, as in (5–11).

Following the method outlined in Article 5–2, we multiply both sides of (5–11) by $\sin (n\pi x/L) \sin (m\pi y/l)$ and integrate over the interval for which $f(x,y)$ is defined. If the intervals are 0 to L for x and 0 to l for y, then

$$\int_{x=0}^{L} \int_{y=0}^{l} f(x,y) \sin \frac{n\pi}{L} x \sin \frac{m\pi}{l} y\,dxdy$$

$$= c_{11} \left[\int_0^L \sin \frac{\pi}{L} x \sin \frac{n\pi}{L} x\,dx \right]\left[\int_0^l \sin \frac{\pi}{l} y \sin \frac{m\pi}{l} y\,dy \right] + \cdots$$

$$+ c_{nm} \left[\int_0^L \sin^2 \frac{n\pi}{L} x\,dx \right]\left[\int_0^l \sin^2 \frac{m\pi}{l} y\,dy \right].$$

Here, by virtue of

$$\int_0^L \sin \frac{\pi}{L} x \sin \frac{n\pi}{L} x\,dx = 0 = \int_0^l \sin \frac{\pi}{l} y \sin \frac{m\pi}{l} y\,dy; \ \ n \neq 1 \neq m,$$

all the integrals on the right side vanish except those associated with the c_{nm} coefficient, which we compute to be

$$\int_0^L \sin^2 \frac{n\pi}{L} x\,dx = \frac{x}{2} - \frac{\sin (2\pi/L)nx}{4\pi(n/L)} \Big]_0^L = \frac{L}{2}; \ \ n = 1, 2, 3, \cdots.$$

This puts us in possession of the required amplitudes, as

$$c_{nm} = \frac{4}{Ll} \int_0^L \int_0^l f(x,y) \sin \frac{n\pi}{L} x \sin \frac{m\pi}{l} y\,dxdy; \ \ n, m = 1, 2, 3, \cdots. \tag{5–12}$$

The expansion of $f(x,y)$ in a cosine series is to be carried out in exactly the same way. In fact, the representation of $f(x,y)$ or $f(x,y,z)$ in either type of Fourier series leads to results analogous in every way to the results for $f(x)$, the correspondence manifesting itself as a product of previously obtained integrals.

5–6 The Fourier integral theorem. A complete treatment of the Fourier series includes the limiting case where $f(x)$ is defined over the infinite interval $-\infty < x < \infty$. This case is of practical importance because we shall later consider systems which may be thought of as having, for all practical purposes, one or more dimensions of infinite extent. We now show that the Fourier series developed for a finite interval of x, $-L < x < L$, passes over to the form of definite integrals for the limiting case where $L \to \infty$ (3).

In the complete Fourier series,

$$f(x) = \frac{1}{2L} \int_{-L}^{L} f(x)dx + \frac{1}{L} \cos \frac{\pi}{L} x \int_{-L}^{L} f(x) \cos \frac{\pi}{L} xdx$$

$$+ \frac{1}{L} \cos \frac{2\pi}{L} x \int_{-L}^{L} f(x) \cos \frac{2\pi}{L} xdx + \cdots + \frac{1}{L} \sin \frac{\pi}{L} x \int_{-L}^{L} f(x) \sin \frac{\pi}{L} xdx$$

$$+ \frac{1}{L} \sin \frac{2\pi}{L} x \int_{-L}^{L} f(x) \sin \frac{2\pi}{L} xdx + \cdots,$$

the variable x may be changed to a new variable x' without changing the value of any integral. Then, since x is independent of the assumed variable of integration x', the cosine function in x (x now being called a "dummy variable") may be entered under each integral and treated as a constant. This also being true of the sine functions in x, we have

$$Lf(x) = \frac{1}{2} \int_{-L}^{L} f(x')dx' + \int_{-L}^{L} f(x') \cos \frac{\pi}{L} x \cos \frac{\pi}{L} x'dx' + \cdots$$

$$+ \int_{-L}^{L} f(x') \sin \frac{\pi}{L} x \sin \frac{\pi}{L} x'dx' + \cdots.$$

Factoring out the integral $\int_{-L}^{L} f(x')dx'$ and using the identity $\cos \alpha \cos \beta + \sin \alpha \sin \beta = \cos (\alpha - \beta)$ gives

$$f(x) = \frac{1}{L} \int_{-L}^{L} \left[\frac{1}{2} + \cos \frac{\pi}{L} (x' - x) + \cdots + \cos \frac{n\pi}{L} (x' - x) \right] f(x')dx' \cdot$$

Then by treating the expression in brackets as a polynomial,

$$a(\tfrac{1}{2} + b + c + \cdots) = \tfrac{1}{2}a(1 + 2b + 2c + \cdots),$$

and remembering that the cosine is even, there results, after some obvious rearrangement,

$$f(x) = \frac{1}{2L} \int_{-L}^{L} \left[\cos \left(\frac{-n\pi}{L} \right) (x' - x) + \cdots \right.$$

$$+ \cos \left(\frac{-\pi}{L} \right) (x' - x) + \cos \frac{(0)\pi}{L} (x' - x)$$

$$\left. + \cos \frac{\pi}{L} (x' - x) + \cdots + \cos \frac{n\pi}{L} (x' - x) \right] f(x')dx',$$

or, equivalently,

$$f(x) = \frac{1}{2\pi} \int_{-L}^{L} \left[\sum_{n=-\infty}^{\infty} \frac{\pi}{L} \cos \frac{n\pi}{L} (x' - x) \right] f(x')dx'. \qquad (5\text{--}13)$$

We now recall the fundamental definition of the definite integral $\int_{0}^{\infty} udu$ as

$$\int_{0}^{\infty} udu = \lim_{\Delta u \to 0} \sum_{n=0}^{\infty} (n\Delta u)\Delta u,$$

which has the legitimate extension

$$\int_{-\infty}^{\infty} udu = \lim_{\Delta u \to 0} \sum_{n=-\infty}^{\infty} (n\Delta u)\Delta u. \qquad (5\text{--}14)$$

The bracketed term in (5–13) is of the form (5–14), where $\Delta u = \pi/L$. On letting L pass to infinitely large values, Δu approaches zero, whereby

$$\sum_{n=-\infty}^{\infty} \frac{\pi}{L} \cos \frac{n\pi}{L} (x' - x) = \int_{-\infty}^{\infty} \cos \lambda (x' - x)d\lambda,$$

in which λ is defined as

$$\lambda = \frac{n\pi}{L}. \qquad (5\text{--}15)$$

This result can be identified with (5–13) as

$$f(x) = \frac{1}{2\pi} \int_{-\infty}^{\infty} f(x')dx' \int_{-\infty}^{\infty} \cos \lambda (x' - x)d\lambda; \quad -\infty < x < \infty. \qquad (5\text{--}16)$$

The double integral (5–16) is known as the *Fourier integral*, and is the limiting case of the complete Fourier series for which the interval of expansion is unbounded, $-\infty < x < \infty$.

5–7 The Fourier sine and cosine integrals. By virtue of the cosine being an even function, the range of integration in the second integral of (5–16) may be divided by simply breaking the integration at the half range as

$$\int_{-\infty}^{\infty} \cos \lambda (x' - x)d\lambda = \int_{0}^{\infty} \cos \lambda (x' - x)d\lambda + \int_{0}^{\infty} \cos \lambda (x' - x)d\lambda.$$

This changes the form of (5–16) to

$$f(x) = \frac{1}{\pi} \int_{-\infty}^{\infty} f(x')dx' \int_{0}^{\infty} \cos \lambda (x' - x)d\lambda. \qquad (5\text{--}17)$$

From (5–17) the exact integral form for either even or odd $f(x)$ can be determined, the integral being in terms of a sine or cosine function, depending on whether $f(x)$ is odd or even. We can first rewrite (5–17) as

$$f(x) = \frac{1}{\pi} \int_{-\infty}^{\infty} f(x')dx' \int_{0}^{\infty} \cos \lambda (x' - x)d\lambda$$

$$= \frac{1}{\pi} \int_{-\infty}^{\infty} f(x') \cos \lambda (x' - x)dx' \int_{0}^{\infty} d\lambda, \qquad (5\text{–}18)$$

since the integration limits belong to x, which is still playing the role of a dummy variable. Then

$$\int_{-\infty}^{\infty} f(x') \cos \lambda (x' - x)dx' = \int_{-\infty}^{0} f(x') \cos \lambda (x' - x)dx'$$

$$+ \int_{0}^{\infty} f(x') \cos \lambda (x' - x)dx'$$

$$= \int_{0}^{\infty} f(-x') \cos \lambda (x' + x)dx'$$

$$+ \int_{0}^{\infty} f(x') \cos \lambda (x' - x)dx',$$

and if $f(x')$ is even,

$$\int_{-\infty}^{\infty} f(x') \cos \lambda (x' - x)dx' = \int_{0}^{\infty} f(x')[\cos \lambda (x' + x) + \cos \lambda (x' - x)]dx'.$$

By employing the identity $\cos (\alpha + \beta) + \cos (\alpha - \beta) = 2 \cos \alpha \cos \beta$, we can reduce the above equation to

$$\int_{-\infty}^{\infty} f(x') \cos \lambda (x' - x)dx' = 2 \int_{0}^{\infty} f(x') \cos \lambda x \cos \lambda x'dx',$$

and this puts (5–18) in the form

$$f(x) = \frac{2}{\pi} \int_{0}^{\infty} f(x') \cos \lambda x \cos \lambda x'dx' \int_{0}^{\infty} d\lambda,$$

or

$$f(x) = \frac{2}{\pi} \int_{0}^{\infty} f(x')dx' \int_{0}^{\infty} \cos \lambda x \cos \lambda x'd\lambda \left. \right\} f(x)_{\text{even}}. \qquad (5\text{–}19)$$

In like fashion, if the function to be expanded is odd, then (5–19) is to be replaced by

$$f(x) = \frac{2}{\pi} \int_{0}^{\infty} f(x')dx' \int_{0}^{\infty} \sin \lambda x \sin \lambda x'd\lambda \left. \right\} f(x)_{\text{odd}}. \qquad (5\text{–}20)$$

The result (5–19) is known as the *Fourier cosine integral* for even $f(x)$, and (5–20) as the *Fourier sine integral* for odd $f(x)$. In analogy to the series, these integrals also have the property that both the sine and cosine representations hold over the positive half-range of x.

Integration of Partial-Differential Equations

Problems in heat conduction thus far considered have all been of the one-dimensional type so that, in general, a characteristic total-differential equation which had to be satisfied by $t(x)$ or $t(r)$ could, in any case, be integrated directly by the elementary methods. The partial-differential equations which must be satisfied by $t(x,y)$ or $t(r,\varphi)$ in problems of the two-dimensional type (Article 1–3) cannot, by contrast, be integrated as easily. The exact methods to be employed in these cases are formalized and two in number, the first being the *separation of variables* method, and the second the *Laplace transform* method.

The separation of variables technique is the classical approach to the solution of two-dimensional boundary-value problems, and will be used here almost exclusively. By this method the partial-differential equation in question is reduced to a set of two total-differential equations, the general solutions of which are well known or to which the usual methods of integration apply. Application of the Laplace transform method to a one-dimensional problem reduces the characteristic differential equation to a simple algebraic equation and, somewhat like the separation method, its application to a two-dimensional problem effects a transformation of the partial-differential equation into a total-differential equation.

There are convincing arguments on both sides as to which of these methods represents the preferred approach. The Laplace transform is generally accepted as being particularly well suited for the more difficult boundary-value problems, and is often "cleaner," more conservative of equations, than the separation method. But for student use, and for those who are not well trained in such topics as the complex variable and contour integration, and particularly for those who are not used to the more abstract manipulations of operational calculus, the separation of variables method represents a perfectly straightforward approach which is nearly always successful. In the infrequent case of an impasse with the separation method, one turns to the Laplace transform technique, for which only the briefest outline can be given here.

5–8 Separation of variables method. Consider the general second-order partial-differential equation

$$f_1(x)\frac{\partial^2 t}{\partial x^2} + f_2(x)\frac{\partial t}{\partial x} + f_3(x)t + g_1(y)\frac{\partial^2 t}{\partial y^2} + g_2(y)\frac{\partial t}{\partial y} + g_3(y)t = 0. \quad (5\text{–}21)$$

To integrate this linear and homogeneous equation by the separation of variables method, we assume a *product solution* for $t(x,y)$ of the form

$$t(x,y) = XY; \quad X = X(x), Y = Y(y),$$

where X is assumed to be a function of x alone and Y a function of y alone.

Substituting this in (5–21) gives the equality

$$-\frac{1}{X}\left(f_1\frac{\partial^2 X}{\partial x^2} + f_2\frac{\partial X}{\partial x} + f_3 X\right) = \frac{1}{Y}\left(g_1\frac{\partial^2 Y}{\partial y^2} + g_2\frac{\partial Y}{\partial y} + g_3 Y\right),$$

which clearly shows that the variables x and y are now separated. Now since, by hypothesis, the left side of this equation is independent of y and the right side is independent of x, each side must be independently equal to a common constant, say μ. Referring to this as a *separation constant*, we have

$$f_1\frac{d^2 X}{dx^2} + f_2\frac{dX}{dx} + (f_3 + \mu)X = 0, \tag{5–22}$$

and

$$g_1\frac{d^2 Y}{dy^2} + g_2\frac{dY}{dy} + (g_3 - \mu)Y = 0. \tag{5–23}$$

The general partial-differential equation (5–21) has thus been reduced by the separation-of-variables method to two total-differential equations. From here on the final solution for $t(x,y)$ is obtained by first finding the general solutions $X(x)$ and $Y(y)$ of the two separated differential equations (5–22) and (5–23). The general product solution $t(x,y) = XY$ is then fitted to the boundary conditions of the problem at hand, and it is during this process that the value of the separation constant μ is determined.

The elementary separation of variables method can also be extended to include three-dimensional cases, such as in steady conduction with $t = t(x,y,z)$ or transient conduction with $t = t(x,y,\theta)$. In the first case, we simply assume $t = XYZ$, and in the second $t = XY\Theta$ or even $t = XYZ\Theta$.

In the strict mathematical sense, not all partial-differential equations have product solutions of the form assumed in the separation of variables method. Fortunately, however, most of the linear partial-differential equations which need be considered here do possess such product solutions. The complete success of the separation method depends not only on effecting the separation itself, but on the possibility of forcing the product solution to satisfy initial and boundary conditions. In some cases this is not possible; when, for example, these conditions are *nonhomogeneous.** However, it is sufficient at this point to say that such difficulties can ordinarily be overcome by a suitable change of variable.

5–9 The Laplace transformation. The Laplace transformation leads to an operational method for integrating either linear or nonlinear differential equations. In contrast to the separation-of-variables method, in which a general solution is first obtained and then arbitrary constants

---

*A boundary condition, like any equation, is said to be *homogeneous* if it is not only satisfied by $t(x)$, but by $ct(x)$ as well, where c is an arbitrary constant.

evaluated so as to satisfy initial and boundary conditions, the transform method introduces the particular conditions of the problem at an early stage of the operational solution. This is to some advantage, since in many cases it eliminates the evaluation of arbitrary constants, which can become quite tedious in the separation method. The operational method is especially adaptable when these boundary conditions are discontinuous.

The *Laplace transformation* of a function $f(x)$, symbolized here as $\mathcal{L}(u)$, is defined as the operation of multiplying $f(x)$ by e^{-ux} and integrating over all positive values of the variable x, as

$$\mathcal{L}(u) = \int_0^\infty e^{-ux} f(x) dx. \tag{5–24}$$

The value of u may be real or imaginary, and in either case its real part must be sufficiently large to ensure the convergence of the integral (5–24). *Transforms* of various functions $f(x)$ can therefore be obtained by direct integration. For example, if $f(x) = \sqrt{x}$, then the transform of this function is $\mathcal{L}(u) = \int_0^\infty e^{-ux} \sqrt{x} dx = (\pi/4u^3)^{1/2}$. The *inverse transform* is the function itself. Thus $\sqrt{x}$ is called the inverse transform of $(\pi/4u^3)^{1/2}$. A few such elementary *transform pairs* are listed in Table 5–1.* The table

TABLE 5–1

LAPLACE-TRANSFORM PAIRS

	$f(x)$	$\mathcal{L}(u)$		$f(x)$	$\mathcal{L}(u)$
(1)	1	$\dfrac{1}{u}$	(5)	$\sin ax$	$\dfrac{a}{u^2 + a^2}$
(2)	e^{ax}	$\dfrac{1}{u - a}$	(6)	$\cos ax$	$\dfrac{u}{u^2 + a^2}$
(3)	* x^n	$\dfrac{n!}{u^{n+1}}$	(7)	$\sinh ax$	$\dfrac{a}{u^2 - a^2}$
(4)	† x^k	$\dfrac{\Gamma(k + 1)}{u^{k+1}}$	(8)	$\cosh ax$	$\dfrac{u}{u^2 - a^2}$

* n integral and > -1.   † k fractional (Article 3–3).

can be extended by noting from the transform pairs (1) and (2) that multiplication of an inverse transform by $e^{\pm mx}$ changes the argument u in the transform to $u \mp m$. For example, if $f(x) = e^{mx} \sin ax$, then according to the transform pair (5), $\mathcal{L}(u) = a/[(u - m)^2 + a^2]$.

---

*For more elaborate tables of Laplace-transform pairs, see Carslaw and Jaeger (4), Churchill (5), and Thomson (6).

With an integration by parts it can be shown that the important Laplace transforms of first and second derivatives are

$$\mathcal{L}\left(\frac{df}{dx}\right) = u\mathcal{L}(u) - f(0), \tag{5-25}$$

and

$$\mathcal{L}\left(\frac{d^2f}{dx^2}\right) = u^2\mathcal{L}(u) - uf(0) - \frac{d}{dx}f(0). \tag{5-26}$$

In these algebraic transforms, $f(0)$ and its derivative represent boundary conditions to be satisfied by $f(x)$.

5–10 Laplace transform method.   We can now examine in a general way how to integrate differential equations by the Laplace transform method, using the transformation (5–24) along with a few of its fundamental properties, notably (5–25) and (5–26).

Consider the total-differential equation

$$\frac{d^2t}{dx^2} + a\frac{dt}{dx} + bt = 0. \tag{5-27}$$

Applying the Laplace transformation to this, as

$$\mathcal{L}\left(\frac{d^2t}{dx^2}\right) + \mathcal{L}\left(a\frac{dt}{dx}\right) + \mathcal{L}(bt) = 0,$$

we obtain, by reference to (5–25) and (5–26),

$$u^2\mathcal{L}(u) - ut(0) - \frac{d}{dx}t(0) + au\mathcal{L}(u) - at(0) + b\mathcal{L}(u) = 0,$$

or

$$\mathcal{L}(u) = \frac{(u + a)t(0) + dt(0)/dx}{u^2 + au + b}. \tag{5-28}$$

The result (5–28) is referred to as the *subsidiary equation* of (5–27). In this case of a total-differential equation, the subsidiary equation is algebraic.

The problem that remains is to find $t(x)$ from the subsidiary equation, and this is to be accomplished by substituting the appropriate boundary conditions $t(0)$ and $dt(0)/dx$ in (5–28), and then rearranging the result in such a fashion that an *inverse transformation* can be performed, i.e., that $t(x)$ can be obtained from $\mathcal{L}(u)$. This operation usually requires that the subsidiary equation be reduced by the method of partial fractions to a form where each term can be identified with a known inverse transform.

EXAMPLE 5–4. Using the Laplace transform method, find the particular solution of

$$\frac{d^2t}{dx^2} + a = 0$$

satisfying both $t = t_0$ and $dt/dx = 0$ at $x = 0$.

Solution. By referring to (5–26) and the transform pair (1) in Table 5–1,

$$\mathcal{L}\left(\frac{d^2t}{dx^2}\right) = u^2\mathcal{L}(u) - ut(0) - \frac{d}{dx}t(0) = u^2\mathcal{L}(u) - ut_0,$$

$$\mathcal{L}(a) = \frac{a}{u}.$$

The subsidiary equation is then obtained in this case from

$$u^2\mathcal{L}(u) - ut_0 + \frac{a}{u} = 0,$$

as

$$\mathcal{L}(u) = \frac{ut_0 - (a/u)}{u^2} = t_0\left(\frac{1}{u}\right) - \frac{a}{2}\left(\frac{2}{u^3}\right).$$

The inverse transformation is easily performed by recognizing the transform pairs (1) and (3) in Table 5–1 as those contained in the subsidiary equation above, the final solution appearing as

$$t = t_0 - \frac{a}{2}x^2.$$

EXAMPLE 5–5. Solve the turbine-blade problem of Article 2–11, using the Laplace transform method. The blade temperature $T(x)$ must satisfy the differential equation

$$\frac{d^2T}{dx^2} - N^2T = 0,$$

and the boundary conditions $T = T_r$ at $x = 0$ and $dT/dx = 0$ at $x = L$.

Solution. In this case we do not have two conditions for $x = 0$. But if we let $C = dT(0)/dx$, then the subsidiary equation becomes

$$\mathcal{L}(u) = \frac{uT_r + C}{u^2 - N^2} = T_r\left(\frac{u}{u^2 - N^2}\right) + \frac{C}{N}\left(\frac{N}{u^2 - N^2}\right),$$

and by using the transform pairs (7) and (8) in Table 5–1 the inverse transformation is

$$T = T_r \cosh Nx + \frac{C}{N}\sinh Nx.$$

But the second boundary condition requires that $C = -T_r N \sinh NL/\cosh NL$, so that

$$\frac{T}{T_r} = \frac{\cosh NL\,(1 - x/L)}{\cosh NL},$$

as in (2–31).

For the application of the Laplace-transform method to partial-differential equations, consider the problem where $t(x,\theta)$ must satisfy

$$\frac{\partial^2 t}{\partial x^2} = \frac{1}{\alpha}\frac{\partial t}{\partial \theta},$$ (5-29)

the boundary conditions $t(x_1,\theta) = t_1$ and $t(x_2,\theta) = t_2$, and the initial condition $t(x,0) = t_i$. Applying the Laplace transformation *with respect to* θ on both sides of (5-29), as

$$\int_0^\infty e^{-u\theta}\frac{\partial^2 t}{\partial x^2}\,d\theta = \frac{1}{\alpha}\int_0^\infty e^{-u\theta}\frac{\partial t}{\partial \theta}\,d\theta,$$

we have, after interchanging the order of integration and differentiation on the left side, and after expressing the right side in terms of its algebraic transform,

$$\frac{\partial^2}{\partial x^2}\int_0^\infty e^{-u\theta}t(x,\theta)d\theta = \frac{1}{\alpha}[u\mathfrak{L}(u) - t(x,0)].$$

The left-hand integral transformation will evidently be a function of u and the single variable x; hence the partial derivative goes over to a total derivative, and with the abbreviation

$$\bar{u} = \mathfrak{L}(u), = \int_0^\infty e^{-u\theta} t(x,\theta)\,d\theta$$ (5-30)

the subsidiary equation becomes

$$\frac{d^2\bar{u}}{dx^2} - \frac{u}{\alpha}\bar{u} = \frac{t_i}{\alpha}.$$ (5-31)

The Laplace transformation has thus reduced the partial-differential equation (5-29) to the total-differential equation (5-31) with $\bar{u} = \bar{u}(x,u)$, and with the boundary conditions transformed into $\bar{u} = t_1$ at $x = x_1$ and $\bar{u} = t_2$ at $x = x_2$. The subsidiary differential equation (5-31) is to be integrated by the usual methods, or again by the Laplace transform method, and these two boundary conditions fitted to the solution $\bar{u}$. An inverse transformation from $\bar{u}$ to t is again the final solution to the original problem.

An inverse transformation is not always so simple that the subsidiary solution can be resolved into functions listed in tables as transform pairs. In many cases t must be determined from $\bar{u}$ by means of the *inversion integral*, which involves a contour integration with complex variables. Space not permitting, the reader is referred here to References (5) and (6) for systematic accounts of these integrations and the procedures whereby a final solution is put in real form.

REFERENCES

1. R. E. Langer, "Fourier Series—The Genesis and Evolution of a Theory," Herbert Ellsworth Slaught Memorial Papers No. 1, *The American Mathematical Monthly*, Aug.-Sept., 1947.

2. D. Jackson, "Fourier Series and Orthogonal Polynomials," The Carus Mathematical Monographs No. 6, *Mathematical Association of America*, 1941.

3. H. S. Carslaw, *Introduction to the Theory of Fourier's Series and Integrals*. London: Macmillan and Co., Limited, 1930.

4. H. S. Carslaw and J. C. Jaeger, *Conduction of Heat in Solids*. London: Oxford University Press, 1947.

5. R. V. Churchill, *Modern Operational Mathematics in Engineering*. New York: McGraw-Hill Book Co., Inc., 1944.

6. W. T. Thomson, *Laplace Transformation*. New York: Prentice-Hall, Inc., 1950.

PROBLEMS

5–1. (a) Develop the following Fourier cosine-series expansion of the function $f(x) = x, 0 < x < L$:

$$f(x) = x = \frac{L}{2} - \frac{4L}{\pi^2}\left(\cos\frac{\pi}{L}x + \frac{1}{9}\cos\frac{3\pi}{L}x + \frac{1}{25}\cos\frac{5\pi}{L}x + \cdots\right).$$

(b) Show that the series in (a) would not hold if $f(x)$ were defined over the complete interval $-L < x < L$. (c) Show that the series in (a) converges to both end points $x = 0, L$.

5–2. (a) Develop the following Fourier sine-series expansion of the function $f(x) = x, 0 < x < L$:

$$f(x) = x = \frac{2L}{\pi}\left(\sin\frac{\pi}{L}x - \frac{1}{2}\sin\frac{2\pi}{L}x + \frac{1}{3}\sin\frac{3\pi}{L}x - \cdots\right).$$

(b) Show that the series in (a) would also hold if $f(x)$ were defined over the complete interval $-L < x < L$. (c) Show that the series in (a) converges to the end point $x = 0$ and mid-point $x = L/2$, but not to the end point $x = L$.

5–3. Plot the sum of the first, the first and second, and the first, second, and third terms for both the sine and cosine expansions of $f(x) = x$ in problems 5–1 and 5–2. See Examples 5–2 and 5–3.

5–4. (a) Develop the Fourier expansion

$$f(x) = \frac{1}{2} + \frac{2}{\pi}\left(\sin\frac{\pi}{L}x + \frac{1}{3}\sin\frac{3\pi}{L}x + \frac{1}{5}\sin\frac{5\pi}{L}x + \cdots\right)$$

for the step function $f(x) = 0, -L < x < 0, f(x) = 1, 0 < x < L$. (b) Show that the series in (a) converges to the function $f(x)$ at the points $x = -L/2$, $L/2$, and converges to the mean of the function at the end points $x = -L$, L and at the discontinuity $x = 0$. (c) Show how this series approximation builds up to $f(x)$, as in problem 5–3.

5-5. Develop the Fourier expansion

$$f(x) = -\frac{\pi}{4} - \frac{2}{\pi} (\cos x + \tfrac{1}{9} \cos 3x + \tfrac{1}{25} \cos 5x + \cdots)$$
$$+ 3 (\sin x + \tfrac{1}{3} \sin 3x + \cdots) - (\tfrac{1}{2} \sin 2x + \tfrac{1}{4} \sin 4x + \cdots)$$

for the step function $f(x) = -\pi$, $-\pi < x < 0$, $f(x) = x$, $0 < x < \pi$.

5-6. Develop the Fourier expansion

$$f(x) = \frac{\pi}{8} + \frac{2}{\pi} \sum_{n=1}^{\infty} \frac{1}{n^2} \left(1 - \cos \frac{n\pi}{2} \right) \cos nx$$

for the step function $f(x) = 0$, $-\pi < x < -\pi/2$, $f(x) = x + \pi/2$, $-\pi/2 < x < 0$, $f(x) = -x + \pi/2$, $0 < x < \pi/2$, $f(x) = 0$, $\pi/2 < x < \pi$.

5-7. Develop the Fourier expansion

$$f(x) = \frac{1}{2} - \frac{4}{\pi} \sum_{n=1}^{\infty} \frac{1}{n} \sin \tfrac{3}{4} n\pi \cos \frac{n\pi}{4} x + \frac{4}{\pi} \sum_{n=1}^{\infty} \frac{1}{n} \left(\cos \tfrac{3}{4} n\pi - \cos \frac{n\pi}{2} \right) \sin \frac{n\pi}{4} x$$

for the discontinuous function of period 4, $f(x) = -1$, $2 < x < 3$, $f(x) = 1$, $3 < x < 6$.

5-8. Develop the following Fourier expansion of the function $f(x) = e^x$, $-\pi < x < \pi$:

$$f(x) = e^x = \frac{2}{\pi} \sinh \pi \left[\frac{1}{2} + \sum_{n=1}^{\infty} \frac{(-1)^n}{1 + n^2} \cos nx - \sum_{n=1}^{\infty} \frac{n(-1)^n}{1 + n^2} \sin nx \right].$$

5-9. Develop the following Fourier expansion of the function $f(x) = \cosh x$, $-\pi < x < \pi$:

$$f(x) = \cosh x = \frac{2}{\pi} \sinh \pi \left[\frac{1}{2} + \sum_{n=1}^{\infty} \frac{(-1)^n}{1 + n^2} \cos nx \right].$$

5-10. Develop the following Fourier cosine and sine integral expansions of the step function $f(x) = 1$, $0 < x < L$, $f(x) = 0$, $L < x < \infty$:

$$f(x) = \frac{2}{\pi} \int_0^{\infty} \frac{1}{\lambda} \sin \lambda L \cos \lambda x d\lambda,$$

$$f(x) = \frac{2}{\pi} \int_0^{\infty} \frac{1}{\lambda} (1 - \cos \lambda L) \sin \lambda x d\lambda.$$

5-11. Show by the separation of variables method that the partial-differential equation

$$\frac{\partial^2 t}{\partial x^2} = \frac{1}{\alpha} \frac{\partial t}{\partial \theta}$$

can be reduced to the set of total-differential equations

$$\frac{d^2 X}{dx^2} - nX = 0, \qquad \frac{d\Theta}{d\theta} - n\alpha\Theta = 0,$$

where n is a separation constant, and where $X = X(x)$ and $\Theta = \Theta(\theta)$.

5–12. Show by the separation of variables method that the partial-differential equation

$$\frac{\partial^2 t}{\partial r^2} + \frac{1}{r}\frac{\partial t}{\partial r} + \frac{1}{r^2}\frac{\partial^2 t}{\partial \varphi^2} = 0$$

can be reduced to the set of total-differential equations

$$\frac{d^2 R}{dr^2} + \frac{1}{r}\frac{dR}{dr} - \frac{n^2}{r^2}R = 0,$$

$$\frac{d^2 \Phi}{d\varphi^2} + n^2 \Phi = 0,$$

where n is a separation constant, and where $R = R(r)$ and $\Phi = \Phi(\varphi)$.

5–13. Using the Laplace transform method, show that the particular solution of

$$\frac{d^2 t}{dx^2} + at = 0,$$

satisfying the boundary conditions $t = t_0$ at $x = 0$ and $dt/dx = b$ at $x = 0$ is

$$t = t_0 \cos \sqrt{a}\,x + \frac{b}{\sqrt{a}} \sin \sqrt{a}\,x.$$

5–14. Show by elementary methods that the general solution of the subsidiary equation (5–31) is

$$\mathcal{L}(u) = C_1 e^{\sqrt{u/\alpha}\,x} + C_2 e^{-\sqrt{u/\alpha}\,x} - \frac{t_i}{u}.$$

CHAPTER 6

STEADY TWO-DIMENSIONAL SYSTEMS

Now that we have reviewed the Fourier series and methods for handling partial-differential equations, we can go on to examine a number of fundamental systems in which the permanent state of temperature is a function of two space coordinates. General and particular solutions of the Laplace equation in rectangular, cylindrical, and spherical coordinates are obtained by the separation of variables method. In this chapter we also extend the approximate graphical method to steady two-dimensional fields, treating first systems with known isothermal boundaries and, second, cases where boundary conditions are of the convective type.

6–1 Semi-infinite adiabatic plate. Consider a plane plate free of internal heat sources and sinks and oriented in the first xy-quadrant with edges $x = 0$, $x = L$, $y = 0$, and $y = \infty$, as in Fig. 6–1. Such a solid is spoken of as *semi-infinite*, since one of its dimensions is unlimited. Let the three edges $x = 0$, $x = L$, and $y = \infty$ be held at a steady and uniform temperature t_1, and the fourth edge, $y = 0$, maintained at a steady but arbitrary temperature distribution $t = f(x)$. Since the plate is considered to be relatively thin, the temperature gradient dt/dz is assumed negligible, and the temperature field in question becomes two-dimensional, as $t(x,y)$.

If the plate is of uniform thermal conductivity, and if its face surfaces are perfectly insulated against heat exchange with the surroundings, then the temperature field $t(x,y)$ in the plate with *adiabatic faces* must satisfy the Laplace partial-differential equation

$$\frac{\partial^2 T}{\partial x^2} + \frac{\partial^2 T}{\partial y^2} = 0, \tag{6–1}$$

and the conditions of temperature on the boundaries as

$$T = 0 \qquad\qquad \text{at } x = 0, L,$$

$$T = 0 \qquad\qquad \text{at } y = \infty, \tag{6–2}$$

$$T = f(x) - t_1 = F(x) \quad \text{at } y = 0,$$

where T is now defined as the temperature difference $T = t - t_1$. Using the separation of variables method of Article 5–8, we assume a product solution for $t(x,y)$ of the form $T = XY$, where $X = X(x)$ and $Y = Y(y)$. This reduces (6–1) to

$$\frac{1}{X}\frac{d^2X}{dx^2} = -\frac{1}{Y}\frac{d^2Y}{dy^2}.$$

The variables x and y are now separated, with the result that each side of the above equation must be independently equal to the same separation constant, say $-\lambda^2$. This gives the two total-differential equations

$$\frac{d^2X}{dx^2} + \lambda^2 X = 0, \qquad (6\text{–}3)$$

and

$$\frac{d^2Y}{dy^2} - \lambda^2 Y = 0. \qquad (6\text{–}4)$$

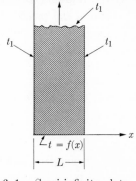

Fig. 6–1.   Semi-infinite plate.

The general solution of (6–3) is obtained by setting $X = e^{ax}$, whereby $a = \pm i\lambda$ ($i^2 = -1$). According to this result,

$$X = C_1 e^{i\lambda x} + C_2 e^{-i\lambda x},$$

and by recalling the identities $e^{\pm i\alpha} = \cos \alpha \pm i \sin \alpha$, the general solution for X takes the form

$$X = C_1 \cos \lambda x + C_2 \sin \lambda x. \qquad (6\text{–}5)$$

From (4–1) the general solution of (6–4) is

$$Y = C_3 e^{\lambda y} + C_4 e^{-\lambda y}. \qquad (6\text{–}6)$$

The general solution of the Laplace equation (6–1) is thus assumed to be given by the product of X in (6–5) and of Y in (6–6).

Now in order for (6–5) to satisfy the first boundary condition in (6–2), that $T = 0$ at $x = 0$, X must vanish at $x = 0$, and this means that $C_1 = 0$. By the same reasoning, $C_3 = 0$ if Y (and thus T) is to vanish at $y = \infty$. The general solution XY is therefore reduced in this case to the form

$$T = C e^{-\lambda y} \sin \lambda x,$$

and if this is to satisfy the second boundary condition in (6–2), that $T = 0$ at $x = L$, then $\sin \lambda L = 0$ or $\lambda = n\pi/L$; $n = 1, 2, 3, \cdots$.* There is, accordingly, a different solution for each consecutive integer n, and a different integration constant C associated with each solution. We express this by summing these solutions for all positive integral n as

$$T = \sum_{n=1}^{\infty} C_n e^{-(n\pi/L)y} \sin \frac{n\pi}{L} x, \qquad (6\text{–}7)$$

*The value $n = 0$ is excluded because it gives only the trivial solution $T = 0$.

the summation being permissible since a solution of a homogeneous and linear partial-differential equation is also the sum of any number of solutions, providing the resulting series is termwise differentiable. Note that (6–7) also satisfies the third boundary condition in (6–2) that $T = 0$ at $y = \infty$. The numbers n are known as *eigenvalues*, and each corresponding solution T_n is called an *eigenfunction*.*

Finally, in order that (6–7) will satisfy the remaining boundary condition in (6–2) that $T = F(x)$ at $y = 0$, we have

$$F(x) = \sum_{n=1}^{\infty} C_n \sin \frac{n\pi}{L} x.$$

This result is recognized as a Fourier expansion (Chapter 5) of the arbitrary function $F(x)$ in an infinite series of sines. In this case the undetermined amplitudes C_n are given by (5–10) as

$$C_n = \frac{2}{L} \int_0^L F(x) \sin \frac{n\pi}{L} x\, dx.$$

The two necessary integration constants λ and C are now completely determined, and herewith the final solution reads

$$T = t - t_1 = \frac{2}{L} \sum_{n=1}^{\infty} e^{-(n\pi/L)y} \sin \frac{n\pi}{L} x \int_0^L F(x) \sin \frac{n\pi}{L} x\, dx. \qquad (6\text{–}8)$$

EXAMPLE 6–1. Determine the plate temperature $t(x,y)$ if $t = t_2$ at $y = 0$. *Solution.* In this case $f(x) = t_2$, so that $F(x) = t_2 - t_1$. Then by evaluating the integral

$$\int_0^L F(x) \sin \frac{n\pi}{L} x\, dx = \frac{L}{n\pi}(t_2 - t_1) \cos \frac{n\pi}{L} x \Big]_0^L = \frac{2L}{n\pi}(t_2 - t_1); \quad n = 1, 3, 5, \cdots,$$

and substituting in (6–8), we have

$$\frac{t - t_1}{t_2 - t_1} = \frac{4}{\pi}\left(e^{-(\pi/L)y} \sin \frac{\pi}{L} x + \tfrac{1}{3} e^{-(3\pi/L)y} \sin \frac{3\pi}{L} x + \cdots \right). \qquad (6\text{–}9)$$

The solution (6–9) is easily shown to satisfy both the differential equation (6–1) and boundary conditions (6–2). Moreover, when a solution like this is in open form, it must be further verified with regard to convergence. Noticing that the sine of $n\pi x/L$ cannot take on values exceeding unity, we are sure that any term in the series (6–9) will be less than $(4/n\pi)e^{-n\pi y/L}$. Then by applying the Cauchy ratio test for uniform convergence (Article 3–2), we find that

$$\lim_{n\to\infty} \left| \frac{M_{n+1}}{M_n} \right| = \lim_{n\to\infty} \left| \frac{n}{n+1} e^{-(\pi/L)y} \right| = e^{-(\pi/L)y},$$

which is evidently less than unity for all positive y. This serves to verify the

---

*In the English literature n and T_n are more frequently called *characteristic values* and *characteristic functions*.

convergence of (6–9), and we conclude that the solution is authentic, since it also satisfies the above-mentioned differential equation and boundary conditions.

In the following article we develop the means whereby (6–9) can be expressed in closed form.

6–2 Conjugate functions. Referring to the theory for functions of a complex variable, we recall that a complex function is made up of the sum of a real and an imaginary part according to

$$w(z) = w(x + iy) = u(x,y) + iv(x,y).$$

The real portions $u(x,y)$ and $v(x,y)$ are known as *conjugate functions*, and have the unique property that each satisfies the Laplace equation, as in (6–1). This property exists only if the complex function $w(z)$ is *analytic* in the sense that $u(x,y)$ and $v(x,y)$ satisfy the *Cauchy-Riemann reciprocity relations*

$$\frac{\partial u}{\partial x} = \frac{\partial v}{\partial y}, \quad \frac{\partial u}{\partial y} = -\frac{\partial v}{\partial x}, \tag{6–10}$$

since then

$$\frac{\partial^2 v}{\partial x \partial y} = -\frac{\partial^2 u}{\partial y^2} = \frac{\partial^2 u}{\partial x^2} \left.\right\} \frac{\partial^2 u}{\partial x^2} + \frac{\partial^2 u}{\partial y^2} = 0,$$

and

$$\frac{\partial^2 u}{\partial x \partial y} = \frac{\partial^2 v}{\partial y^2} = -\frac{\partial^2 v}{\partial x^2} \left.\right\} \frac{\partial^2 v}{\partial x^2} + \frac{\partial^2 v}{\partial y^2} = 0.$$

Thus, *if a complex function is analytic, then both its real and imaginary components u and v will satisfy the Laplace equation.* Complex analytic functions are therefore useful here in that they supply us with two solutions of the Laplace equation for each analytic function.

A second important property of conjugate functions is the geometric one of orthogonality. Consider two curves $u(x,y) = c_1$ and $v(x,y) = c_2$, as in Fig. 6–2. If the complex function of which u and v are the conju-

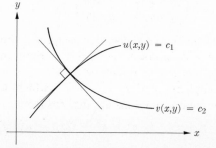

Fig. 6–2.   Conjugate components of a complex analytic function.

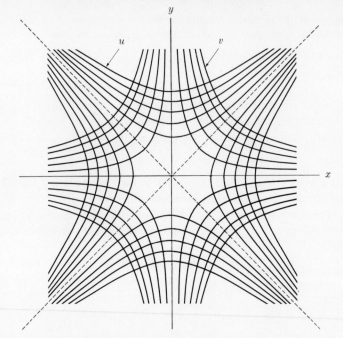

Fig. 6–3.   Orthogonality property of the complex analytic function $w(z) = z^2$.

gate components is analytic according to (6–10), then the slopes of these two curves can be expressed as

$$\left(\frac{dy}{dx}\right)_{u=c_1} = \frac{\partial u}{\partial x}\frac{\partial y}{\partial u} = \frac{\partial v}{\partial y}\frac{\partial y}{\partial u},$$

and

$$\left(\frac{dy}{dx}\right)_{v=c_2} = \frac{\partial v}{\partial x}\frac{\partial y}{\partial v} = -\frac{\partial u}{\partial y}\frac{\partial y}{\partial v}.$$

As a consequence of this, the product of their slopes is

$$\left(\frac{\partial v}{\partial y}\frac{\partial y}{\partial u}\right)\left(-\frac{\partial u}{\partial y}\frac{\partial y}{\partial v}\right) = -1.$$

The fact that the two slopes are negative reciprocals implies that the two curves $u = c_1$ and $v = c_2$ intersect each other at right angles. Such curves are said to be *orthogonal* one to the other.

Consider the complex function $w(z) = z^2$, which is clearly analytic. In this case the conjugate functions are derived from

$$w(z) = z^2 = (x + iy)^2 = x^2 - y^2 + i2xy = u(x,y) + iv(x,y)$$

as

$$u(x,y) = x^2 - y^2, \quad v(x,y) = 2xy,$$

and the conjugate curves are the rectangular hyperbolas $x^2 - y^2 = c_1$ and $2xy = c_2$. The families of hyperbolas are shown in Fig. 6–3 to be not only normal at all points of intersection, but to intersect the x- and y-axes and asymptotes at right angles as well.*

We shall use these properties in Article 6–3 to develop a more convenient closed-form solution corresponding to (6–9), and again in Article 6–8 for approximate graphical solutions of the Laplace equation.

6–3 Closed solution for semi-infinite plate. It has been shown that the conjugate functions u and v of a complex analytic function have the property that each satisfies the Laplace equation, and the property that each describe mutually orthogonal curves. This suggests that in any steady potential field problem, one of the components of a properly chosen complex analytic function can be made to correspond to the equipotential lines of the field, and the other component made to correspond to the lines of potential flux in the field, since by definition such lines are mutually orthogonal in a Laplacian field. A development in complex functions may therefore be used to advantage here in determining the analogous *isothermal* and *adiabatic* (heat flow) lines in the semi-infinite plate of Article 6–1.

Consider for this case the complex function

$$w(z') = \ln z' = u + iv,$$

where $z' = 1 + z = (1 + x) + iy$. Expressing z' in equivalent polar form,

$$z' = re^{i\alpha}; \quad r^2 = (1 + x)^2 + y^2, \quad \alpha = \tan^{-1}\frac{y}{1 + x},$$

we have

$$\ln z' = \ln re^{i\alpha} = \ln r + i\alpha = u + iv,$$

and thus the particular conjugate functions

$$u = \ln [(1 + x)^2 + y^2]^{\frac{1}{2}}, \quad v = \tan^{-1}\frac{y}{1 + x}.$$

With these we check the analyticity of $w(z')$ according to (6–10) as

---

*The reader is reminded here that complex-variable theory includes a systematic method for the solution of the Laplace equation known as *conformal mapping*, of which Fig. 6–3 is but one example, where the complex analytic function z^2 in the z-plane is mapped into hyperbolas in the so-called w-plane. Conformal mapping is useful for distorting the boundaries of a given region into a simple form for which the exact solution for the potential field is either tractable or known, the success of the method depending on just the right selection of complex function. For a practical treatment of conformal mapping, see Bewley (1).

$$\frac{\partial u}{\partial x} = \frac{1+x}{(1+x)^2 + y^2}, \qquad \frac{\partial u}{\partial y} = \frac{y}{(1+x)^2 + y^2},$$

$$\frac{\partial v}{\partial y} = \frac{1+x}{(1+x)^2 + y^2}, \qquad -\frac{\partial v}{\partial x} = \frac{y}{(1+x)^2 + y^2}.$$

Having proved that the particular conjugate functions u and v above are solutions of (6–1), we now proceed to expand the complex function $\ln (1 + z)$ and $\ln (1 - z)$ with the idea that the imaginary component will be similar to the series solution (6–9). We begin with the well-known series expansions

$$\ln (1 + z) = z - \frac{z^2}{2} + \frac{z^3}{3} - \cdots; \qquad z < 1,$$

and

$$\ln (1 - z) = -z - \frac{z^2}{2} - \frac{z^3}{3} - \cdots; \qquad z < 1.$$

Then by substituting for z the equivalent trigonometric form $z = r(\cos \alpha + i \sin \alpha)$, and recalling the identity

$$\ln z = \ln (x \pm iy) = \tfrac{1}{2} \ln (x^2 + y^2) \pm i \tan^{-1} \frac{y}{x},$$

there results

$$\tfrac{1}{2} \ln \left[(1 + r \cos \alpha)^2 + (r \sin \alpha)^2\right] + i \tan^{-1} \frac{r \sin \alpha}{1 + r \cos \alpha}$$
$$= z - \frac{z^2}{2} + \frac{z^3}{3} - \cdots,$$

and

$$\tfrac{1}{2} \ln \left[(1 - r \cos \alpha)^2 + (r \sin \alpha)^2\right] - i \tan^{-1} \frac{r \sin \alpha}{1 - r \cos \alpha}$$
$$= -z - \frac{z^2}{2} - \frac{z^3}{3} - \cdots.$$

Subtracting the latter from the former, and noting that $\tan^{-1} \alpha + \tan^{-1} \beta = \tan^{-1} [(\alpha + \beta)/(1 - \alpha\beta)]$ and $\sin^2 \alpha + \cos^2 \alpha = 1$, we have

$$\frac{1}{2} \ln \left[\frac{1 + 2r \cos \alpha + r^2}{1 - 2r \cos \alpha + r^2}\right] + i \tan^{-1} \frac{2r \sin \alpha}{1 - r^2} = 2 \left(z + \frac{z^3}{3} + \frac{z^5}{5} + \cdots \right)$$
$$= 2 \{r(\cos \alpha + i \sin \alpha) + \tfrac{1}{3}[r(\cos \alpha + i \sin \alpha)^3] + \cdots\}$$
$$= 2 \left[r(\cos \alpha + i \sin \alpha) + \frac{r^3}{3} (\cos 3\alpha + i \sin 3\alpha) + \cdots \right],$$

the last reduction following from DeMoivre's theorem, which gives $z^a = r^a (\cos a\alpha + i \sin a\alpha)$. Finally, by equating real and imaginary parts,

u and v become

$$u = \frac{1}{4} \ln \left[\frac{1 + 2r \cos \alpha + r^2}{1 - 2r \cos \alpha + r^2} \right] = r \cos \alpha + \frac{r^3}{3} \cos 3\alpha + \cdots, \quad (6\text{–}11)$$

and

$$v = \frac{1}{2} \tan^{-1} \frac{2r \sin \alpha}{1 - r^2} = r \sin \alpha + \frac{r^3}{3} \sin 3\alpha + \cdots. \quad (6\text{–}12)$$

The temperature distribution for the special case of an adiabatic semi-infinite plate with $f(x) = t_2$ on $y = 0$ is given by (6–9), and is seen to be of the same form as v in (6–12). Thus v and T are identical for $r = e^{-\pi y/L}$ and $\alpha = \pi x/L$. Then, since the argument $e^{-\pi y/L}$ is less than unity for positive y, we can rewrite (6–9) in the alternate closed form

$$\frac{t - t_1}{t_2 - t_1} = \frac{2}{\pi} \tan^{-1} \left(\frac{\sin (\pi/L)x}{\sinh (\pi/L)y} \right), \quad (6\text{–}13)$$

which again satisfies both (6–1) and (6–2) for $f(x) = t_2$.

Using the closed-form solution (6–13), we find the equation of any isothermal line in the plate as

$$\frac{2}{\pi} \tan^{-1} \left(\frac{\sin (\pi/L)x}{\sinh (\pi/L)y} \right) = c_2,$$

or, in a form convenient for computation,

$$y = \frac{L}{\pi} \sinh^{-1} \left(\frac{\sin (\pi/L)x}{\tan (\pi/2)c_2} \right). \quad (6\text{–}14)$$

Then by setting $r = e^{-\pi y/L}$ and $\alpha = \pi x/L$ in (6–11), we get the orthogonal set of adiabatic lines

$$\frac{1}{\pi} \ln \left[\frac{\cosh (\pi/L)y + \cos (\pi/L)x}{\cosh (\pi/L)y - \cos (\pi/L)x} \right] = c_1,$$

which can be reduced, by employing the identity

$$\tanh^{-1} a = \tfrac{1}{2} \ln [(1 + a)/(1 - a)],$$

to

$$\frac{2}{\pi} \tanh^{-1} \left(\frac{\cos (\pi/L)x}{\cosh (\pi/L)y} \right) = c_1.$$

Again, for ease of computation we express the equation of the adiabatic heat-flow lines as

$$y = \frac{L}{\pi} \cosh^{-1} \left(\frac{\cos (\pi/L)x}{\tanh (\pi/2)c_1} \right). \quad (6\text{–}15)$$

An illustrative set of orthogonal isothermal-adiabatic lines in the semi-infinite plate is shown in Fig. 6–4.

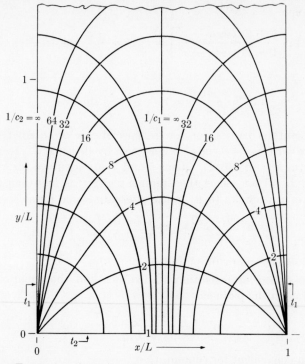

Fig. 6–4.   Trace of isothermal and adiabatic points in a semi-infinite adiabatic plate.

6–4 Rectangular adiabatic plate.

In this article we go on to consider a thin adiabatic plate bounded by $x = 0$, $x = L$, $y = 0$, and $y = l$ in which the temperature field $T(x,y)$ must satisfy (6–1) and the set of completely arbitrary boundary temperatures

$$
\begin{aligned}
T &= F_1(x) && \text{at } y = l, \\
T &= F_2(x) && \text{at } y = 0, \\
T &= G_1(y) && \text{at } x = L, \\
T &= G_2(y) && \text{at } x = 0,
\end{aligned}
\tag{6–16}
$$

where, in this case, it is more convenient to define T as $T = (t - t_1)/(t_2 - t_1)$. This problem can be easily handled by adding together four solutions corresponding to the four less arbitrary sets of boundary temperatures

$$
\left.\begin{array}{ll}
T = F_1(x) & \text{at } y = l \\
T = 0 & \text{at } y = 0 \\
T = 0 & \text{at } x = L \\
T = 0 & \text{at } x = 0
\end{array}\right\} \ (1)
\qquad
\left.\begin{array}{ll}
T = 0 & \text{at } y = l \\
T = F_2(x) & \text{at } y = 0 \\
T = 0 & \text{at } x = L \\
T = 0 & \text{at } x = 0
\end{array}\right\} \ (2)
$$

$$\begin{cases} T = 0 & \text{at } y = l \\ T = 0 & \text{at } y = 0 \\ T = G_1(y) & \text{at } x = L \\ T = 0 & \text{at } x = 0 \end{cases} \text{(3)} \qquad \begin{cases} T = 0 & \text{at } y = l \\ T = 0 & \text{at } y = 0 \\ T = 0 & \text{at } x = L \\ T = G_2(y) & \text{at } x = 0 \end{cases} \text{(4)},$$

this being permissible because the differential equation in question is both homogeneous and linear.

Consider first the case represented by (1). Here the primitive product solutions (6–5) and (6–6) apply, and again we find that $C_1 = 0$ and $\lambda = n\pi/L$, $n = 1, 2, 3, \cdots$, if X and thus T is to vanish at both $x = 0$ and L. If T is also to vanish at $y = 0$, then $C_3 = -C_4$ and the general solution XY becomes

$$T = \sum_{n=1}^{\infty} C_n [e^{(n\pi/L)y} - e^{-(n\pi/L)y}] \sin \frac{n\pi}{L} x.$$

Finally, for this to satisfy the remaining boundary condition in (1), the C_n must be the undetermined amplitudes of the Fourier sine-series expansion

$$F_1(x) = 2 \sum_{n=1}^{\infty} C_n \sinh n\pi \frac{l}{L} \sin \frac{n\pi}{L} x,$$

which are given by (5–10) as

$$2C_n \sinh n\pi \frac{l}{L} = \frac{2}{L} \int_0^L F_1(x) \sin \frac{n\pi}{L} x dx.$$

The complete solution corresponding to the particular set of boundary temperatures (1) is herewith determined to be

$$T_{(1)} = \frac{2}{L} \sum_{n=1}^{\infty} \frac{\sinh (n\pi/L)y}{\sinh n\pi(l/L)} \sin \frac{n\pi}{L} x \int_0^L F_1(x) \sin \frac{n\pi}{L} x dx.$$

Alternate solutions for the three remaining sets of boundary conditions (2), (3), and (4) can be written down directly by simply rotating coordinates in the above solution. Thus

$$T_{(2)} = \frac{2}{L} \sum_{n=1}^{\infty} \frac{\sinh \dfrac{n\pi}{L} (l - y)}{\sinh n\pi \dfrac{l}{L}} \sin \frac{n\pi}{L} x \int_0^L F_2(x) \sin \frac{n\pi}{L} x dx,$$

$$T_{(3)} = \frac{2}{l} \sum_{n=1}^{\infty} \frac{\sinh \dfrac{n\pi}{l} y}{\sinh n\pi \dfrac{L}{l}} \sin \frac{n\pi}{l} y \int_0^l G_1(y) \sin \frac{n\pi}{l} y dy,$$

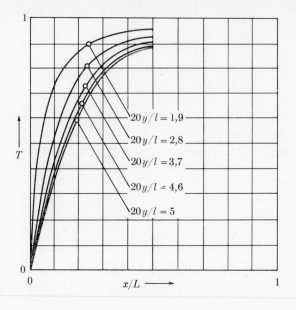

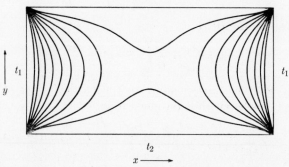

Fig. 6–5. Temperature field in a rectangular adiabatic plate.

$$T_{(4)} = \frac{2}{l} \sum_{n=1}^{\infty} \frac{\sinh \dfrac{n\pi}{l} (L - x)}{\sinh n\pi \dfrac{L}{l}} \sin \frac{n\pi}{l} y \int_0^l G_2(y) \sin \frac{n\pi}{l} y dy,$$

and in this way we build the final solution

$$T = T_{(1)} + T_{(2)} + T_{(3)} + T_{(4)}, \tag{6–17}$$

which satisfies both (6–1) and (6–16).

EXAMPLE 6–2. Determine the plate temperature $t(x,y)$ if $t = t_1$ at $x = 0,L$ and $t = t_2$ at $y = 0,l$, and graph the temperature field for a particular plate size, say $L = 2l$.

Solution. With $F_1(x) = [f_1(x) - t_1]/(t_2 - t_1) = 1 = F_2(x)$ and $G_1(y) = 0 = G_2(y)$, the solution (6–17) takes the form

$$T = \frac{4}{\pi}\left[\frac{\cosh\dfrac{\pi}{L}\left(\dfrac{l}{2} - y\right)}{\cosh\dfrac{\pi}{2}\dfrac{l}{L}}\sin\frac{\pi}{L}x + \frac{1}{3}\frac{\cosh\dfrac{3\pi}{L}\left(\dfrac{l}{2} - y\right)}{\cosh\dfrac{3\pi}{2}\dfrac{l}{L}}\sin\frac{3\pi}{L}x + \cdots\right]. \quad (6\text{–}18)$$

Now in order to compute a family of isothermal lines from this solution, we could attempt a development in complex variables (Article 6–3) to find a closed-form expression equivalent to (6–18), or simply resort to the computation of T at a large number of points in the plate and then fit in lines of constant temperature by visual interpolation.

A much easier method than the former and far more accurate method than the latter is to treat y as a parameter. Then x can be chosen at will, and corresponding values of T computed by (6–18). These T's are then to be plotted against x with y a parameter, as in the upper curves of Fig. 6–5. Finally, corresponding values of x and y are read from these curves at successive ordinates T = constant, and the results transposed to appropriate points in the plate, as shown by the lower illustration of Fig. 6–5.

In Article 8–12 we use this scheme again in connection with the problem of finding the temperature field in a nuclear reactor, and in Article 11–8 in connection with the problem of a moving source of heat.

6–5 Long solid semicylinder.

By way of examining solutions of the two-dimensional Laplace equation in cylindrical coordinates, we consider the temperature field $t(r,\varphi)$ in a long solid semicylinder bounded by the surface $r = r_1$ held at an arbitrary temperature distribution $t = f(\varphi)$, and the diameter surface $2r_1$ maintained at a uniform temperature t_0, as in Fig. 6–6. If, in this case, we define a temperature difference as $T = t - t_0$, then $T(r,\varphi)$ must satisfy the partial-differential equation

$$\frac{\partial^2 T}{\partial r^2} + \frac{1}{r}\frac{\partial T}{\partial r} + \frac{1}{r^2}\frac{\partial^2 T}{\partial \varphi^2} = 0, \quad (6\text{–}19)$$

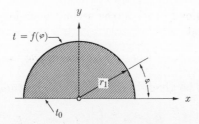

Fig. 6–6.   Solid semicylinder.

and the boundary conditions

$$T = 0 \qquad \text{at } r = r \quad \text{and} \quad \varphi = 0, \pi,$$
$$T = F(\varphi) \quad \text{at } r = r_1 \quad \text{and} \quad 0 < \varphi < \pi,$$

(6–20)

where now $F(\varphi) = f(\varphi) - t_0$.

In problem 5–12 it was shown that by assuming a product solution for T in the form $T = R\Phi$, where $R = R(r)$ and $\Phi = \Phi(\varphi)$, (6–19) could be separated into the two total-differential equations

$$r^2 \frac{d^2R}{dr^2} + r \frac{dR}{dr} - n^2R = 0,$$

(6–21)

and

$$\frac{d^2\Phi}{d\varphi^2} + n^2\Phi = 0.$$

(6–22)

The general solution of the Euler equation (6–21) is determined by setting $R = r^a$, whereby $a = \pm n$, giving

$$R = C_1 r^n + C_2 r^{-n},$$

and the general solution of (6–22) is given by (6–5) as

$$\Phi = C_3 \cos n\varphi + C_4 \sin n\varphi.$$

These two general solutions put us in possession of a general product solution $R\Phi$ of Laplace's equation in terms of the *nth-degree circular harmonics*

$$T = r^n (A \cos n\varphi + B \sin n\varphi) + r^{-n}(C \cos n\varphi + D \sin n\varphi). \quad (6\text{–}23)$$

To fit the general solution (6–23) to the boundary temperatures (6–20), we observe that the terms in r^{-n} cannot exist if t is to remain finite as r approaches zero. In what remains with $C = 0 = D$, it is clear that $A = 0$ if T is to vanish at $\varphi = 0$ for all r. If T is also to vanish at $\varphi = \pi$, then $n = 1, 2, 3, \cdots$, and $B = B_n$. This reduces our solution to

$$T = \sum_{n=1}^{\infty} B_n r^n \sin n\varphi; \quad 0 < \varphi < \pi,$$

and if this is to finally satisfy the second boundary condition in (6–20), which requires that

$$F(\varphi) = \sum_{n=1}^{\infty} B_n r_1^n \sin n\varphi,$$

then the B_n must be given by the Fourier amplitudes (5–5) as

$$B_n r_1^n = \frac{2}{\pi} \int_0^\pi F(\varphi) \sin n\varphi d\varphi.$$

The complete solution must therefore read

$$t = t_0 + \frac{2}{\pi} \sum_{n=1}^{\infty} \left(\frac{r}{r_1}\right)^n \sin n\varphi \int_0^{\pi} F(\varphi) \sin n\varphi d\varphi. \qquad (6\text{--}24)$$

EXAMPLE 6–3.   Determine the semicylinder temperature $t(r,\varphi)$ if $f(\varphi) = t_1$.
Solution.   This is a simple case for which $F(\varphi) = t_1 - t_0$, so that by (6–24)

$$\frac{t - t_0}{t_1 - t_0} = \frac{4}{\pi} \left[\left(\frac{r}{r_1}\right) \sin \varphi + \frac{1}{3}\left(\frac{r}{r_1}\right)^3 \sin 3\varphi + \cdots \right]. \qquad (6\text{--}25)$$

This result immediately suggests the possibility of an equivalent solution in closed form, since (6–25) closely resembles v of the two conjugate functions developed in Article 6–3. Thus, by taking r/r_1 for r and φ for α in (6–12), we have

$$\frac{t - t_0}{t_1 - t_0} = \frac{2}{\pi} \tan^{-1} \frac{2r_1 r \sin \varphi}{r_1^2 - r^2},$$

so that any isothermal line in the semicylinder is given by

$$r = \left[\left(\frac{\sin \varphi}{\tan(\pi C_2/200)} \right)^2 + 1 \right]^{\frac{1}{2}} - \frac{\sin \varphi}{\tan\left(\dfrac{\pi c_2}{200}\right)}.$$

In like manner, the orthogonal adiabatic lines are found from u in (6–11) with r/r_1 for r and φ for α, as

$$r = \frac{\cos \varphi}{\tanh(\pi c_1/200)} - \left[\left(\frac{\cos \varphi}{\tanh(\pi c_1/200)} \right)^2 - 1 \right]^{\frac{1}{2}}.$$

6–6 Short solid cylinder. In the case of a short cylinder the axial temperature gradient dt/dz must be considered. Then if the temperature of the surface $r = r_1$ is uniform, the temperature field in question is two-dimensional, as $t(r,z)$.

Consider a short cylinder of length L with $t = t_1$ at both $r = r_1$ and $z = 0$, and $t = t_2$ at $z = L$. The solution for $t(r,z)$ is derived for this case in problem 6–9 as

$$\frac{t - t_1}{t_2 - t_1} = 2 \sum_{n=1}^{\infty} \frac{\sinh(\lambda_n/r_1)z}{\lambda_n \sinh(\lambda_n L/r_1) J_1(\lambda_n)} J_0\left(\lambda_n \frac{r}{r_1}\right), \qquad (6\text{--}26)$$

wherein the λ_n are consecutive roots of the equation $J_0(\lambda r_1) = 0$ (Table A–11).

The dimensionless temperature uniformity along the cylinder axis $r = 0$ is shown in Fig. 6–7. We see that when the axial length of the cylinder becomes large compared with the cylinder radius, then the effect of the end temperature t_2 becomes very small; the axial temperature is then nearly t_1 along a large proportion of L. The mean profile temperature

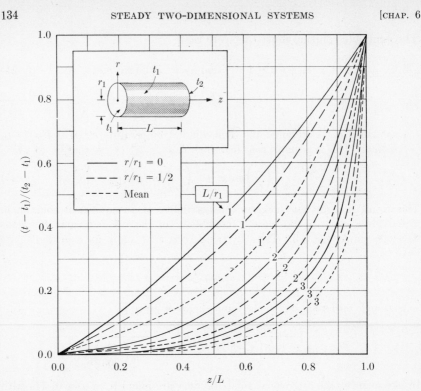

Fig. 6–7. Effect of axial length on the temperature uniformity in a short solid cylinder.

at any axial station can be found by simply averaging the radial temperature as

$$\bar{T}_z = \frac{1}{\pi r_1^2} \int_0^{r_1} 2\pi r T dr.$$

Then with the necessary portion of the integration evaluated as

$$\int_0^{r_1} r J_0 \left(\lambda_n \frac{r}{r_1} \right) dr = \frac{r_1^2}{\lambda_n} J_1(\lambda_n),$$

we have

$$\frac{t - t_1}{t_2 - t_1} = 4 \sum_{n=1}^{\infty} \frac{\sinh (\lambda_n/r_1)z}{\lambda_n^2 \sinh (\lambda_n/r_1)L} \cdot$$

The mean radial temperature, along with the mid-radius temperature at $r = r_1/2$, is compared with the axial temperature distribution in Fig. 6–7.

6–7 Spherical shell. For a particular solution of Laplace's equation in spherical coordinates, we consider the steady temperature at any point in the shell of a hollow sphere. The outer surface of the sphere at $r = r_1$

is to be held at a uniform temperature t_1, and the inner surface $r = r_2$ is to be maintained at some arbitrary temperature distribution $t = f(\psi)$, as in Fig. 6–8. Here φ is the angle between the x-axis and the projection of r on the xy-plane, according to Fig. 1–3. It is also to be carefully noted that the temperature field in this case of *zonal symmetry* is independent of the reflected angle φ^* (Fig. 1–3), and therefore the temperature difference $T(r,\psi) = t - t_1$ must satisfy the partial-differential equation

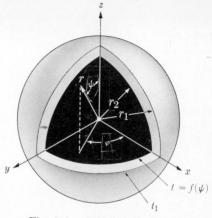

Fig. 6–8.   Spherical shell.

$$r \frac{\partial^2}{\partial r^2}(rT) + \frac{1}{\sin\psi}\frac{\partial}{\partial\psi}\left(\sin\psi\frac{\partial T}{\partial\psi}\right) = 0, \qquad (6\text{–}27)$$

and the boundary conditions

$$\begin{aligned} T &= 0 & \text{at } r = r_1, \\ T &= F(\psi) & \text{at } r = r_2, \end{aligned} \qquad (6\text{–}28)$$

where again $F(\psi) = f(\psi) - t_1$.

Separating variables in (6–27) by an assumed product solution $R\Psi$, we have

$$\frac{r^2}{R}\frac{d^2R}{dr^2} + \frac{2r}{R}\frac{dR}{dr} = -\frac{1}{\Psi}\frac{d^2\Psi}{d\psi^2} - \frac{1}{\Psi}\frac{\cos\psi}{\sin\psi}\frac{d\Psi}{d\psi},$$

wherewith the two total-differential equations

$$\frac{d^2R}{dr^2} + \frac{2}{r}\frac{dR}{dr} - \frac{\eta}{r^2}R = 0, \qquad (6\text{–}29)$$

and

$$\frac{d^2\Psi}{d\psi^2} + \frac{\cos\psi}{\sin\psi}\frac{d\Psi}{d\psi} + \eta\Psi = 0, \qquad (6\text{–}30)$$

in which η is a common separation constant.

The general solution of the Euler equation (6–29) is determined by the roots of the quadratic $a^2 + a - \eta = 0$ as

$$R = C_1 r^{a_1} + C_2 r^{a_2} = C_1 r^{-\frac{1}{2}+(\frac{1}{4}+\eta)^{\frac{1}{2}}} + C_2 r^{-\frac{1}{2}-(\frac{1}{4}+\eta)^{\frac{1}{2}}}$$

---

*Such a field is often spoken of as being *axisymmetrical*.

But inasmuch as a_1 and a_2 are arbitrary constants, let $m = -\frac{1}{2} + (\frac{1}{4} + \eta)^{\frac{1}{2}}$, so that $\eta = m(m + 1)$ and $-\frac{1}{2} - (\frac{1}{4} + \eta)^{\frac{1}{2}} = -1 - m$. The general solution of (6–29) is then

$$R = C_1 r^m + C_2 r^{-m-1}.$$

The second differential equation (6–30) can be reduced to a recognized form by a change in independent variable according to $\xi = \cos \psi$. The transformation gives

$$(1 - \xi^2) \frac{d^2 \Psi}{d\xi^2} - 2\xi \frac{d\Psi}{d\xi} + m(m + 1)\Psi = 0 ,$$

which we recognize as the exact form of the Legendre differential equation (3–31) of Article 3–8. We recall that the first-kind solutions of Legendre's equation are the Legendre polynomials $P_m(\psi) = P_m(\cos \psi)$ if m is either zero or a positive integer. The Legendre polynomials therefore constitute a general solution of (6–30) as

$$\Psi_m = P_m (\cos \psi),$$

and the general solution of Laplace's equation in spherical coordinates for this special case of zonal symmetry becomes $R\Psi$, as

$$T = \sum_{m=0}^{\infty} (A_m r^m + B_m r^{-m-1}) P_m (\cos \psi). \tag{6–31}$$

In fitting the general primitive solution (6–31) to the boundary conditions (6–28), we first note that the polynomial in r must vanish at $r = r_1$. Hence $B_m = -A_m r_1^{2m+1}$, and

$$T = \sum_{m=0}^{\infty} A_m \left(\frac{r^{2m+1} - r_1^{2m+1}}{r^{m+1}} \right) P_m (\cos \psi).$$

Now at $r = r_2$, the polynomial in r must be unity if T is to be a function of ψ alone along the inner radius. This adjustment is easily accomplished by multiplying $f(r)$ by $1/f(r)$ at r_2, as

$$\left(\frac{r^{2m+1} - r_1^{2m+1}}{r^{m+1}} \right) \left(\frac{r_2^{m+1}}{r_2^{2m+1} - r_1^{2m+1}} \right),$$

so that

$$T = \sum_{m=0}^{\infty} A_m \left(\frac{r_1^{2m+1} - r^{2m+1}}{r_2^{2m+1} - r_1^{2m+1}} \right) \left(\frac{r_2}{r} \right)^{m+1} P_m (\cos \psi),$$

which clearly satisfies (6–28).

If, in our present problem, $f(\psi)$ is to be some $f(\cos \psi)$, then the A_m must be chosen so as to satisfy

$$F(\cos \psi) = \sum_{m=0}^{\infty} A_m P_m(\cos \psi),$$

which is an expansion of the arbitrary function $F(\cos \psi) = f(\cos \psi) - t_1$ in a series of Legendre polynomials as considered in Article 3–10. At points where $F(\cos \psi)$ is continuous, the general coefficients A_m of this series are given by (3–44) as

$$A_m = \tfrac{1}{2}(2m + 1)\int_{-1}^{1} P_m(\xi)F(\xi)d\xi; \quad m = 0, 1, 2, \cdots,$$

or in terms of the transformation $\xi = \cos \psi$ by (3–45) for the Legendre coefficients as

$$A_m = \tfrac{1}{2}(2m + 1)\int_{0}^{\pi} P_m(\cos \psi)F(\cos \psi) \sin \psi d\psi.$$

This serves to complete the final solution in the form

$$t = t_1 + \sum_{m=0}^{\infty} (m + \tfrac{1}{2}) \left(\frac{r_1^{2m+1} - r^{2m+1}}{r_1^{2m+1} - r_2^{2m+1}}\right)\left(\frac{r_2}{r}\right)^{m+1} P_m(\cos \psi)$$
$$\int_{0}^{\pi} P_m(\cos \psi)F(\cos \psi) \sin \psi d\psi. \quad (6\text{--}32)$$

EXAMPLE 6–4. Compute and sketch the temperature field $t(r,\psi)$ in a spherical shell $r_1/r_2 = 2$ having a temperature distribution along the inner surface according to $f(\cos \psi) = 100 \cos^2 \psi$ °F, and a uniform temperature on the outer surface of $t_1 = 0$°F.

Solution. The integrals in the solution (6–32) are most conveniently handled in terms of $\xi = \cos \psi$. By referring to (3–37) for the $P_m(\xi)$

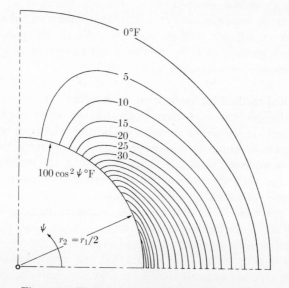

Fig. 6–9. Temperature field in a spherical shell.

$$\int_0^\pi P_m(\cos\psi)\cos^2\psi\sin\psi d\psi = \int_{-1}^1 P_0(\xi)\xi^2 d\xi = \int_{-1}^1 \xi^2 d\xi = \tfrac{2}{3},$$

$$\int_{-1}^1 P_1(\xi)\xi^2 d\xi = \int_{-1}^1 \xi^3 d\xi = 0,$$

$$\int_{-1}^1 P_2(\xi)\xi^2 d\xi = \int_{-1}^1 \frac{\xi^2}{2}(3\xi^2 - 1)d\xi = \tfrac{4}{15},$$

.
.
.

we find that all the integrals vanish except those for which $m = 0$ and 2, and these lead to the particular solution

$$t = \frac{1}{3}\left(1 - \frac{r}{r_1}\right)\left(\frac{r_1}{r}\right) + \frac{2}{93}\left[1 - \left(\frac{r}{r_1}\right)^5\right]\left(\frac{r_1}{r}\right)^3 (3\cos 2\psi + 1), \quad (6\text{--}33)$$

and the temperature field illustrated in Fig. 6–9.

GRAPHICAL METHOD

In many practical problems of conduction heat transfer the order of accuracy required in the evaluation of a temperature field does not justify a detailed analytical investigation. This is certainly the case in exploratory research, and even in the final design of structures whose thermal properties and boundary conductances are known with only marginal accuracy. Of considerably more importance is the fact that many of these practical problems are very difficult, if at all possible, to handle by exact analytical means. In such instances one has no choice but to turn to an *approximate* graphical, numerical, or experimental method.

6–8 Graphical method for isothermal boundaries. A structure may be considered as being elementary insofar as its having isothermal boundaries, but if these boundaries are of complex shape then the temperature field within the structure cannot be determined exactly. On the other hand, no matter how complex the boundary shape may be, if the surface temperatures are uniform, then the problem can be solved at least approximately by simple *free-hand sketching of the temperature field.* The basis for this approximate graphical approach is to be found in Article 6–2, where, according to complex-variable theory, it was shown that the locus of isothermal and adiabatic points in a Laplacian field must be orthogonal, one to the other (Fig. 6–3). This means that one simply has to fill in the given region with a net of isothermal-adiabatic lines, carrying out the construction by trial and error until the criterion that these lines meet at right

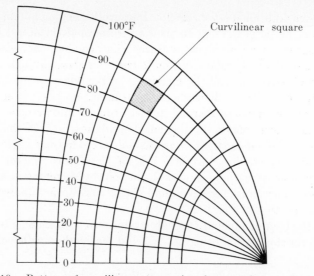

Fig. 6–10. Pattern of curvilinear squares in a long solid semicylinder.

angles at all points of intersection is satisfied. By this method the temperature field is obtained directly, and the heat rate becomes a by-product of the necessary construction.

To evaluate the internal heat transfer rate, it is necessary that the graphical construction be performed in such a way that the isothermal-adiabatic lines form a net of *curvilinear squares*, i.e., that the distance between the two isothermal sides of a square be equal to the distance between the two adiabatic sides of the same square. Such a network can be obtained analytically for only a few simple cases, such as from the results of Example 6–3. The isothermal-adiabatic net computed from these results for a unit-radius semicylinder with $t_0 = 0$ and $t_1 = 100°F$ (Fig. 6–6) is thus shown in Fig. 6–10 to contain a large number of such true curvilinear squares.

Wall of odd shape. Consider, as in Fig. 6–11, a unit length of what might be considered the cross-sectional design of a long kiln used for heating high aspect-ratio bar stock. Given that the surfaces 1 and 2 are isothermal $(t_1 < t_2)$, the problem is to compute how much heat is lost during steady operation of the kiln.

From the observed symmetry we need consider only the removed one-eighth (hatched) section having uniform surface temperatures t_1 and t_2. Since the kiln is imagined to be long compared with its width and height dimensions, no heat flows in the longitudinal direction and, moreover, no heat passes the cut boundaries because they are planes of geometric symmetry and hence adiabatic. These two planes serve to indicate the general direction of internal adiabatic surfaces, and in this case we arbitrarily fill in with five additional adiabatic flow lines while keeping in mind that these lines must be perpendicular to the two isothermal surfaces 1 and 2. By the definition of an adiabatic surface, whatever heat Δq passes through the increment of boundary a-d on 2 must all pass through the *channel* a-b-c-d and leave through the increment of boundary b-c on 1. Next, we superimpose a number of isothermal surfaces (in this case six) generally parallel to the known isothermal surfaces 1 and 2 and perpendicular to the known adiabatic planes in the cut boundaries. *If the construction is correct, then all intersections of isothermal and adiabatic lines are at right angles, and the resulting net is a field of curvilinear squares.* The final accuracy of construction can also be checked by sketching in a network of diagonals which must form a second net of curvilinear squares, as seen in the lower portion of Fig. 6–11.

Now the heat conducted through a typical *element* such as 1-2-3-4 is Δq, the area for conduction being $\Delta l_a \times 1$ and the conducting length being Δl_i. Thus

$$\Delta q_{1\text{-}2\text{-}3\text{-}4} = K\Delta t = k\frac{\Delta l_a}{\Delta l_i}\,\Delta t, \qquad (6\text{--}34)$$

in which Δt represents the positive temperature difference between isothermals 1–4 and 2–3; i.e., $(t_{2\text{-}3} - t_{1\text{-}4})$. Since we have deliberately chosen the construction so that

$$\Delta l_a = \Delta l_i, \qquad (6\text{--}35)$$

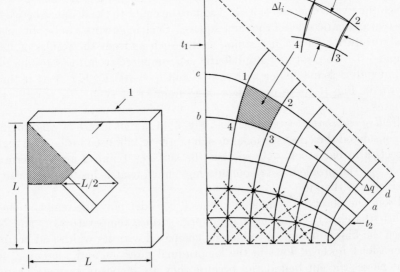

Fig. 6–11.   Free-hand sketch of isothermal and adiabatic lines in a wall of odd shape.

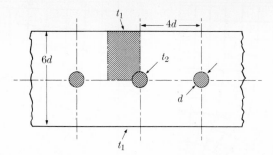

Fig. 6–12.   Plane wall with isothermal heating elements.

by (6–34) the value of Δt must be the same for each curvilinear square element in the channel for which Δq is constant.   A channel may then be thought of as a composite wall with series resistances (Article 2–2), whereby

$$\Delta q_{a\text{-}b\text{-}c\text{-}d} = \frac{k}{S}\,(t_2 - t_1),$$

where S denotes the number of curvilinear squares in the channel.   Finally, for C channels,

$$q = \frac{C}{S}\,k\,(t_2 - t_1). \tag{6–36}$$

The temperature drop between each isothermal is $\Delta t = (t_2 - t_1)/S$, and the quotient C/S is called the *shape factor*.

Referring again to Fig. 6–11, we see that the number of channels is $C = 6$ and the number of squares per channel $S = 7$.   Therefore, by (6–36), if $k = 1$ Btu/hr-ft-°F, $t_1 = 100°$F, and $t_2 = 300°$F, then

$q = 8\,(6/7)\,(1)\,(300 - 100) = 1{,}371$ Btu/hr per foot length of kiln.*

In working out the network of curvilinear squares for a given region, both the conditions of orthogonality and (6–35) must eventually be satisfied by trial and error, and this means that only after working out a large number of cases will the eye become experienced enough to obtain a satisfactory net after several attempts.   In a large majority of cases the number of channels or squares will not be integral, and a fraction of a channel or square will have to be interpolated.   In other words, if one chooses to make C (or S) an integer, then S (or C) will likely be a fraction after the construction is completed.   One therefore selects as fine a net as he has patience for in order to increase the accuracy of this interpolation, and also to make the pattern of isothermal-adiabatic lines more nearly approach a network of true squares.

Heating wall.   As a second example in free-hand field plotting, we consider a large heating wall with isothermal surfaces and having dimensions as shown in Fig. 6–12.   Heating elements (electrical cables, steam

*The solution to this particular problem will be considered again by both *fluid-flow analogy* and *electrical analogy* in Chapter 13.

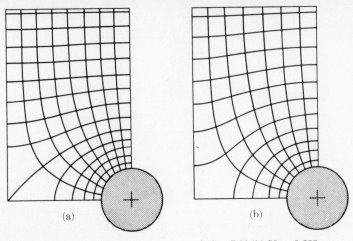

$$C/S = 8.00/13.25 = 0.604 \qquad C/S = 7.00/11.50 = 0.608$$

Fig. 6–13. Free-hand sketch of isothermal and adiabatic lines for structure in Fig. 6–12.

pipes, etc.) with surface temperatures at t_2 are embedded at uniform intervals along the center line of the wall.*

The field plotting for this problem is carried out twice in Fig. 6–13. In both (a) and (b) the number of flow channels is arbitrarily fixed and isothermals started at the source. Examination of (a) shows that $C/S = 0.604$, and for the slightly less dense net in (b), $C/S = 0.608$, which is in substantial agreement with (a).

Equation (6–36) holds for nonintegral S as well as nonintegral C. Then if, say, $k = 10$ Btu/hr-ft-°F, $t_1 = 120$°F, and $t_2 = 400$°F, we take the mean $C/S = 0.606$ and obtain $q = 1,697$ Btu/hr for each symmetrical section with 2d ft^2 of surface.†

In Article 8–3 we shall consider another wall with embedded heating elements, but for which the face surface temperature is unknown.

6–9 Graphical method for nonisothermal boundaries. Graphical solutions become quite tedious for cases in which the boundary temperatures are unknown, i.e., cases for which the boundary heat exchange must be

---

*The assumption of a uniform t_2 is justified only in the practical case where d (Fig. 6–12) is very small compared with the wall thickness. If this condition is not satisfied, then the surface temperature of the heating elements will be nonuniform, and the solution will give only an upper or lower limit to the heat rate according as to whether the boundary 2 is assumed to be isothermal at the minimum or maximum temperature.

†Schofield (2) treats the problem of a single tube in an infinite wall by the method of conformal mapping. The solution is approximate since, in order to effect a conformal transformation, the circular boundary 2 in Fig. 6–12 must be replaced by a line source of heat.

considered.   Pollmann (3) illustrates
how to treat such problems by first
assuming the temperature field and
then analytically checking the flow
net at the boundaries to see if the
assumed field orientation is correct.
This amounts to varying the Laplacian temperature field within the
given region until it corresponds to
required boundary conditions.

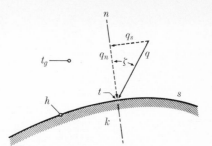

Fig. 6–14.   Normal and surface components of boundary heat exchange.

Lutz (4) reports a more general and
positive graphical method which uses
the inverse procedure.   By this method we first assume the flow direction through the boundaries and then check to see if the internal flow
net corresponds to a Laplacian field.   The chief advantage of this trial-
and-error graphical technique is that it gives the important distribution of
surface temperature directly.

To illustrate the Lutz graphical method, consider a general region free of
heat sources and of uniform thermal conductivity k, receiving steady heat
along a boundary s from an ambient gas at a uniform temperature t_g as in
Fig. 6–14.   If the flow q enters the surface at an angle ζ with the normal n
to the surface, then the normal and surface components of the flow are

$$q_n = -k\frac{\partial t}{\partial n}, \quad q_s = -k\frac{\partial t}{\partial s},$$

where t is the boundary temperature
at the particular point on s in question.   But according to the convective
boundary condition, with h denoting
the uniform unit surface conductance,

$$q_n = h(t_g - t),$$

whereby

$$q_s = -k\frac{\partial t}{\partial s} = \frac{k}{h}\frac{\partial q_n}{\partial s} = q_n \tan \zeta.$$

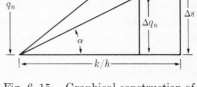

Fig. 6–15.   Graphical construction of
(6–37).

For the graphical determination we replace the differentials with finite
differences and obtain as the basis of the Lutz method

$$\Delta q_n = \left(\frac{\Delta s}{k/h}\right) q_n \tan \zeta. \tag{6–37}$$

The construction shown in Fig. 6–15 evidently satisfies (6–37); it represents the basic operation of the Lutz graphical method.

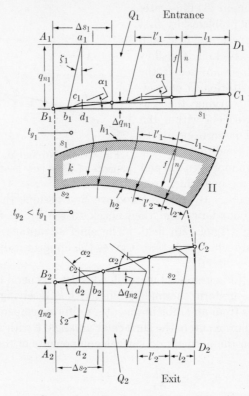

Fig. 6–16. General application of the Lutz graphical method.

Consider the application of (6–37) to the general two-dimensional structure shown in Fig. 6–16. The region in question is bounded by two free surfaces s_1 and s_2, and two adiabatic planes I and II. We begin developing the flow distribution for the entrance surface s_1 by laying off an assumed normal entering flow q_{n1}, and arbitrarily subdividing s_1 into say three equal increments Δs_1. With uniform subdivision, the angle $\alpha_1 = \tan^{-1}(\Delta s_1 h_1/k)$ is constant. Following the construction illustrated in Fig. 6–15, we begin at the center of the first increment and lay off the line a_1-b_1 corresponding to an assumed flow angle ζ_1. Line b_1-c_1 is laid off next at the computed angle α_1. Then c_1-d_1 represents the decrease in flow Δq_{n1}, and this is to be referred to the end of the increment Δs_1. This step-by-step construction is carried along the complete entrance surface s_1, and the enclosed area A_1-B_1-C_1-D_1 then represents the entire entering flow Q_1.

To find appropriate entrance points on the actual surface s_1, we arbitrarily divide the total flow Q_1 into say four equal parts $Q_1/4$, as in Fig. 6–16, and then locate corresponding points $l_1, l'_1, \cdots$ along s_1. The orientation of the entering flow lines f with respect to the normal n to s_1 are

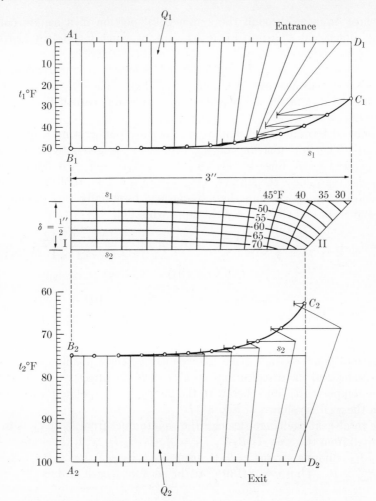

Fig. 6–17. Graphical solution for square corner by the Lutz method.

interpolated from the assumed flow directions developed in the entrance diagram.

The construction is now repeated for the exit surface s_2, where obviously $Q_2 = Q_1$. This means that if we choose $q_{n1} = q_{n2}$, then A_2-B_2-C_2-$D_2 = A_1$-B_1-C_1-D_1. Again the total flow Q_2 represented by A_2-B_2-C_2-D_2 is divided into four equal parts $Q_2/4$, and three exit flow lines are drawn in on s_2. Since corresponding flow lines do not meet, the construction must be corrected by assuming different flow angles ζ_{1i} and ζ_{2i} until this condition is fulfilled.

Square corner. To carry through a complete graphical solution by the Lutz method, consider the problem of finding the temperature field and total heat transfer through the symmetrical portion of a square corner having dimensions shown in Fig. 6–17, and for which $k = 1$ Btu/hr-ft-°F, $h_1 = 12$ Btu/hr-ft^2-°F, $h_2 = 2h_1$, $t_{g_1} = 0$, and $t_{g_2} = 100$°F.

Let the entrance surface be uniformly subdivided into 12 increments Δs_1, and the exit surface into 10 increments Δs_2. Then $\alpha_1 = \tan^{-1}\left(\frac{1}{4}\right)$, $\alpha_2 = \tan^{-1}\left(\frac{1}{2}\right)$, and the developed surfaces give nine correct flow lines, as seen in Fig. 6–17.

We now determine the distribution of surface temperature t_1 on s_1 and t_2 on s_2. The flow distribution q_{n_1} through s_1 is given by B_1-C_1, and since q_{n_1} and t_1 are linearly related as $q_{n_1} = h_1(t_1 - t_{g_1})$, it follows that B_1-C_1 also reproduces the surface temperature t_1. To establish the actual temperature scale, we note that B_1-B_2 acts essentially as a plane wall independent of end effects. By this approximation

$$t_{1B_1} = t_{g_1} + \frac{(t_{g_2} - t_{g_1})/h_1}{(1/h_1 + \delta/k + 1/h_2)} = 0 + \frac{(100 - 0)/12}{(1/12 + 0.5/12 \times 1 + 1/24)}$$
$$= 50.0,$$

$$t_{2B_2} = t_{g_2} - \frac{(t_{g_2} - t_{g_1})/h_2}{(1/h_1 + \delta/k + 1/h_2)} = 100 - \frac{(100 - 0)/24}{(1/12 + 0.5/12 \times 1 + 1/24)}$$
$$= 75.0.$$

The second point on each scale is evidently t_g, corresponding to $q_n = 0$. These scales and the distributions B_1-C_1 and B_2-C_2 directly determine the surface temperatures, and therewith the family of interpolated isothermals within the wall, as shown in Fig. 6–17.

The total heat exchange through the square duct from t_{g_2} to t_{g_1} is to be computed from the area A_1-B_1-C_1-$D_1 = A_2$-B_2-C_2-D_2 with the scale A_1-B_1 or A_2-B_2 running from $q_n = 0$ to $q_n = h_1(t_1 - t_{g_1}) = h_2(t_{g_2} - t_2) = 600$ Btu/hr-ft. Thus $q = 8(139)$ Btu/hr per foot length of duct.*

REFERENCES

1. L. V. Bewley, *Two-Dimensional Fields in Electrical Engineering*. New York: The Macmillan Co., 1948.

2. F. H. Schofield, "The Heat Loss from a Cylinder Embedded in an Insulating Wall," *Philosophical Magazine*, Vol. 12, 1931, pp. 329–349.

3. E. Pollmann, "Temperatures and Stresses on Hollow Blades for Gas Turbines" (Translation from German), *NACA TM* No. 1183. Washington: 1947.

4. O. Lutz, "Graphical Determination of Wall Temperatures for Heat Transfer Through Walls of Arbitrary Shape" (Translation from German), *NACA TM* No. 1280. Washington, 1950.

---

*Lutz (5) also reports an extension of this graphical method to include axially symmetrical forms as well as nonuniform unit surface conductances and nonuniform ambient temperatures.

5. O. Lutz, "Graphical Determination of Wall Temperatures During Heat Transfer," *R.T.P. Translation* No. 2500, Durand Reprinting Committee, California Institute of Technology.

PROBLEMS

6-1. A rectangular plate with adiabatic faces has uniform edge temperatures t_1 at $x = 0$, t_2 at $x = L$, t_1 at $y = 0$, and t_2 at $y = l$. Show that the temperature field $t(x,y)$ in the plate is given by

$$\frac{t - t_1}{t_2 - t_1} = \frac{4}{\pi}\left(\frac{\sinh (\pi/L)y}{\sinh \pi(l/L)} \sin \frac{\pi}{L} x + \frac{1}{3} \frac{\sinh (3\pi/L) y}{\sinh 3\pi(l/L)} \sin \frac{3\pi}{L} x + \cdots \right.$$

$$\left. + \frac{\sinh (\pi/l)x}{\sinh \pi (L/l)} \sin \frac{\pi}{l} y + \frac{1}{3} \frac{\sinh (3\pi/l)x}{\sinh 3\pi (L/l)} \sin \frac{3\pi}{l} y + \cdots \right),$$

and plot this solution for a plate size $L = 3l$.

6-2. A square adiabatic plate has uniform edge temperatures t_1 at $x = 0$ and L, t_2 at $y = 0$, and t_1 at $y = l$. A second square adiabatic plate has uniform edge temperatures t_1 at $x = 0$ and L, and t_2 at $y = 0$ and l. Show that the temperature at the center of the second plate is twice that at the center of the first plate.

6-3. A rectangular plate of uniform thermal conductivity k and of thickness δ loses heat from its two face surface $z = 0,\delta$ to an ambient gas at a uniform temperature t_g on both sides. If the unit thermal conductances on the face surfaces 1 and 2 are uniform as h_1 and h_2, then show that $t(x,y)$ in the plate must satisfy the partial-differential equation

$$\frac{\partial^2 t}{\partial x^2} + \frac{\partial^2 t}{\partial y^2} - H(t - t_g) = 0,$$

wherein $H = (h_1 + h_2)/k\delta$.

6-4. The nonadiabatic plate of problem 6-3 has edge temperatures t_g at $x = 0$, t_g at $y = 0$ and l, and $g_2(y)$ at $x = L$. Show that in this case $t(x,y)$ in the plate is given by

$$t = t_g + \frac{2}{l} \sum_{n=1}^{\infty} \frac{\sinh (H + n^2\pi^2/l^2)^{\frac{1}{2}}x}{\sinh (H + n^2\pi^2/l^2)^{\frac{1}{2}}L} \sin \frac{n\pi}{l} y \int_0^l G_2(y) \sin \frac{n\pi}{l} ydy,$$

where $G_2(y) = g_2(y) - t_g$.

6-5. A long semicylinder has a uniform temperature of t_0 along its diameter surface $r = r$; $\varphi = 0$, π, and a temperature distribution $t = f(\varphi) = t_1 \sin \varphi$ on its cylindrical surface $r = r_1$. (a) Show that the temperature field $t(r,\varphi)$ in the semicylinder is given by

$$t = t_0 + \left(t_1 - \frac{4}{\pi} t_0\right)\left(\frac{r}{r_1}\right) \sin \varphi - \frac{4}{\pi} t_0 \sum_{n=3}^{\infty} \frac{1}{n}\left(\frac{r}{r_1}\right)^n \sin n\varphi; \quad n = 3, 5, 7, \cdots.$$

(b) Show that the temperature distribution along r at $\varphi = \pi/2$ is

$$t = t_0\left[1 - \frac{4}{\pi} \tan^{-1}\left(\frac{r}{r_1}\right)\right] + t_1\left(\frac{r}{r_1}\right).$$

(c) Show that the isothermals in this semicylinder are straight lines parallel to the diameter surface for the special case where this diameter is at 0°F.

6–6. Consider a long quarter-cylinder with boundary radii at $\varphi = 0$ and $\pi/2$ held at a uniform temperature t_0, and with the outer surface at r_1 maintained at an arbitrary temperature distribution $t = f(\varphi)$.   (a) Show that the temperature field $t(r,\varphi)$ in the quarter-cylinder is

$$t = t_0 + \frac{4}{\pi} \sum_{n=1}^{\infty} \left(\frac{r}{r_1}\right)^{2n} \sin 2n\varphi \int_0^{\pi/2} F(\varphi) \sin 2n\varphi\, d\varphi.$$

(b) Show that for the particular case where $f(\varphi) = t_1$, we have

$$\frac{t - t_0}{t_1 - t_0} = \frac{4}{\pi}\left[\left(\frac{r}{r_1}\right)^2 \sin 2\varphi + \frac{1}{3}\left(\frac{r}{r_1}\right)^6 \sin 6\varphi + \frac{1}{5}\left(\frac{r}{r_1}\right)^{10} \sin 10\varphi + \cdots\right].$$

(c) Show that the particular solution in (b) can be expressed in the closed form

$$\frac{t - t_0}{t_1 - t_0} = \frac{2}{\pi} \tan^{-1} \frac{2r_1^2 r^2 \sin 2\varphi}{r_1^4 - r^4}.$$

6–7. Show that the temperature field $t(r,z)$ in a short solid cylinder of length L and with a uniform temperature t_1 at both its surface r_1 and the end $z = 0$ is satisfied by the general solution

$$t = t_1 + \sum_{n=1}^{\infty} C_n \sinh \frac{\lambda_n}{r_1} z\, J_0\left(\lambda_n \frac{r}{r_1}\right),$$

where the λ_n are consecutive roots of the equation $J_0(\lambda r_1) = 0$.

6–8. The end $z = L$ of the cylinder in problem 6–7 is maintained at some arbitrary temperature distribution $t(r,L) = f(r)$.   Show that the complete solution for $t(r,z)$ in the cylinder is given by

$$t = t_1 + \frac{2}{r_1^2} \sum_{n=1}^{\infty} \frac{\sinh\,(\lambda_n/r_1)z}{\sinh\,(\lambda_n L/r_1)J_1^2(\lambda_n)} J_0\left(\lambda_n \frac{r}{r_1}\right) \int_0^{r_1} rF(r) J_0\left(\lambda_n \frac{r}{r_1}\right) dr,$$

in which $F(r) = f(r) - t_1$.

6–9. Show that if $f(r) = t_2$ at $z = L$ for the cylinder of problem 6–8, then $t(r,z)$ is given by

$$\frac{t - t_1}{t_2 - t_1} = 2 \sum_{n=1}^{\infty} \frac{\sinh\,(\lambda_n/r_1)z}{\lambda_n \sinh\,(\lambda_n L/r_1)J_1(\lambda_n)} J_0\left(\lambda_n \frac{r}{r_1}\right),$$

as in (6–26).

6–10. An infinite plate with adiabatic faces contains a single hole of radius r_1 which is maintained at an arbitrary temperature distribution $t = f_1(\varphi)$. If the plate edges attain a uniform temperature t_∞ as $r \to \infty$, then show that the general plate temperature is

$$t = t_\infty + \sum_{n=1}^{\infty} \left(\frac{r_1}{r}\right)^n (A_n \cos n\varphi + B_n \sin n\varphi),$$

where

$$A_n = \frac{1}{\pi} \int_0^{2\pi} f_1(\varphi) \cos n\varphi\, d\varphi,$$

and

$$B_n = \frac{1}{\pi} \int_0^{2\pi} f_1(\varphi) \sin n\varphi d\varphi.$$

6–11. With reference to the spherical-shell problem of Article 6–7: (a) Show that the solution (6–32) reduces to the appropriate one-dimensional form for the elementary case of uniform temperature on the inner surface $r = r_2$. (b) For the special case of $t_1 = 0$, $f(\cos \psi) = (\cos \psi - 1)^2$, and $r_1/r_2 = 2$, show that the solution (6–32) gives

$$t = \frac{4}{3}\left(1 - \frac{r}{r_1}\right)\left(\frac{r_1}{r}\right) - \frac{4}{7}\left[1 - \left(\frac{r}{r_1}\right)^3\right]\left(\frac{r}{r_1}\right)^2 \cos \psi$$

$$+ \frac{2}{43}\left[1 - \left(\frac{r}{r_1}\right)^5\right]\left(\frac{r_1}{r}\right)^3 (3 \cos 2\psi + 1).$$

6–12. The square cross section of a long furnace is $L \times L$ on the outside and $(L/2) \times (L/2)$ on the inside, and surface temperatures are uniform at $t_1 = 100°F$ on the outer surface and $t_2 = 600°F$ on the inner surface. Estimate the heat loss from each foot length of this furnace, using the approximate graphical method represented by free-hand sketching of an isothermal-adiabatic net as in Article 6–8. The inside of the furnace is to be oriented as in Fig. 6–11.

6–13. Repeat problem 6–12 for the inside of the furnace oriented in the usual way with uniform wall thickness.* These graphical results will be checked against an approximate numerical solution in problem 7–5.

6–14. Figure 6–18 shows a plane insulating wall with alternately spaced ribs projecting from both surfaces 1 and 2 into the wall. If the ribs are of high thermal conductivity, then their temperature can be considered as being essentially the same as that of the high-conductivity sheet-metal surfaces to which they are attached. The space between these surfaces and ribs is filled with mineral-wool insulation of thermal conductivity 0.022 Btu/hr-ft-°F. (a) Estimate the heat rate conducted through this wall if $t_1 = 310°F$ and $t_2 = 92°F$.† (b) Estimate the percentage reduction in heat loss through this wall if the structural ribs could be removed by using surfaces of heavier-gage.

6–15. Repeat the Lutz graphical solution of Article 6–9 for the case where the inner square corners of the duct are replaced by fillets of $\frac{1}{2}''$ radius.

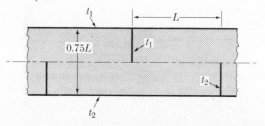

Fig. 6–18.   Plane wall with isothermal ribs.

*See Fig. 13–12.
†See Fig. 13–13.

CHAPTER 7

STEADY-STATE
NUMERICAL METHOD

This chapter introduces the approximate steady-state numerical-relaxation method of Emmons and Southwell. Numerical solutions for several elementary one- and two-dimensional problems are compared with exact analytical values, and in addition a number of systems are considered for which exact solutions are not available.

7-1 Introduction. In previous chapters we have developed exact analytical solutions for one- and two-dimensional temperature distributions by the direct method of integrating an appropriate differential equation, and with a solution of this sort we could then calculate the temperature at any point in the system. By contrast to this method, in the numerical approach we revert to the fundamental heat balance in finite-difference form, and therewith compute the temperature at only preselected points in the system. This is equivalent to familiar techniques used in approximate integration. For example, by Simpson's trapezoidal rule we take the mid-ordinate of a nonrectangular area as being representative of the true average ordinate. By an analogous approximation, in the numerical method the temperature of a finite volume is assumed to be that at its center. We shall see that the approximate numerical approach based on this simplification has great advantage over the exact method by effectively reducing a multidimensional system to a number of elementary one-dimensional systems for which required boundary conditions can be more easily satisfied. In other words, the eventual success of an exact approach nearly always depends upon the possibility of exactly satisfying required boundary conditions; this possibility either exists or does not exist at all, whereas by the numerical approach it is always possible to at least approximately satisfy the boundary conditions of the problem.

The basis of approximate numerical techniques is to be found in Sir Richard Southwell's work on applied mechanics (1), and while the first application of the numerical method to conduction heat-transfer is due to Emmons (2), we are indebted to Dusinberre for a good deal of its generalization in this field. For the many important details of both numerical and relaxation techniques which cannot be included in this and succeeding chapters, the reader will want to refer to the more recent accounts of Dusinberre (3) and Southwell's associate, Allen (4). Many of these details relate to variations of the fundamental method to be outlined here, such modifications enabling the computer to take advantage of the great flexibility of the numerical approach and thereby arrive at answers with a minimum expense of time and effort.

7–2 Approximate numerical method. The first step in a numerical solution is to subdivide the given system into a suitable number of small volumes and assign a reference number to the central point in each of these subvolumes. For purposes of illustration we consider first the simplest one-dimensional system, represented by a long rectangular bar with insulated surfaces and of unit width and depth δ as in (a) of Fig. 7–1. Here an arbitrary length 3δ is subdivided into three equal subvolumes $\delta \times \delta \times 1$ with central *nodal points* ①, ②, and ③. These subvolumes are then replaced by a network of "fictitious" heat-conducting *rods* between nodal points, as indicated in (b) of Fig. 7–1. Now if an appropriate internal thermal conductance K (Article 1–6) is assigned to a particular rod, then the steady and linear heat flow q in this rod will approximate the steady heat flow by conduction between the nodal points of the two sub-volumes for which the rod was substituted. We say "approximately" because we shall later assume that each subvolume is at its nodal-point temperature throughout. Actually, the temperature varies through each subvolume with a gradient dt/dx, and the approximation can only be improved if Δx is chosen smaller, so that $\Delta t/\Delta x$ approaches dt/dx.

Now a heat balance for a general nodal point such as ① in Fig. 7–1 is simply $q_{21} - q_{13} = 0$, or $q_{21} + q_{31} = 0$, where $q_{ij} = K_{ij}(t_i - t_j)$. If we write this as

$$\bar{q}_1' = K_{21}(t_2 - t_1) + K_{31}(t_3 - t_1),$$

then in the steady state $\bar{q}_1'$ must be zero. In this case the conducting area for each rod is $\delta \times 1$ and the length of path for each rod is δ, and this fixes the internal conductance (1–16) of each rod (based on a uniform thermal conductivity k) as $K_{21} = k(\delta \times 1)/\delta = k = K_{31}$. Herewith $\bar{q}_1' = kt_2 + kt_3 - 2kt_1$, or simply

$$\bar{q}_1 = t_2 + t_3 - 2t_1, \tag{7–1}$$

where again $\bar{q}_1$ must be zero.

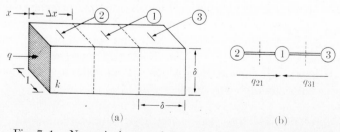

(a)   (b)

Fig. 7–1. Numerical network for a one-dimensional system.

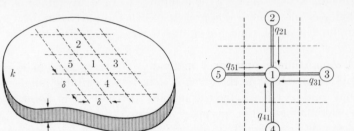

Fig. 7–2. Numerical network for a two-dimensional system.

The quantity $\bar{q}_1$ is called a *residual*, and (7–1) itself is referred to as a *residual equation*.*

The scheme for a two-dimensional system is much the same as in one dimension. Referring to Fig. 7–2, we select a square subdivision $\delta \times \delta \times 1$ so that for a general nodal point such as ① we have $q_{21} + q_{31} + q_{41} + q_{51} = 0$, or

$$\bar{q}_1' = K_{21}(t_2 - t_1) + K_{31}(t_3 - t_1) + K_{41}(t_4 - t_1) + K_{51}(t_5 - t_1).$$

A square subdivision has the advantage that each internal conductance is again independent of network size, so that $K_{21} = k(\delta \times 1)/\delta = k = K_{31} = K_{41} = K_{51}$, and

$$\bar{q}_1 = t_2 + t_3 + t_4 + t_5 - 4t_1. \tag{7–2}$$

A residual equation according to (7–1) for a one-dimensional system or (7–2) for a two-dimensional system is written for each of n nodal points in the numerical network. The result, *which represents the fundamental development of the numerical method*, is a system of n linear algebraic residual equations in n unknown temperatures. The determination of these n unknown temperatures can then be accomplished by any one of the orthodox methods of solving a system of n simultaneous algebraic equations in n unknowns. However, when n is large (corresponding to a dense network) such methods as solution by determinants become tedious, and this is especially so in cases where the residual equations have nonintegral coefficients. In Article 7–4 we show how this portion of the work can be handled most conveniently by the *Southwell relaxation method*. But before doing this, it is best that we first gain some appreciation of the approximations already considered.

---

*In reality (7–1) is a *difference equation* which results from substituting finite differences for differentials.

7–3 Nature of the finite-difference approximation. In pointing up the errors which are inherent to the finite-difference approximation represented by either (7–1) or (7–2), we keep in mind that these residual equations are replacements for the one- and two-dimensional Laplace equations

$$\left(\frac{d^2t}{dx^2}\right)_1 = 0 = \bar{q}_1 \quad \text{and} \quad \left(\frac{\partial^2t}{\partial x^2}\right)_1 + \left(\frac{\partial^2t}{\partial y^2}\right)_1 = 0 = \bar{q}_1.$$

Let the temperature t be expanded in a Taylor's series (4) about the nodal point ① as

$$t = t_1 + (x - x_1)\left(\frac{dt}{dx}\right)_1 + \frac{(x - x_1)^2}{2!}\left(\frac{d^2t}{dx^2}\right)_1$$
$$+ \frac{(x - x_1)^3}{3!}\left(\frac{d^3t}{dx^3}\right)_1 + \cdots . \quad (7\text{--}3)$$

Then according to this expansion, the temperatures for the nodal points ② at $x_1 - \delta$ and ③ at $x_1 + \delta$ are

$$t_2 = t_1 - \delta\left(\frac{dt}{dx}\right)_1 + \frac{\delta^2}{2}\left(\frac{d^2t}{dx^2}\right)_1 - \frac{\delta^3}{6}\left(\frac{d^3t}{dx^3}\right)_1 + \cdots ,$$

and

$$t_3 = t_1 + \delta\left(\frac{dt}{dx}\right)_1 + \frac{\delta^2}{2}\left(\frac{d^2t}{dx^2}\right)_1 + \frac{\delta^3}{6}\left(\frac{d^3t}{dx^3}\right)_1 + \cdots .$$

If we add together the series for t_2 and t_3, neglecting all terms whose δ-coefficients are of order 4 or higher, then the finite-difference approximation to the second derivative $(d^2t/dx^2)_1$ becomes

$$\delta^2\left(\frac{d^2t}{dx^2}\right)_1 = t_2 + t_3 - 2t_1,$$

and this is seen to be the same approximation as implied by (7–1). A similar development for the two-dimensional case leads to (7–2).

The residual equations (7–1) and (7–2) are therefore reasonable approximations to an exact solution only when δ^4 is small. Maximum errors of order δ^4 in numerical solutions are thus minimized if we select a subdivision size as small as practicable. However, as the subdivision is made finer, the number of nodal points and associated residual equations is increased, so from the viewpoint of the labor involved we also want to select as coarse a network as possible. The best network size is therefore a compromise, and there is no criterion other than experience for selecting the best size in a given situation. Until one gains this facility he has no way of judging the errors introduced by too coarse a network other than that of noting the change in t with successively finer subdivisions. This means that, ideally, one would carry through repeated solutions with increasingly finer networks (i.e., smaller and smaller δ) until no appreciable change in t is noted.

7–4 Longitudinal temperature distribution in a turbine blade.

This is a practical one-dimensional problem for which the numerical results can be compared directly with an exact solution developed in Chapter 2. The numerical solution will be carried through for this case with a detailed account of the Southwell relaxation procedure.

Let the turbine blade be of length $L = 2''$, cross-sectional profile area $A = 0.005$ ft^2, perimeter $p = 0.400$ ft, uniform thermal conductivity $k = 15$ Btu/hr-ft-°F, and select a uniform unit surface conductance of $h = 120$ Btu/hr-ft^2-°F, a uniform ambient gas temperature of $t_g = 1500$°F, and a blade root temperature of $t_r = 1000$°F.

We choose the *uniform linear network* shown in Fig. 7–3 with half subvolumes at the root and tip. In this case heat gain on the surface of each subvolume must be considered, so that for a typical nodal point such as ② we have

$$\bar{q}_2 = K_{12}(t_1 - t_2) + K_{32}(t_3 - t_2) + K_{g2}(t_g - t_2),$$

in which the surface area for each subvolume is $p(L/4)$ for nodal points ②, ③, and ④, and one-half this value for root and tip nodal points ① and ⑤. The internal conductances are evaluated as $K_{12} = (15 \times 0.005)/(0.5/12) = 1.8 = K_{23} = K_{34} = K_{45}$, and the surface conductances as $K_{g2} = 120(0.4 \times 0.5/12) = 2.0 = K_{g3} = K_{g4}$, and $K_{g1} = 1.0 = K_{g5}$. Note that while in this case blade-tip heat loss is neglected in the evaluation of the surface conductance K_{g5}, this effect could easily be included by taking $K_{g5} = 120[(0.4 \times 0.25/12) + 0.005]$. We are now equipped to write out the residual equations for the four nodal points ②, ③, ④, and ⑤ (the nodal point ① not being considered since the blade root temperature t_r is known) as

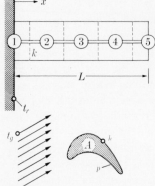

$$\bar{q}_2 = 1.8t_1 + 1.8t_3 + 2t_g - 5.6t_2,$$

$$\bar{q}_3 = 1.8t_2 + 1.8t_4 + 2t_g - 5.6t_3,$$

$$\bar{q}_4 = 1.8t_3 + 1.8t_5 + 2t_g - 5.6t_4, \tag{7-4}$$

$$\bar{q}_5 = 1.8t_4 \qquad + t_g - 2.8t_5.$$

This leaves us with the problem of finding the t_2, t_3, t_4, and t_5 that satisfy the residual equations (7–4) with $t_1 = t_r = 1000$, $t_g = 1500$, and with $\bar{q}_2 = \bar{q}_3 = \bar{q}_4 = \bar{q}_5 = 0$. The most elementary approach would be to ven-

Fig. 7–3. Numerical network for turbine blades.

ture a guess at these unknown temperatures and then compute the $\bar{q}_2$, $\bar{q}_3$, $\bar{q}_4$, and $\bar{q}_5$. In all probability these $\bar{q}$'s would not be zero as required, and consequently the t's would have to be repeatedly changed until this condition was satisfied. The *relaxation method of Southwell* is simply a convenient tabular means of carrying out these successive guesses and cumulative corrections.

Now we see by the residual equations (7–4) that a change in t_2 of amount Δt_2 will affect both residuals $\bar{q}_2$ and $\bar{q}_3$. Likewise, a change in t_3 of amount Δt_3 will affect the three residuals $\bar{q}_2$, $\bar{q}_3$, and $\bar{q}_4$, and so on. The magnitude of these changes is in direct proportion to the coefficient of the term affected by the temperature change. Thus a change in t_2 of amount Δt_2 will change the residual $\bar{q}_2$ by $\Delta \bar{q}_2 = -5.6\Delta t_2$, and the residual $\bar{q}_3$ by $\Delta \bar{q}_3 = 1.8\Delta t_2$. *A change in temperature at a given point in the network is therefore seen to cause a redistribution of residuals according to a fixed pattern.* We can either set up a convenient pattern of the coefficients as

	Δt_2	Δt_3	Δt_4	Δt_5
$\Delta \bar{q}_2$	-5.6	1.8		
$\Delta \bar{q}_3$	1.8	-5.6	1.8	
$\Delta \bar{q}_4$		1.8	-5.6	1.8
$\Delta \bar{q}_5$			1.8	-2.8

or else refer directly to the residual equations (7–4). The relaxation itself is to be carried out according to the following set of general rules:

(a) *Compute and record all residuals in the network which result from initial temperature guesses.*

(b) *Choose the nodal point at which the residual is numerically the largest and relax it, "overrelaxing" or "underrelaxing" as suggested by the sign of dependent residuals.*

(c) *Compute the changes in dependent residuals resulting from the relaxation of the largest residual in step* (b), *and record their algebraic sums.*

(d) *Again select the numerically largest residual and repeat steps* (b) *and* (c), *continuing in this fashion until all residuals in the network are reduced as nearly to zero as accuracy requires.*

From these basic rules we see that the underlying objective of the relaxation* procedure is to reduce all network residuals as nearly to zero as accuracy requires, the numerical solution being complete when and only when such a condition is finally fulfilled.

---

*The use of the word *"relaxation"* appears (4) to have its origin in Southwell's treatment of mechanical problems in loaded frames, where *residual forces* are carried by constraints. The operation of relaxation corresponds to applying selected displacements until the system is in a state of static equilibrium and all constraints are relaxed.

TABLE 7-1

RELAXATION OF RESIDUAL EQUATIONS (7-4)

	$\bar{q}_2$	t_2	$\bar{q}_3$	t_3	$\bar{q}_4$	t_4	$\bar{q}_5$	t_5
(1)	0	1000	0	1000	0	1000	0	1000
(2)	1000		1000		1000		500	
(3)	1000	1000	1000	1000	1000	1000	500	1000
(4)	−1775	317	570					
(5)	−775	1317	1570					
(6)	776		−2420	432	776			
(7)	1		−850	1432	1776			
(8)			849		−2640	471	849	
(9)			−1		−864	1471	1349	
(10)					865		−1349	481
(11)					1		0	1481

The particular relaxation of the residual equations (7-4) is contained in Table 7-1. As an initial guess we set all the temperatures equal to 1000 and all the residuals equal to zero on line (1). This satisfies the root temperature $t_1 = 1000$ but not the gas temperature $t_g = 1500$. A change in gas temperature of $\Delta t_g = 1500 - 1000 = 500$ is seen from (7-4) to change all residuals by $\Delta \bar{q}_2 = 2 \times 500 = 1000 = \Delta \bar{q}_3 = \Delta \bar{q}_4$, and $\Delta \bar{q}_5 = 1 \times 500 = 500$. These changes are entered in appropriate columns on line (2), and their algebraic sums on line (3). Now it appears that if t_2 is changed by approximately 179, then $\bar{q}_2$ would vanish as required. However, it is necessary to purposely overestimate this required temperature change, since $\bar{q}_2$ will be later affected by a change in t_3. With this in mind, let $\Delta t_2 = 317$, so that $\Delta \bar{q}_2 = -5.6 \times 317 = -1775$ and $\Delta \bar{q}_3 = 1.8 \times 317 = 570$, and enter these changes on line (4) along with their algebraic sums on line (5). Now increase t_3 by 432. This gives $\Delta \bar{q}_3 = -2420$, $\Delta \bar{q}_2 = 776$, and $\Delta \bar{q}_4 = 776$ on line (6), and the sums on line (7).

The relaxation is continued in this way with nearly correct temperature guesses in order to shorten the illustrated computation. The residuals remaining at the end as 1, −1, and 1 could be reduced closer to zero only if temperature changes of less than one degree are considered; hence we stop here, as this represents reasonable precision. It would certainly be unreasonable in this case to go to fractions of a degree, since the subdivision chosen in Fig. 7-3 is a relatively crude one from the very start.

The numerical results in Table 7-1 are compared in Table 7-2 with exact values computed from the analytical solution (2-31) as

$$\frac{t - t_g}{t_r - t_g} = \frac{\cosh NL(1 - x/L)}{\cosh NL},$$

in which, for this example, $N^2 = 120 \times 0.4/15 \times 0.005 = 640$.   The agreement is fairly substantial despite the choice of a relatively crude subdivision, and we note in particular that the error is most pronounced in the vicinity of the blade root, where the temperature gradient is steepest.   If we wish to improve these results, we would simply choose either a finer subdivision throughout the entire length of integration or a finer subdivision in the root portion of the blade, although in this case the additional work of, say, three or four more nodal points would hardly seem worth while.

TABLE 7–2

EXACT AND NUMERICAL TEMPERATURES IN TURBINE BLADE

x/L	Exact	Numerical	% Error
0.25	1325	1317	-0.60
0.50	1438	1432	-0.42
0.75	1476	1471	-0.34
1.00	1485	1481	-0.28

7–5 Corrugated wall.   As a first example in the use of *uniform square networks*, we consider the problem of finding the steady temperature field and heat flow through a wall with continuous indented and protuberant corners, as in Fig. 7–4.   The wall material is of uniform thermal conduc-

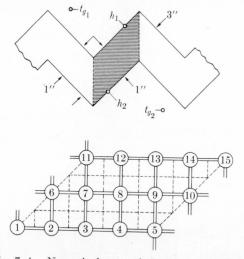

Fig. 7–4.   Numerical network for a corrugated wall.

tivity $k = 1$ Btu/hr-ft-°F, and it receives heat from an ambient gas at $t_{g_1} = 100°$F on surface 1, where the unit conductance is $h_1 = 24$ Btu/hr-ft²-°F, and loses heat to an ambient gas at $t_{g_2} = 0°$F on surface 2, where the unit conductance is $h_2 = \frac{1}{2}h_1$. Both ambient gas temperatures and unit surface conductances are assumed to be uniform.

Let a unit-depth symmetrical section of the wall (Fig. 7–4) be subdivided into squares of uniform size with half subvolumes at the surfaces 1 and 2, and then number the nodal points ①–⑮. When dealing with only a symmetrical portion of the structure, we simply remember to double the effects of, say, nodal point ② on ①, ② on ⑥, and ⑦ on ⑥, and so on. Thus for a typical internal nodal point such as ⑥, we have

$$\bar{q}_6 = 2K_{26}(t_2 - t_6) + 2K_{76}(t_7 - t_6),$$

and for typical surface nodal points such as ① and ⑪,

$$\bar{q}_1 = 2K_{21}(t_2 - t_1) + K_{g_21}(t_{g_2} - t_1),$$

$$\bar{q}_{11} = 2K_{711}(t_7 - t_{11}) + 2K_{1211}(t_{12} - t_{11}) + K_{g_111}(t_{g_1} - t_{11}),$$

in which $K_{26} = k = 1 = K_{76}$ (all internal rods), $K_{21} = k(\frac{1}{4}/\frac{1}{2}) = \frac{1}{2} = K_{1211}$ (all surface rods), $K_{g_21} = 12(\frac{1}{2}/12) = \frac{1}{2}$ (all surface 2 conductances), and $K_{g_111} = 24(\frac{1}{2}/12) = 1$ (all surface 1 conductances).

The reader can check his residual equations against the relaxation pattern given here, and then carry out the relaxation itself. When dealing with a relatively large number of nodal points it is helpful to first relax a coarser network such as ①–③–⑤–⑪–⑬–⑮ and then use these tempera-

	Δt_1	Δt_2	Δt_3	Δt_4	Δt_5	Δt_6	Δt_7	Δt_8	Δt_9	Δt_{10}	Δt_{11}	Δt_{12}	Δt_{13}	Δt_{14}	Δt_{15}
$\Delta \bar{q}_1$	−1.5	1.0													
$\Delta \bar{q}_2$	0.5	−2.5	0.5			1.0									
$\Delta \bar{q}_3$		0.5	−2.5	0.5			1.0								
$\Delta \bar{q}_4$			0.5	−2.5	0.5			1.0							
$\Delta \bar{q}_5$				1.0	−3.5				2.0						
$\Delta \bar{q}_6$		2.0				−4.0	2.0								
$\Delta \bar{q}_7$		1.0				1.0	−4.0	1.0			1.0				
$\Delta \bar{q}_8$			1.0				1.0	−4.0	1.0			1.0			
$\Delta \bar{q}_9$				1.0				1.0	−4.0	1.0			1.0		
$\Delta \bar{q}_{10}$									2.0	−4.0				2.0	
$\Delta \bar{q}_{11}$						2.0					−4.0	1.0			
$\Delta \bar{q}_{12}$							1.0				0.5	−3.0	0.5		
$\Delta \bar{q}_{13}$								1.0				0.5	−3.0	0.5	
$\Delta \bar{q}_{14}$									1.0				0.5	−3.0	0.5
$\Delta \bar{q}_{15}$														1.0	−2.0

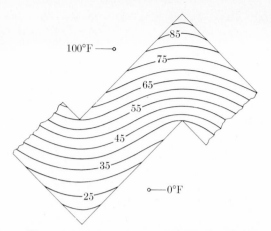

Fig. 7–5. Temperature field in the corrugated wall of Fig. 7–4.

tures as a first approximation in the network of Fig. 7–4.* The final results can be checked against those in Table 7–3, and a visualization of the temperature field obtained by interpolating a system of isothermals from these local temperatures, as shown in Fig. 7–5.

TABLE 7–3

NUMERICAL TEMPERATURES IN CORRUGATED WALL

i	t_i	i	t_i	i	t_i
1	18	6	39	11	70
2	26	7	51	12	78
3	34	8	59	13	83
4	40	9	67	14	88
5	50	10	77	15	94

If the final temperatures in Table 7–3 are correct, then the total heat rate transferred to g_2 must balance the total heat rate conducted through a single symmetrical section from g_1; that is,

$$12(0.25/12)18 + 12(0.5/12)(26 + 34 + 40) + 12(0.25/12)50 \overset{(?)}{=}$$

*The reader should be aware that a number of useful techniques have been devised for speeding up the ordinary relaxation process and, in general, for shortening the tabulated computation. The *overrelaxation* technique used in Table 7–1 is one example, and two more such devices are known as *block relaxation*, where unit temperature changes are simultaneously applied at more than one point, and *group relaxation*, where temperature changes of different size are simultaneously applied at more than one point in the network. For details of block and group relaxation, see Allen (4).

$$24(0.25/12)(100-70)+24(0.5/12)[(100-78)+(100-83)+(100-88)]$$
$$+24(0.25/12)(100-94).$$

This gives (on the left) 67.0 Btu/hr lost from surface 2 and (on the right) 69.0 Btu/hr transferred to surface 1, and this checks close enough.

It is interesting to compute the change in heat transferred for a straight wall of the same $1''$ thickness. The comparison is to be made on the basis of one symmetrical section which is of length $\sqrt{2}''$. For this section, $1/UA = 12/24 \times 1.414 + 12/12 \times 1.414 + 12/12 \times 1.414 = 1.768$, and therefore $q = 100/1.768 = 56.5$ Btu/hr. The corrugated wall in this example is thus seen to transfer nearly 20% more heat than an equivalent straight wall of the same length and thickness.

7–6 Nonrectangular boundaries. The general problem of treating a region in the vicinity of an irregular curved boundary can be handled in one of several ways. By a first method, we attempt to fill out the boundary regions with a square network which is somewhat finer than that used in the main portion of the region, or to fill out the boundary regions with networks other than square.* Such variations are known as *graded nets*, and are not only used for boundary regions, but are useful as well for portions of the field which are either of most general interest or which contain the highest temperature gradients occurring in the field. We note that the use of fine boundary nets is the least conservative of nodal points, while the use of networks other than square requires a more elaborate computation of conductances.

A second, and usually the preferred, approach to the problem of curved boundaries is to modify the residual equations for a uniform square network. The general case is shown in Fig. 7–6. Here a curved boundary cuts across, at most, two of the conducting rods (in this case rods 1–2 and 1–5) so that (7–2) cannot be applied to the central nodal point ①. Now since the boundary condition is known at points I and II, rather than at the now fictitious nodal points ② and ⑤, we want to write a residual equation for ① in terms of I, ③, ④, and II. To do this we consider again, as in Article 7–3, the expansion of t in a Taylor's series about ①, keeping in

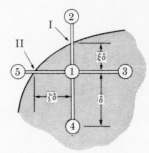

Fig. 7–6.   Uniform square network in the vicinity of a curved boundary.

---

*Dusinberre (3) reviews a large number of irregular subdivisions. For examples of triangular and rectangular networks, see Articles 7–8 and 12–9 respectively.

mind that we are looking for the replacement of Laplace's two-dimensional equation.

Rewriting (7–3) in terms of both x and y as

$$t(x) = t_1 + (x - x_1)\left(\frac{dt}{dx}\right)_1 + \frac{(x - x_1)^2}{2!}\left(\frac{d^2t}{dx^2}\right)_1 + \frac{(x - x_1)^3}{3!}\left(\frac{d^3t}{dx^3}\right)_1 + \cdots,$$

and

$$t(y) = t_1 + (y - y_1)\left(\frac{dt}{dy}\right)_1 + \frac{(y - y_1)^2}{2!}\left(\frac{d^2t}{dy^2}\right)_1 + \frac{(y - y_1)^3}{3!}\left(\frac{d^3t}{dy^3}\right)_1 + \cdots,$$

and substituting therein, according to Fig. 7–6, $x = x_1 + \delta$, $x = x_1 - \zeta\delta$, $y = y_1 - \delta$, and $y = y_1 + \xi\delta$, we have

$$t_3 = t_1 + \delta\left(\frac{dt}{dx}\right)_1 + \frac{\delta^2}{2}\left(\frac{d^2t}{dx^2}\right)_1 + \cdots,$$

$$t_{II} = t_1 - \zeta\delta\left(\frac{dt}{dx}\right)_1 + \frac{\zeta^2\delta^2}{2}\left(\frac{d^2t}{dx^2}\right)_1 + \cdots,$$

$$t_4 = t_1 - \delta\left(\frac{dt}{dy}\right)_1 + \frac{\delta^2}{2}\left(\frac{d^2t}{dy^2}\right)_1 + \cdots,$$

$$t_I = t_1 + \xi\delta\left(\frac{dt}{dy}\right)_1 + \frac{\xi^2\delta^2}{2}\left(\frac{d^2t}{dy^2}\right)_1 + \cdots.$$

We now add the first two of these series expansions, neglecting all δ-coefficients of order 3 or higher, and obtain

$$\delta^2\left(\frac{d^2t}{dx^2}\right)_1 = \frac{2}{(\zeta + 1)}t_3 + \frac{2}{\zeta(\zeta + 1)}t_{II} - \frac{2}{\zeta}t_1.$$

A similar addition of the last two series expansions leads in parallel to

$$\delta^2\left(\frac{d^2t}{dy^2}\right)_1 = \frac{2}{(\xi + 1)}t_4 + \frac{2}{\xi(\xi + 1)}t_I - \frac{2}{\xi}t_1.$$

The *modified residual equation* for this general case is therefore

$$\bar{q}_1 = \frac{2}{\xi(\xi + 1)}t_I + \frac{2}{(\zeta + 1)}t_3 + \frac{2}{(\xi + 1)}t_4 + \frac{2}{\zeta(\zeta + 1)}t_{II}$$
$$-2\left(\frac{1}{\xi} + \frac{1}{\zeta}\right)t_1. \quad (7\text{–}5)$$

Particular cases are encompassed in (7–5) by either ξ or ζ equal to 1, and evidently (7–5) reduces appropriately to (7–2) for the special case $\xi = 1 = \zeta$ when points I and II coincide with real nodal points ② and ⑤. Note that in this derivation, terms in δ^3 or higher have been neglected; the finite-difference error in the modified residual equation is thus somewhat greater than with a full square network, where terms in δ^4 or higher are neglected.

The method of modifying residual equations for a square network is generally convenient to apply in practice, although such a residual equation is certainly not as convenient as the standard form (7–2). In this respect, Allen (4) recommends computing temperatures at the fictitious nodal points in terms of temperatures at real nodal points and then using these in the standard residual equation (7–2). To demonstrate this, consider the two-dimensional case represented by (7–2) for a regular square network, and by (7–5) as

$$\bar{q}_1 = \frac{2}{\xi(\xi + 1)}\, t_{\mathrm{I}} + t_3 + \frac{2}{(\xi + 1)}\, t_4 + t_5 - 2\left(\frac{1}{\xi} + 1\right)t_1 \qquad (7\text{–}6)$$

for a modified square network in which the boundary cuts across the single conducting rod 1–2 ($\zeta = 1$). By equating (7–2) to (7–6), and solving for the temperature t_2 of the fictitious nodal point ②, we have

$$t_2 = \frac{2}{\xi(\xi + 1)}\, t_{\mathrm{I}} + \left(\frac{1 - \xi}{\xi + 1}\right) t_4 - \frac{2}{\xi}\,(1 - \xi)t_1. \qquad (7\text{–}7)$$

This result allows us to use the simple residual equation (7–2), if temperatures at the fictitious nodal point ② are then calculated according to (7–7).

7–7 Temperature field in turbine-blade profile.

The methods of Articles 7–2 and 7–4 can also be shown to encompass the effects of a non-uniform surface conductance. An analysis of the temperature field in the cross-sectional profile of a turbine blade is a practical example which includes this nonuniformity, for if one applies conventional boundary-layer theory and Reynolds analogy to compute local conductances along the outer surface of airfoils, he finds that these unit conductances vary along the chordwise surface at any spanwise station.

Livingood and Sams (5) have examined the temperature field in the profile of a water-cooled turbine blade whose computed gas-side unit surface conductance was distributed as shown in Fig. 7–7. The blade was of uniform thermal conductivity $k = 15$ Btu/hr-ft-°F, the average cooling-water temperature $t_w = 200$°F, the unit surface conductance in the two circular cooling passages a uniform $h_w = 2370$ Btu/hr-ft²-°F, and the effective outer gas temperature $t_g = 2000$°F.

The numerical computation of the temperature field can be carried out with a uniform square network approximating the actual contour of the blade profile (Fig. 7–7), or with a uniform square network and the method of modified residual equations as discussed in Article 7–6. Then for the residual equation at any outer-surface nodal point we simply estimate the unit conductance from the distribution of h_g shown.

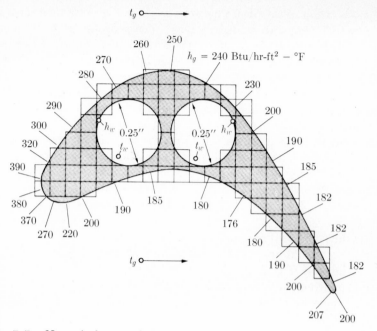

Fig. 7–7.   Numerical network for a turbine-blade profile.   (Data courtesy of NACA.)

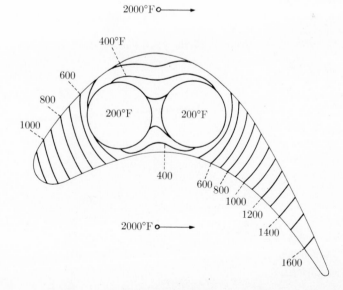

Fig. 7–8.   Temperature field in the turbine-blade profile of Fig. 7–7.   (Courtesy of NACA.)

The relaxation of this dense network was based on analytical estimates of the actual temperature distribution. Temperature estimates for the blade leading edge were obtained by a calculation of the temperature gradient in a tube, and for the trailing edge by a calculation of the temperature gradient in a wedge of equivalent dimensions. The final numerical results, using these precomputed temperatures as a first approximation in the numerical solution, are shown in Fig. 7–8.

7–8 Straight trapezoidal fin. In a nonrectangular area the number of required nodal points can be kept to a minimum by using a network other than square. We illustrate this by finding the temperature field and heat dissipation from a straight trapezoidal fin of width $w = 0.08'$. Let the fin be of uniform thermal conductivity $k = 18$ Btu/hr-ft-°F, its base temperature be 100°F, and assume a unit surface conductance of 500 Btu/hr-ft²-°F and an ambient gas temperature of 0°F.

For a trapezoidal profile, Dusinberre (3) suggests the *uniform triangular network* shown in Fig. 7–9. The conductance of a typical internal rod in the triangular network, such as 2–4, is a function of the cotangent of the opposite angle such that $K_{24} = k \cot(4\text{–}1\text{–}2)$, and for the conductance of a typical boundary rod such as 1–4 we get one-half this value, just as in a uniform square network. Then $K_{24} = 3.0 = K_{25} = K_{35} = K_{56} = K_{57}$, $K_{14} = 1.5 = K_{46}$, $K_{45} = k \cot(4\text{–}2\text{–}5) = 52.4$, $K_{67} = 26.2$, $K_{g1} = h(w/4)/\sin(4\text{–}1\text{–}2) = 10.2$, $K_{g4} = 20.4$, $K_{g6} = K_{g1} + h(w/12) = 13.5$, $K_{g7} = h(w/6) = 6.7$, and by observing temperature symmetry,

$$\bar{q}_4 = 1.5t_1 + \quad 3.0t_2 + 52.4t_5 + \quad 1.5t_6 + 20.4t_g - 78.8t_4,$$

$$\bar{q}_5 = 3.0t_2 + \quad 3.0t_3 + 52.4t_4 + \quad 3.0t_6 + \quad 3.0t_7 - 64.4t_5,$$

$$\bar{q}_6 = 1.5t_4 + \quad 3.0t_5 + 26.2t_7 + 13.5t_g \qquad\qquad - 44.2t_6, \tag{7-8}$$

$$\bar{q}_7 = 6.0t_5 + 52.4t_6 + \quad 6.7t_g \qquad\qquad\qquad - 65.1t_7.$$

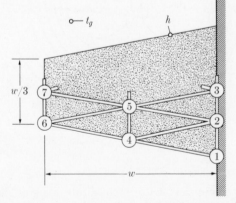

Fig. 7–9. Numerical network for a straight trapezoidal fin.

TABLE 7–4

RELAXATION OF RESIDUAL EQUATIONS (7–8)

$\bar{q}_4$	t_4	$\bar{q}_5$	t_5	$\bar{q}_6$	t_6	$\bar{q}_7$	t_7
0	0	0	0	0	0	0	0
450	0	600	0	0	0	0	0
−2175	27.6	1445		41			
−1725	27.6	2045		41			
1712		−2105	32.7	98		196	
−13		−60	32.7	139		196	
14		29		−419	9.5	498	
1		−31		−280	9.5	694	
		32		280		−696	10.7
		1		0		−2	10.7

A relaxation of the residual equations (7–8) is exhibited in Table 7–4, with all initial residuals and temperatures taken as zero. Here we see the necessity of considering a two-dimensional temperature distribution when dealing with thick fins.

From the temperature field we compute the heat dissipation per unit length of fin as $q = 2(10.2 \times 100 + 20.4 \times 27.6 + 13.5 \times 9.5 + 6.7 \times 10.7)$ $= 3566$ Btu/hr.

7–9 Cylinder of nonuniform thermal conductivity.

In this article we use the numerical method to investigate the steady temperature in a structure for which the thermal conductivity is known to vary with local temperature according to the linear function $k_t = k_0(1 + \beta_0 t)$.

In the general case of variable thermal conductivity, the temperature field must satisfy the characteristic partial-differential equation

$$\frac{\partial}{\partial x}\left(k_t \frac{\partial t}{\partial x}\right) + \frac{\partial}{\partial y}\left(k_t \frac{\partial t}{\partial y}\right) = 0.$$

But for the special case of linear conductivity, $k_t = A + Bt$, we can substitute $t = k_t/B - A/B$ and therewith obtain the new partial-differential equation

$$\frac{\partial}{\partial x}\left(\frac{k_t}{B} \frac{\partial k_t}{\partial x}\right) + \frac{\partial}{\partial y}\left(\frac{k_t}{B} \frac{\partial k_t}{\partial y}\right) = 0,$$

or

$$\frac{\partial}{\partial x}\left(2k_t \frac{\partial k_t}{\partial x}\right) + \frac{\partial}{\partial y}\left(2k_t \frac{\partial k_t}{\partial y}\right) = 0,$$

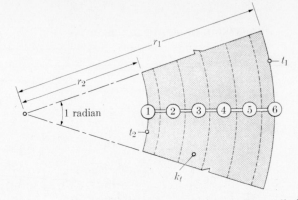

Fig. 7–10.   Uniform numerical network for a hollow cylinder.

and by inspection we see that this last result is equivalent to

$$\frac{\partial^2}{\partial x^2}(k_t^2) + \frac{\partial^2}{\partial y^2}(k_t^2) = 0.$$

This suggests that we simply relax the numerical system in terms of k_t^2 and then reinterpret the results in terms of local nodal-point temperatures t. This scheme is useful only when boundary temperatures are known or when boundaries are adiabatic.

By way of example, consider a hollow cylinder with $r_1 = 1''$, $r_2 = r_1/2$, $k_0 = 50$ Btu/hr-ft-°F, $\beta_0 = 0.01/°$F, $t_1 = 0°$F, and $t_2 = 100°$F.   This is a one-dimensional solution for which the k_t^2 must satisfy

$$\frac{\partial^2}{\partial r^2}(k_t^2) + \frac{1}{r}\frac{\partial}{\partial r}(k_t^2) = 0.$$

There are several possible ways of subdividing a circular region, and for this example we choose the simple method of subdividing at uniform increments along the radius with a half subvolume at each boundary as in Fig. 7–10.   With such a *uniform radial network* the internal conductance increases with the radius.   We can eliminate π from the computation of these conductances by considering a segment of the cylinder bounded by radii only one radian apart, since then the radius and arc length are equal at all radial stations.   For this particular system $K_{12} = 50 \times 0.55/0.1 = 275$, $K_{23} = 325$, $K_{34} = 375$, $K_{45} = 425$, and $K_{56} = 475$, and these lead to the set of four required residual equations

$$\bar{q}_2 = 0.275t_1 + 0.325t_3 - 0.6t_2,$$

$$\bar{q}_3 = 0.325t_2 + 0.375t_4 - 0.7t_3,$$

$$\bar{q}_4 = 0.375t_3 + 0.425t_5 - 0.8t_4,\qquad\qquad(7\text{--}9)$$

$$\bar{q}_5 = 0.425t_4 + 0.475t_6 - 0.9t_5.$$

TABLE 7–5

RELAXATION OF RESIDUAL EQUATIONS (7–9) AS k_t^2

$\bar{q}_2$	k_2^2	$\bar{q}_3$	k_3^2	$\bar{q}_4$	k_4^2	$\bar{q}_5$	k_5^2
0	0	0	0	0	0	0	0
2750	0	0	0	0	0	1189	0
−4820	8040	2610					
−2070	8040	2610					
0		−4460	6360	2385			
		−1850	6360	2385			
		1850		−3940	4920	2094	
		0		−1555	4920	3283	
				1555		−3283	3650
				0		0	3650

The relaxation of equations (7–9) is now carried out in terms of k_t^2, as in Table 7–5. We begin by setting all residuals and k_t^2's equal to zero. But this does not satisfy the k_t^2's on the boundary nodal points ⑥ and ①, where $k_6^2 = [50(1 + 0.01 \times 0)]^2 = 2500$ and $k_1^2 = [50(1 + 0.01 \times 100)]^2 = 10{,}000$. The boundary corrections for residuals $\bar{q}_2$ and $\bar{q}_5$ are therefore $\Delta \bar{q}_2 = 0.275 \times 10{,}000 = 2750$ and $\Delta \bar{q}_5 = 0.475 \times 2500 = 1189$. Finally, with the completed relaxation of k_t^2 in Table 7–5 we convert to corresponding temperatures according to $t_i = [(k_{ti}/k_0) - 1]/\beta_0$, as contained in Table 7–6. The corresponding temperatures in parentheses are those for the case of uniform thermal conductivity.

TABLE 7–6

NUMERICAL TEMPERATURES IN HOLLOW CYLINDER

i	t_i	
1	100.0	
2	79.2	(73.8)
3	59.6	(51.5)
4	40.2	(32.2)
5	20.8	(15.3)
6	0.0	

7–10 Cross-flow heat-exchanger tube. In this final example we consider the practical situation where the unit surface conductance is nonuniform over the outer surface of a heat-exchanger tube of unit thermal conductivity and with boundary radii $r_1 = 1''$ and $r_2 = r_1/2$. Imagine that the tube transports a high-temperature gas at $t_{g_2} = 370°F$, and that a cooling gas at $t_{g_1} = 70°F$ is flowing normal to the tube on the outer surface. The unit surface conductances in Btu/hr-ft²-°F on r_1 and r_2 are assumed to be distributed as in Table 7–7.

TABLE 7-7

DISTRIBUTION OF UNIT SURFACE CONDUCTANCES

$\varphi°$	h_1	h_2
0	25	55
20	24	55
40	22	55
60	18	55
80	12	55
100	10	55
120	9	55
140	9	55
160	9	55
180	9	55

In Article 7–9 we used a uniform radial subdivision for a hollow cylinder, and in the present case we choose a *logarithmic network*. A logarithmic subdivision in cylindrical coordinates leads to true curvilinear squares (Article 6–8); it is analogous to a uniform square subdivision in rectangular coordinates, and thus retains the advantage that all internal conductances are once again $K = k$. The logarithmic network shown in Fig. 7–11 is

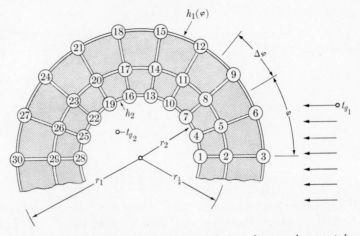

Fig. 7–11.   Logarithmic numerical network for a heat-exchanger tube.

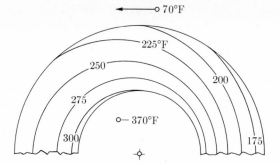

Fig. 7–12.　Temperature field in the heat-exchanger tube of Fig. 7–11.

obtained by taking equal increments of $\ln r$. The radial location of the single set of internal nodal points will then be given by $(\ln r_1 - \ln r_2)/2 = 0.347$ as $r_{1/2} = e^{-0.347} = 0.706''$. The angle between nodal points is then simply $\Delta\varphi = 0.347 \times 57.3 = 19.9°$, and for simplicity we take this to be $\Delta\varphi = 20°$.

The reader can now write out the thirty required residual equations, or the relaxation pattern itself, keeping in mind that with a logarithmic network the conductance of each internal rod is k and of each boundary rod is $k/2$. The area for boundary heat exchange on r_1 is $0.347/12$ and on r_2 is $0.347/24$. Then, for example, $K_{g_1 15} = 12 \times 0.347/12$ and $K_{g_2 13} = 55 \times 0.347/24$.

A relaxation of this relatively large set of residual equations gives the nodal-point temperatures in Table 7–8, and the interpolated temperature field in the tube wall illustrated in Fig. 7–12. From Table 7–8 we compute the total heat exchange through the tube as approximately $q = 1038$ Btu/hr per foot length of tube.

TABLE 7–8

NUMERICAL TEMPERATURES IN HEAT-EXCHANGER TUBE

i	t_i	i	t_i	i	t_i
1	290	11	242	21	223
2	227	12	183	22	313
3	162	13	304	23	269
4	291	14	252	24	227
5	229	15	201	25	313
6	164	16	309	26	270
7	294	17	260	27	229
8	234	18	215	28	313
9	171	19	312	29	270
10	298	20	266	30	229

7–11 Closure. In this chapter we have found approximate solutions to a variety of steady-state conduction problems by the numerical-relaxation method. We have seen that the general method is useful in two as well as in one dimension, and for cases of nonuniform thermal conductivity and nonuniform boundary conductance. Aside from this pronounced flexibility, the numerical approach has the additional asset of simplicity, which rests rather uniquely on a little algebra and the elementary operations of addition and multiplication.

On the other side of the ledger, one frequently hears the complaint that numerical solutions lack the possible parametrization of an exact solution. While this criticism excludes the large class of problems which are in themselves analytically intractable, for the case which does not resist exact solution one is faced with the problem of selection. The turbine problem of Article 7–4 is a case in point. Here an exact solution requires a good deal less effort than a corresponding numerical solution. Indeed, to work out a family of longitudinal temperature profiles by numerical means would require a change in one, several, or all of the coefficients of each residual equation and a new relaxation for each profile, where, by contrast, in an exact solution one would simply have to change a single parameter in an analytical formula.

In other cases, especially those in which the temperature distribution is two-dimensional and certain nonuniformities are present, the problem of selecting the most realistic of these two methods of solution is more difficult. According to Gardner: "The choice between such a solution (numerical) and an analytical approach (if possible) appears to be comparable to a machine-shop problem: A certain operation may require one hour setup time for fifteen minutes of actual machining; by spending eight hours on making a suitable jig the setup time may be reduced to ten minutes. If less than ten parts are to be made it will not pay to make the jig; for any greater number it will."

REFERENCES

1. R. V. Southwell, *Relaxation Methods in Engineering Science*. New York: Oxford University Press, 1940.

2. H. W. Emmons, "The Numerical Solution of Heat-Conduction Problems," *Trans. ASME*, Vol. 65, No. 6, 1943, pp. 607–612.

3. G. M. Dusinberre. *Numerical Analysis of Heat Flow*. New York: McGraw-Hill, 1949.

4. D. N. de G. Allen, *Relaxation Methods*. New York: McGraw-Hill, 1954.

5. J. N. B. Livingood and E. W. Sams, "Cooling of Gas Turbines; VI—Computed Temperature Distribution Through Cross-Section of Water-Cooled Turbine Blade," *NACA RM* No. E7B11F. Washington: May, 1947.

PROBLEMS

7-1. Find the unknown temperatures t_5, t_6, t_8, t_9, t_{11}, and t_{12} in the numerical network of Fig. 7–13 for a long rod of square cross section.

7-2. With reference to problem 7–1: (a) Check numerical temperatures with the exact solution

$$\frac{t - t_1}{t_2 - t_1} = \frac{4}{\pi}\left[\frac{\sinh \pi(1 - y/w)}{\sinh \pi}\sin\frac{\pi}{w}x + \frac{1}{3}\frac{\sinh 3\pi(1 - y/w)}{\sinh 3\pi}\sin\frac{3\pi}{w}x + \cdots\right].$$

(b) Check the balance of heat conducted to the three sides 1 from side 2, and show that this amounts to approximately $161k$ Btu/hr.

7-3. Let the face surfaces of the rod in problem 7–1 be exposed to ambient gases $t_{g_1} = 0°F$ on all three sides 1 and $t_{g_2} = 100°F$ on side 2. Assign unit surface conductances $h_1 = 2k/w$ and $h_2 = 4k/w$ Btu/hr-ft²-°F, and compare numerical temperatures with

i	t_i	i	t_i	i	t_i
1	58	6	50	11	21
2	70	7	22	12	23
3	73	8	31	13	9
4	34	9	34	14	13
5	46	10	15	15	14

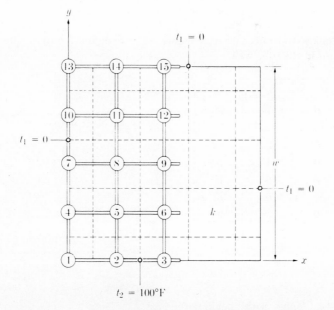

Fig. 7–13. Numerical network for a long square rod.

7–4. With reference to problem 7–3 : (a) Check the balance of heat conducted to the three sides 1 from side 2, and show that approximately $129k$ Btu/hr are transferred from g_2 to g_1. (b) Draw a family of interpolated isothermals in the cross section for $t = 10, 20, \cdots, 70°F$.

7–5. Repeat problem 6–13, using the numerical method of solution, and check the heat rate against the graphical results of that problem.

7–6. A straight fin of triangular profile is of thermal conductivity $k = 15$ Btu/ hr-ft-°F, and operates in 70°F ambient air. The fin width is $w = 0.6''$, its semithickness $\delta_1 = 0.1''$, its base temperature $t_0 = 200°F$, and its unit surface conductance $h = 8$ Btu/hr-ft²-°F. Compute the temperature field in this fin, using the numerical method with a uniform triangular network.

7–7. Compute the heat dissipated by the fin in problem 7–6, and compare with the one-dimensional exact solution (4–18).

7–8. Repeat problem 7–1 for the case of linear nonuniform conductivity with $k_t = 50(1 + 0.01t)$ Btu/hr-ft-°F.

7–9. A tube with dimensions $r_1 = 1''$ and $r_2 = r_1/2$ has uniform unit surface conductances $h_1 = 7$ and $h_2 = 100$ Btu/hr-ft²-°F, and uniform ambient temperatures $t_{g_1} = 70$ and $t_{g_2} = 300°F$. Compute the total heat transferred from g_2 to g_1 per foot length of tube, using the numerical method with a uniform radial subdivision, and check with the corresponding exact solution given in Article 2–6.

7–10. A tube with dimensions $r_1 = 1.4''$ and $r_2 = 0.5''$ is half embedded in a vertical insulating wall, as in Fig. 7–14, and loses heat by natural convection to ambient air. The tube transports a gas at $t_{g_2} = 180°F$, and the inside unit surface conductance is $h_2 = 12$ Btu/hr-ft²-°F. The outer unit surface conductance and ambient air temperature are nonuniformly distributed as listed below. (a) Compute the heat lost by g_2, using a uniform logarithmic subdivision with a single set of internal nodal points. (b) Sketch a family of interpolated isothermals in the tube wall.

$\varphi°$	h_{g_1}	t_{g_1}
0	1	75
30	2	73
60	2	72
90	4	70
120	5	79
150	6	87
180	7	93

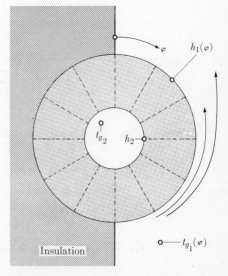

Fig. 7–14. Tube with nonuniform ambient gas temperature and nonuniform surface conductance.

CHAPTER 8

STEADY HEAT-SOURCE SYSTEMS

In this chapter we consider a number of important problems in which heat is either generated or absorbed at one or more local points in the structure, or generated or absorbed throughout its entire volume.

LOCAL HEAT SOURCES

An exothermic or endothermic system in which heat is permanently generated or absorbed at one or more points is said to contain *local heat sources*, while a system permanently generating or absorbing heat at all points is said to contain *distributed heat sources*. Both of these systems are exemplified by a large number of practical engineering applications, and to first illustrate structures with local sources we consider the experimental problem of thermocouple conduction errors, and the applied problem of an electrically heated radiation wall. The first of these two problems will be treated analytically, and the second will be examined by the approximate numerical method of Chapter 7.

8–1 Local heat source in a nonadiabatic plate. Before dealing directly with the problem of thermocouple conduction errors, it will be necessary to first consider the steady temperature distribution in an uninsulated infinite flat plate with a cylindrical heat source located in the plate, as suggested in Fig. 8–1. Let this source develop a total of q_0 Btu/hr in its

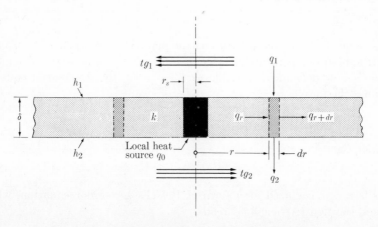

Fig. 8–1. Local heat source in a nonadiabatic plate.

cylindrical volume $\pi r_s^2 \delta$, and assume that the source is at a uniform temperature t_0 throughout; both q_0 and t_0 are to be considered as known quantities. The plate itself is of thickness δ, and its thermal conductivity is assumed to be uniform. In addition to the central heat source s, the plate gains heat on face 1 from an ambient gas at t_{g_1} and loses heat on face 2 to an ambient gas at t_{g_2}, where unit surface conductances are assigned as h_1 and h_2 respectively. The quantities t_{g_1}, t_{g_2}, h_1, and h_2 are considered to be uniform, and if the plate is thin and of high conductivity we may assume additionally that no temperature gradient exists normal to the plate faces 1 and 2. The problem is then one of determining the steady temperature distribution $t(r)$ for $r_s < r < \infty$.

In this case the individual heat transfers by conduction and convection to and from a differential annulus of the plate (Fig. 8–1) are identified as

$$q_r = -kA_r \frac{d}{dr} t_r = -2\pi\delta k r \frac{dt}{dr},$$

$$q_{r+dr} = -kA_{r+dr} \frac{d}{dr} t_{r+dr} = -2\pi\delta k r \left(\frac{d^2 t}{dr^2} dr + \frac{1}{r} \frac{dt}{dr} dr + \frac{dt}{dr} \right),$$

$$\left. \begin{array}{l} q_1 = 2\pi r h_1 (t_{g_1} - t)dr \\ q_2 = 2\pi r h_2 (t - t_{g_2})dr \end{array} \right\} t_{g_1} > t_{g_2},$$

and in the steady state $q_1 + q_r - q_2 - q_{r+dr} = 0$, so that

$$r^2 \frac{d^2 t}{dr^2} + r \frac{dt}{dr} - \frac{r^2}{k\delta} (h_1 + h_2)[t - (h_1 t_{g_1} + h_2 t_{g_2})/(h_1 + h_2)] = 0.$$

But without the source q_0 the plate would be isothermal, and at $r = \infty$ the plate is isothermal regardless of q_0. Therefore, as $r \to \infty$, dt/dr and $d^2 t/dr^2$ approach zero, or

$$t_{r=\infty} = (h_1 t_{g_1} + h_2 t_{g_2})/(h_1 + h_2) = \zeta. \tag{8-1}$$

This value of ζ is the temperature of the plate at $r = r$ when $q_0 = 0$, and is the true plate temperature at large distances $r \gg r_s$ if $q_0 \neq 0$. Then if we define a new dependent variable as $T = t - \zeta$, the differential equation assumes the form

$$r^2 \frac{d^2 T}{dr^2} + r \frac{dT}{dr} - \epsilon^2 r^2 T = 0,$$

wherein

$$\epsilon^2 = (h_1 + h_2)/k\delta. \tag{8-2}$$

This is now recognized as a form of Bessel's zero-order equation, whose general solution (Article 3–5) reads

$$T = t - \zeta = C_1 I_0(\epsilon r) + C_2 K_0(\epsilon r),$$

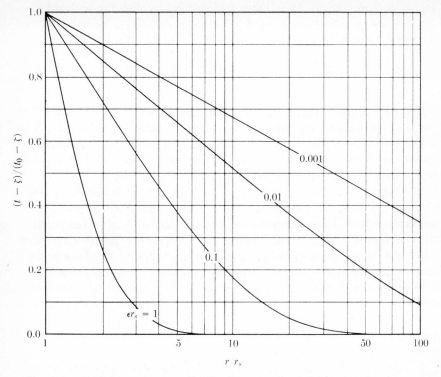

Fig. 8–2.   Radial temperature distribution around a local heat source in a non-adiabatic plate.

where the I_0 and K_0 are recalled as being the modified Bessel functions of the first and second kind respectively.   According to Fig. 3–3, the modified function $I_0(\epsilon r)$ grows indefinitely as the argument ϵr approaches infinity. Thus, in order for the temperature $t(r)$ to remain finite as $r \rightarrow \infty$, as required by (8–1), the integration constant C_1 must be zero.

In the absence of the local source q_0, no heat would be conducted in the plate parallel to its face surfaces, and accordingly the temperature gradient dt/dr must be attributed to the conduction heat flow originating from the source.   At $r = r_s$,

$$q_0 = -kA_s(dt/dr)_{r_s} = -2\pi k\delta r_s \frac{d}{dr}[C_2 K_0(\epsilon r)]_{r_s} = 2\pi k\delta r_s C_2 \epsilon K_1(\epsilon r_s),$$

and from this we retrieve the second integration constant as

$$C_2 = q_0/2\pi k\delta \epsilon r_s K_1(\epsilon r_s).$$

The radial temperature distribution $t(r)$ is thus given by

$$t = \zeta + \frac{q_0}{2\pi k\delta \epsilon r_s} \frac{K_0(\epsilon r)}{K_1(\epsilon r_s)} . \qquad (8\text{–}3)$$

In Fig. 8–2 we plot (8–3) in dimensionless form by dividing both sides by $(t_0 - \zeta)/(t_0 - \zeta)$ as $(t - \zeta)/(t_0 - \zeta) = K_0(\epsilon r_s r/r_s)/K_0(\epsilon r_s)$, and resorting to the following asymptotic approximation to $K_0(x)$ for small x:

$$K_0(x) \doteq \ln\left(\frac{2}{x}\right) - 0.577; \quad x < 0.05.$$

8–2 Application to thermocouple conduction error. It is well known that surface temperatures measured by a common thermocouple are subject to a number of electrical, metallurgical, and thermal errors. Perhaps the most serious of these encountered in the usual type of thermocouple temperature measurement is the so-called *conduction error*.

The origin of thermocouple conduction errors is best visualized by reference to Fig. 8–3. If the thermocouple leads τ and τ' are exposed to an ambient medium whose temperature is higher than the surface temperature to be measured $(t_{g_1} > t_{g_2})$, then these leads will operate at a higher temperature than that of the plate, and heat will be conducted by the thermocouple leads to the lower-temperature plate. This, in turn, causes a local temperature rise in the plate at just the point where the thermocouple junction is to measure its temperature. In this case the recorded temperature will err on the high side. Conversely, if the leads are exposed to a lower-temperature medium $(t_{g_1} < t_{g_2})$, then the leads will record a plate temperature which errs on the low side.

Conduction errors can be eliminated entirely only if the thermocouple is installed in such a fashion as to maintain the leads at the same temperature as the plate temperature to be measured. Since only rarely is it possible to achieve this ideal installation, it becomes important to estimate the actual

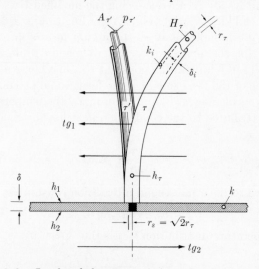

Fig. 8–3. Insulated thermocouple in a nonadiabatic plate.

conduction error in the general case where lead-wire and junction temperatures are not the same. If we take the point of view that the thermocouple leads supply source heat q_0, then (8–3) can be used to determine this error for thermocouple installations in a flat plate.

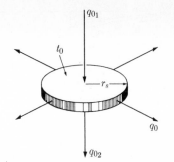

Fig. 8–4.   Thermocouple-junction heat balance.

Consider the case where t_{g_1} exceeds t_{g_2}. Then the thermocouple becomes a source, and q_0 becomes the difference between the heat conducted by the leads to the source area (junction) and that dissipated on face 2 of the source circle, as shown in Fig. 8–4. In terms of general thermal conductances K^t (the superscript t being used here to distinguish between thermal conductances and modified Bessel functions of the second kind),

$$q_{01} = K_1^t(t_{g_1} - t_0), \quad q_{02} = K_2^t(t_0 - t_{g_2}),$$

wherewith

$$q_0 = q_{01} - q_{02} = (K_1^t t_{g_1} + K_2^t t_{g_2}) - (K_1^t + K_2^t)t_0.$$

Then, by (8–3),

$$t_0 - \zeta = \frac{(K_1^t t_{g_1} + K_2^t t_{g_2}) - (K_1^t + K_2^t)t_0}{2\pi k\delta\epsilon r_s} \frac{K_0(\epsilon r_s)}{K_1(\epsilon r_s)},$$

or

$$t_0 - \zeta = \frac{K_1^t(t_{g_1} - \zeta) + K_2^t(t_{g_2} - \zeta)}{(K_1^t + K_2^t) + 2\pi k\delta\epsilon r_s K_1(\epsilon r_s)/K_0(\epsilon r_s)}. \tag{8–4}$$

The value of t_0 is that temperature recorded by the thermocouple, and ζ is either the plate temperature in the absence of the thermocouple ($q_0 = 0$) or the plate temperature at an infinite distance from the thermocouple junction. The difference $(t_0 - \zeta)$ is therefore the absolute thermocouple temperature error.

In practice, the internal conductance K_1^t of the thermocouple leads will greatly exceed the surface conductance K_2^t on one side of the small source circle. With this in mind, we let $K_2^t = 0$, and identify the following solution as a close approximation to (8–4):

$$\frac{t_0 - \zeta}{t_{g_1} - \zeta} = \frac{1}{1 + 2\pi(k\delta/K_1^t)\epsilon r_s K_1(\epsilon r_s)/K_0(\epsilon r_s)}. \tag{8–5}$$

The approximate solution (8–5) is shown in Fig. 8–5 with the abscissa representing the ratio of plate to thermocouple conductance. The small-x approximation for $K_1(x)$ needed here is

$$K_1(x) \doteq x^{-1}; \quad x < 0.05.$$

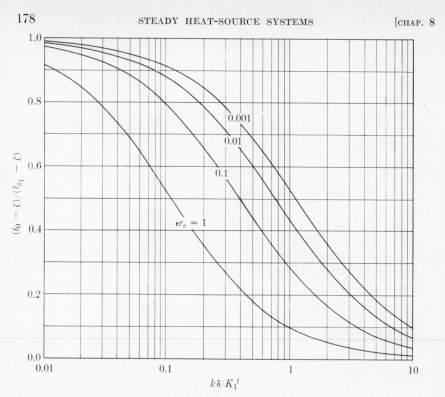

Fig. 8–5.   General thermocouple conduction error for nonadiabatic plates.

Now in order to evaluate the actual temperature error, it becomes necessary to formulate an appropriate expression for the internal thermocouple conductance K_1^t. In this connection we can use some results of the turbine-blade problem in Chapter 2, namely, the solution for the heat rate conducted to the blade root r at $x = 0$ (problem 2–12), as

$$-q_r = \sqrt{hpkA}\ (t_g - t_r)\ \tanh NL.$$

The present problem of a conducting thermocouple lead-wire is analogous to this turbine-blade problem with the single exception that here the wire length L is very long, such that $\tanh NL = 1$. Thus, by an appropriate reidentification of symbols according to Figs. 8–3 and 8–4,

$$q_{01} = (H_\tau p_\tau k_\tau A_\tau)^{\frac{1}{2}}(t_{g_1} - t_0),$$

whereby for the two thermocouple leads in parallel (Article 2–4)

$$K_1^t = (H_\tau p_\tau k_\tau A_\tau)^{\frac{1}{2}} + (H_{\tau'} p_{\tau'} k_{\tau'} A_{\tau'})^{\frac{1}{2}}. \tag{8–6}$$

If the thermocouple is not insulated, then simply $H_\tau = H_{\tau'} = h_\tau$, the average unit surface conductance for flow over a wire of small diameter. With insulated thermocouples heat is gained or lost, as the case may be, in a series path. If, for simplicity, we imagine this path to be the same as in a plane composite wall, then we have simply to compute the reciprocal sum of the surface and insulation resistivities to arrive at an approximate interface unit conductance as $H_\tau = 1(1/h_\tau + \delta_i/k_i)$, and likewise for $H_{\tau'}$. An approximate explicit solution for the conduction error is then obtained by evaluating (8–6) in this way, and combining it with the implicit solution (8–5).

To be more specific, consider the usual case of equal lead-wire size and identical insulation. Then $H_\tau = H_{\tau'}$, $A_\tau = A_{\tau'} = \pi r_\tau^2$, $p_\tau = p_{\tau'} = 2\pi r_\tau$, and the conductance (8–6) reduces to

$$K_1^t = \pi \omega r_\tau (2H_\tau r_\tau)^{\frac{1}{2}}.$$

The solution (8–5) then takes the form

$$\frac{t_0 - \zeta}{t_{g_1} - \zeta} = \frac{1}{1 + \nu K_1(\epsilon r_s)/K_0(\epsilon r_s)}, \qquad (8\text{–}7)$$

where ω and ν are abbreviations for

$$\omega = k_\tau^{\frac{1}{2}} + k_{\tau'}^{\frac{1}{2}} \quad \text{and} \quad \nu = \frac{2}{\omega}[k\delta(h_1 + h_2)/H_\tau r_\tau]^{\frac{1}{2}}.$$

The value of the source radius in (8–7) may be taken as the $\sqrt{2}$ times the wire radius as $r_s = 1.414 r_\tau$.

EXAMPLE 8–1. It is required to measure the temperature of a flat $0.1''$ thick plate whose thermal conductivity is 33.8 Btu/hr-ft-°F. The plate is exposed to a 1655°F gas flow on face 1 where the unit surface conductance is known to be 17.1 Btu/hr-ft²-°F, and a gas flow at 140°F on face 2 where the unit surface conductance is 16.9 Btu/hr-ft²-°F. An iron-constantan thermocouple is to be installed on face 1, the thermocouple being made up of #18-gage lead wires of thermal conductivity 35.7 and 14.6 Btu/hr-ft-°F. Both lead wires are insulated with a $0.005''$ thick layer of insulation whose thermal conductivity is 0.025 Btu/hr-ft-°F. The unit surface conductance over each insulated lead is known to be 181 Btu/hr-ft²-°F. What is the true plate temperature if t_0 is the apparent temperature recorded by the thermocouple?

Solution. Here $\zeta = (17.1 \times 1655 + 16.9 \times 140)/(17.1 + 16.9) = 902$°F, $\omega = \sqrt{35.7} + \sqrt{14.6} = 9.80$, $H_\tau = 1/(1/181 + 0.005/12 \times 0.025) = 45.1$, so that with #18-gage wire $= 0.04''$ diameter the value of the parameter ν becomes

$$\nu = \frac{2}{9.80}\left[\frac{0.1 \times 33.8(17.1 + 16.9)}{45.1 \times 0.02}\right]^{\frac{1}{2}} = 2.3.$$

Then with

$$\epsilon = \left(\frac{17.1 \times 16.9}{33.8 \times 0.1/12}\right)^{\frac{1}{2}} = 10.99 \quad \text{and} \quad \epsilon r_s = 10.99 \times 1.414 \times 0.02/12 = 0.026,$$

and using asymptotic approximations to $K(x)$ as

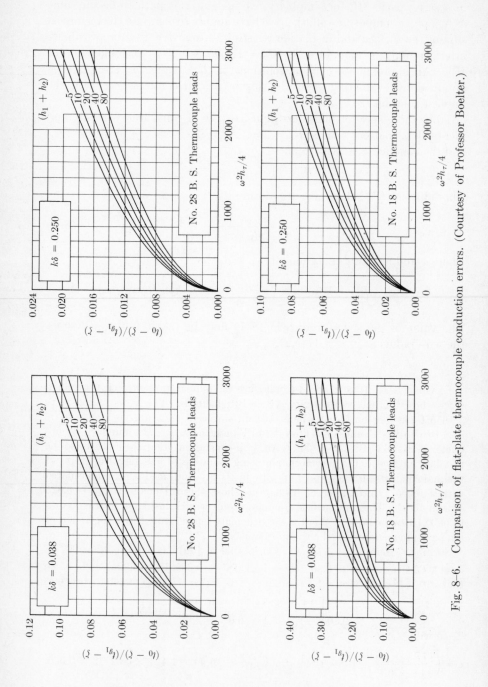

Fig. 8-6. Comparison of flat-plate thermocouple conduction errors. (Courtesy of Professor Boelter.)

$$K_0(\epsilon r_s) = \ln\left(\frac{2}{0.026}\right) - 0.577 = 3.8 \quad \text{and} \quad K_1(\epsilon r_s) = 1/0.026 = 38.6,$$

we have

$$\frac{t_0 - \zeta}{t_{g_1} - \zeta} = \frac{1}{1 + 2.3 \times 38.6/3.8} = 0.041.$$

The thermocouple conduction error is therefore estimated to be $t_0 - \zeta = 0.041$ $(1655 - 902) = 31°F$. The true plate temperature is then taken to be $t = t_0 - 31$.

Boelter $et\ al.$ (1) have developed, by the analysis presented here, a number of graphs for illustrating the separate effects involved in thermocouple conduction errors. These curves, as reproduced in Fig. 8–6, suggest that the conduction error is more sensitive to the unit surface conductance over the lead wires, h_τ, than to the unit surface conductance on either side of the plate, h_1 and h_2. The curves also indicate that for a fixed wire radius, r_τ, a smaller conduction error is to be expected with thick plates of high thermal conductivity k. Corresponding changes for the lead wires apparently have an opposite effect. Thus, for minimum conduction errors, insulated leads of small radius r_τ and low thermal conductivity k_τ should be used.

8–3 Insulated radiation wall.

An extension of the numerical-relaxation method of Chapter 7 to regions with either local or distributed sources or sinks offers no particular difficulty. In fact, the flexibility of the numerical approach encompasses all such extensions without losing its power to approximately solve problems which would otherwise be, at best, awkward to handle analytically.

To illustrate the manner in which the residual equations are altered for systems developing or absorbing heat at one or more local points, consider a given nodal point i located at a point heat source. The steady heat flow into i from all adjacent nodal points j together with the generated heat at i is given by

$$\bar{q}_i' = q_{0i} + \sum_j q_j = q_{0i} + \sum_j K_J \Delta t_J, \tag{8–8}$$

if the heat generation and thermal conductivity of the region are both independent of local temperature. Here $K_J = K_{ji} = k(A/\delta)_{ji}$ for an internal conductance (Fig. 7–2), $K_J = hA_i$ for a surface conductance, and $\Delta t_J = t_j - t_i$. For example, if $i = 1$ and the four adjacent nodal points in a square network are $j = 2, 3, 4$, and 5, then

$$\bar{q}_1' = q_{01} + K_{21}\Delta t_2 + K_{31}\Delta t_3 + K_{41}\Delta t_4 + K_{51}\Delta t_5,$$

or, equivalently,

$$\bar{q}_1 = \frac{q_{01}}{k} + \left(\frac{A}{\delta}\right)_{21} (t_2 - t_1) + \left(\frac{A}{\delta}\right)_{31} (t_3 - t_1)$$

$$+ \left(\frac{A}{\delta}\right)_{41} (t_4 - t_1) + \left(\frac{A}{\delta}\right)_{51} (t_5 - t_1).$$

By way of example, we consider a section of a plane composite radiation wall, as in Fig. 8–7. The $2''$ thick main portion of the wall has equally spaced electrical wires of diameter d embedded along its horizontal center line, each of which generates uniform local "Joulean" heat in permanent amount q_0''' Btu/hr per unit volume of the source when under a particular current-carrying load. The outer face of the $1''$ thick insulation is isothermal at a measured temperature of t_s, and the outer face of the $2''$ wall dissipates heat by radiation to a plane receiver at a uniform temperature t_r. The unit surface conductance for this radiation exchange is assumed to be a uniform H_R. Finally, let the thermal conductivity of wall 1 be uniform throughout as k_1, and consider the insulation as being anisotropic with $k_2 = k_2$ in the horizontal direction, and $k_2 = k_1$ in the vertical direction.

Select $q_0''' = 10^5$ Btu/hr-in.^{3}, $k_1 = 10$ and $k_2 = 1$ Btu/hr-in.-°F, $H_R = 1$ Btu/hr-in.^{2}-°F, $d = 1/5\sqrt{\pi}''$, and $t_s = 0$ and $t_r = 100$°F. Then the wire volume per inch length is $V_i = \pi d^2/4 = 0.01$ in.^{3}, and the heat release associated with each such length of wire is $q_{0i} = q_0'''V_i = 1000$ Btu/hr. This is the quantity of heat generated per hour at the nodal point ③ in the numerical network of Fig. 8–7. If we let k of the wire

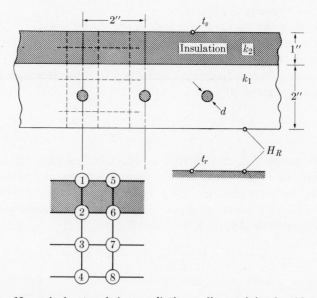

Fig. 8–7. Numerical network for a radiation wall containing local heat sources.

be k_1, and further assume no contact resistances between wire and wall and between walls 1 and 2, then residual equations for nodal points such as ②, ③, and ④ read

$$\bar{q}_2 = \qquad K_{12}(t_1 - t_2) + K_{32}(t_3 - t_2) + 2K_{62}(t_6 - t_2),$$

$$\bar{q}_3 = q_{03} + K_{23}(t_2 - t_3) + K_{43}(t_4 - t_3) + 2K_{73}(t_7 - t_3),$$

$$\bar{q}_4 = \qquad K_{34}(t_3 - t_4) + K_{r4}(t_r - t_4) + 2K_{84}(t_8 - t_4),$$

where the factors of 2 account for geometric symmetry. The internal conductance K_{62} can be approximated by using the mean thermal conductivity as $K_{62} = k(A/\delta)_{62} = \frac{1}{2}(k_1 + k_2)\,(A/\delta)_{62}$.

TABLE 8–1

TABULATION OF THERMAL CONDUCTANCES

$K_{12} = 1$	$K_{34} = 10$	$K_{48} = \frac{10}{2}$	$K_{67} = 10$	$K_{r4} = 1$
$K_{23} = 10$	$K_{37} = 10$	$K_{56} = 1$	$K_{78} = 10$	$K_{r8} = 1$
$K_{26} = \frac{11}{2}$				

Tabulating all conductances per inch depth of section as in Table 8–1 leads to the six required residual equations

$$\bar{q}_2 = \qquad 0.1t_1 + \qquad t_3 + 1.1t_6 - 2.2t_2,$$

$$\bar{q}_3 = 100 + \qquad t_2 + \qquad t_4 + 2.0t_7 - 4.0t_3,$$

$$\bar{q}_4 = \qquad t_3 + \qquad t_8 + 0.1t_r - 2.1t_4,$$

$$\bar{q}_6 = \qquad 1.1t_2 + 0.1t_5 + \qquad t_7 - 2.2t_6,$$

$$\bar{q}_7 = \qquad 2.0t_3 + \qquad t_6 + \qquad t_8 - 4.0t_7,$$

$$\bar{q}_8 = \qquad t_4 + \qquad t_7 + 0.1t_r - 2.1t_8,$$

$$(8–9)$$

and their relaxation in Table 8–2. Note here, in contrast to a nongenerating system (Chapter 7), that the procedure is begun by assuming all $\bar{q}_i$ and t_i as zero and then correcting for the generated heat at each nodal point as well as correcting for the change in t_r from zero to its correct value of 100°F. The former amounts to a correction of 100 for the single nodal point ③, and the latter to a correction of $0.1 \times 100 = 10$ for nodal points ④ and ⑧, as shown on the first line of Table 8–2. Checking the heat generated at the nodal point ③ against that conducted to nodal points ②, ④, and ⑦ gives

$$1000 = 10(315 - 279) + 10(315 - 289) + 2 \times 10(315 - 296)$$
$$= 1000 \text{ Btu/hr},$$

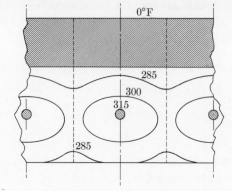

Fig. 8–8. Temperature field in the composite wall of Fig. 8–7.

TABLE 8–2

RELAXATION OF RESIDUAL EQUATIONS (8–9)

$\bar{q}_2$	t_2	$\bar{q}_3$	t_3	$\bar{q}_4$	t_4	$\bar{q}_6$	t_6	$\bar{q}_7$	t_7	$\bar{q}_8$	t_8
0	0	100	0	10	0	0	0	0	0	10	0
−614	279	279				307					
−614	279					307					
315		−1260	315	315				630			
−299		−881	315	325				630			
		289		−607	289					289	
		−592		−282	289					299	
301						−603	274	274			
2						−296	274	904			
		592				296		−1184	296	296	
		0				0		−280	296	595	
				282				282		−595	283
				0				2		0	283

and computing the total heat transferred by radiation per square foot of radiating surface, we find that

$$q_R = 12\,[6 \times 1(289 - 100) + 6 \times 1(283 - 100)] = 26{,}784 \text{ Btu/hr.}$$

The temperature pattern is illustrated in Fig. 8–8.

DISTRIBUTED HEAT SOURCES

The subject of distributed sources has an even more diversified field of application than that for local sources. In this connection we think almost immediately of chemical reactions as being identified with a class of problems in which heat is liberated or absorbed in either uniform or nonuniform amount throughout the volume of the structure. In these cases the source is the heat of reaction. Also in this class are systems undergoing phase changes. The more common situation is that of distributed sources, as occurs in problems of heat release in decomposing systems, the hydration of cement in large concrete structures such as dams, and many others.

In the following articles, we consider first the important industrial problem of predicting maximum operating temperatures in electrical coils. Here the source is the *Joulean* heat generated within the current-carrying wires of the coil, and the problem is somewhat complicated by the fact that the strength of this source is a function of local temperature. We shall treat the problem of electrical coils by both analytical and numerical methods.

A second problem to be considered here, but in less detail than the first, is that of predicting the temperature field in a nuclear reactor in which the heat generation is associated with the processes of fission and gamma-ray absorption. For the particular reactor configuration considered, only an approximate analytical solution can be obtained.

8–4 Electrical coils. The electrical coil in one form or another is an important component of so many electrical devices as to preclude enumeration of all but a few examples such as core-coils of transformers, field coils of generators, and so on. Formulas for the precise description of the general temperature distribution in such conductors, as well as the peak or "hot-spot" temperature, are of considerable interest to the designer of electrical coils, since often the maximum permissible coil current (the maximum electrical loading) is predetermined by a fixed allowable peak temperature for the coil material. New designs, extending the performance of existing equipment, and estimating safe overload limits all depend on such information.

The ordinary coil is helical or quasi-toroidal in form, as shown in (a) of Fig. 8–9. It is usually permissible, however, to disregard the effects of

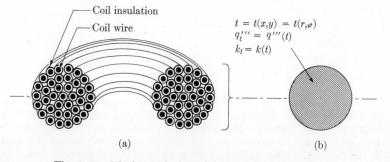

Fig. 8–9.   Mathematical model of an electrical coil.

curvature in the longitudinal axis of the coil, and to assume that this axis is long relative to the cross-sectional *profile* dimensions. This implies that the thermal resistance in the longitudinal direction so far exceeds the transverse profile resistance that all generated heat flows transversely to the coil surface, where it is dissipated to a lower temperature ambient medium. Commonly, this medium is simply the atmosphere, such as in field coils of generators, or the coil may be submerged in a liquid bath, as in many transformers. Submerged liquid cooling or gas cooling of coil surfaces does not necessarily justify the assumption that these surfaces are isothermal.

A plane cutting normal to the longitudinal axis of a coil reveals a profile of lightly insulated wires of small diameter. If the profile area of each wire is a small percent of the total coil profile area, then the development of Joulean heat is essentially uniform over the entire coil profile. In other words, a large number of quasi-homogeneous areas are combined into a single equivalent area, and as such any variation in the heat developed from point to point in the profile must be attributed only to changes in the electrical resistivity of the metal from point to point, such changes being a function of local profile temperature. The net effect of these assumptions is to reduce the actual toroidal coil to a straight homogeneous bar generating distributed heat as a function of local temperature, as in (b) of Fig. 8–9.*

If the coil has an electrical resistivity ρ and carries constant electric current I, then the Joulean heat generated is $q''' = I^2\rho$ at a coil temperature t. The heat developed at a reference temperature $t = 0$ is correspondingly $q_0''' = I^2\rho_0$. In the temperature range of normal coil operation, ρ varies with local temperature as the linear function $\rho = \rho_0(1 + \alpha_0 t)$. If $\alpha_0 \ll 1$, then simply $q_t''' = q_0'''$, while if α_0 is not small, $q_t''' = q_0'''(1 + \alpha_0 t)$.

8–5 Coil of solid circular profile.

Consider an electrical coil of solid circular profile and of uniform thermal conductivity $k_t = k$. The coil is to generate linear nonuniform Joulean heat $q_t''' = q_0'''(1 + \alpha_0 t)$, and its surface temperature $t(r_1,\varphi)$ is to be an arbitrary function of the azimuthal angle φ as $t = f(\varphi)$ in Fig. 8–10.

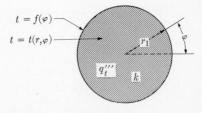

Fig. 8–10.   Coil of solid circular profile.

---

*Difficulties in the actual situation stem from attempts to analytically specify the variation in current density over the profile of each wire, and to account for the heat conducted through the interface between wire and insulation and between insulation and insulation. In the mathematical model the current density is assumed to be uniform over each small-diameter wire, all contact resistances are disregarded, and an equivalent thermal conductivity is assigned.

The steady profile temperature $t(r,\varphi)$ is that solution which satisfies the partial-differential equation

$$\frac{\partial^2 t}{\partial r^2} + \frac{1}{r}\frac{\partial t}{\partial r} + \frac{1}{r^2}\frac{\partial^2 t}{\partial \varphi^2} + a + bt = 0,$$

wherein

$$a = q_0'''/k \quad \text{and} \quad b = a\alpha_0,$$

or the alternate separable partial-differential equation

$$\frac{\partial^2 T}{\partial r^2} + \frac{1}{r}\frac{\partial T}{\partial r} + \frac{1}{r^2}\frac{\partial^2 T}{\partial \varphi^2} + bT = 0, \qquad (8\text{--}10)$$

if T represents the linear transformation $T = a + bt$. An assumed product solution (Article 5–8) for $T(r,\varphi)$ of the form $T = R\Phi$, where $R = R(r)$ and $\Phi = \Phi(\varphi)$, leads to the separation of (8–10) into the two total-differential equations

$$\frac{d^2 R}{dr^2} + \frac{1}{r}\frac{dR}{dr} + \left(b - \frac{\lambda^2}{r^2}\right)R = 0,$$

and

$$\frac{d^2 \Phi}{d\varphi^2} + \lambda^2 \Phi = 0,$$

whose respective general solutions are now well known as

$$R = C_1 J_\lambda(\sqrt{b}\,r) + C_2 Y_\lambda(\sqrt{b}\,r), \qquad (8\text{--}11)$$

and

$$\Phi = C_3 \cos \lambda\varphi + C_4 \sin \lambda\varphi. \qquad (8\text{--}12)$$

Since the separation constant λ is not restricted in any way to a finite number of values, there exist all possible solutions of the type

$$T_\lambda = [C_1 J_\lambda(\sqrt{b}\,r) + C_2 Y_\lambda(\sqrt{b}\,r)][C_3 \cos \lambda\varphi + C_4 \sin \lambda\varphi].$$

However, the cyclic nature of the temperature field in this problem as $T(r,\varphi) = T(r,\varphi \pm 2n\pi)$ forces λ to take on only integral values $\lambda = 0, 1, 2, \cdots$, so that the sum of all possible solutions of the type $R\Phi$, $\lambda = 0, 1, 2, \cdots$, is the solution of (8–10). It is also noted that since $T(r,\varphi)$ must remain finite as $r \to 0$, the second Bessel solution $Y_\lambda(\sqrt{b}\,r)$ must be discarded by taking $C_2 = 0$. Thus

$$T = \sum_{\lambda=0}^{\infty} (M_\lambda \sin \lambda\varphi + N_\lambda \cos \lambda\varphi) J_\lambda(\sqrt{b}\,r). \qquad (8\text{--}13)$$

The general solution (8–13) must now be adjusted to fit the boundary condition on temperature (Fig. 8–10) as

$$t = f(\varphi) \quad \text{at } r = r_1.$$

In terms of the linear transformation variable T this means that

$$T = a + bf(\varphi) = F(\varphi) \quad \text{at } r = r_1,$$

whence

$$F(\varphi) = \sum_{\lambda=0}^{\infty} (M_\lambda \sin \lambda\varphi + N_\lambda \cos \lambda\varphi) J_\lambda(\sqrt{b}\, r_1).$$

This is recognized as a Fourier expansion of the arbitrary function $F(\varphi)$. For such an expansion in a 2π interval, the constant amplitudes M_λ and N_λ are given by (5–5) and (5–7) as

$$J_\lambda(\sqrt{b}\, r_1)M_\lambda = \frac{1}{\pi} \int_0^{2\pi} F(\varphi) \sin \lambda\varphi d\varphi,$$

and

$$J_\lambda(\sqrt{b}\, r_1)N_\lambda = \frac{1}{\pi} \int_0^{2\pi} F(\varphi) \cos \lambda\varphi d\varphi,$$

where it is to be recalled that the leading coefficient is $N_0/2$. This serves to complete the final solution as

$$a + bt = \frac{1}{\pi} \sum_{\lambda=0}^{\infty} \left[\sin \lambda\varphi \int_0^{2\pi} F(\varphi) \sin \lambda\varphi d\varphi + \cos \lambda\varphi \int_0^{2\pi} F(\varphi) \cos \lambda\varphi d\varphi \right]$$
$$\times \frac{J_\lambda(\sqrt{b}\, r)}{J_\lambda(\sqrt{b}\, r_1)}. \qquad (8\text{–}14)$$

EXAMPLE 8–2. The coil of Article 8–5 is half submerged in an oil bath. If the free surface is at t_0 and the submerged surface at t_1, find $t(r,\varphi)$.

Solution. The boundary temperatures are expressed in $F(\varphi)$ as

$$F(\varphi) = a + bt_0 \quad \text{at } r = r_1 \text{ and } 0 < \varphi < \pi,$$

$$F(\varphi) = a + bt_1 \quad \text{at } r = r_1 \text{ and } \pi < \varphi < 2\pi.$$

The integral coefficients in (8–14) are then evaluated by breaking them up into the half range 0–π and π–2π, the leading coefficient for $\lambda = 0$ being

$$\frac{1}{2} \int_0^{2\pi} F(\varphi)d\varphi = \frac{1}{2} \int_0^{\pi} (a + bt_0)d\varphi + \frac{1}{2} \int_\pi^{2\pi} (a + bt_1)d\varphi = \pi a + \frac{\pi b}{2}(t_0 + t_1).$$

The remaining coefficients for $\lambda = 1, 2, 3, \cdots$ are computed as

$$\int_0^{2\pi} F(\varphi) \sin \lambda\varphi d\varphi = \frac{2b}{\lambda}(t_0 + t_1); \quad \lambda = 1, 3, 5, \cdots,$$

$$\int_0^{2\pi} F(\varphi) \cos \lambda\varphi d\varphi = 0,$$

and herewith the particular solution $t(r,\varphi)$ satisfying the required set of boundary temperatures is

$$t = \tfrac{1}{2}(t_0 + t_1) \frac{J_0(\psi)}{J_0(\psi_1)} + \frac{2}{\pi}(t_0 + t_1)\left[\sin\varphi \frac{J_1(\psi)}{J_1(\psi_1)} + \tfrac{1}{3}\sin 3\varphi \frac{J_3(\psi)}{J_3(\psi_1)} + \cdots \right],$$
(8–15)

in which $\psi = \sqrt{b}\,r$ and $\psi_1 = \sqrt{b}\,r_1$.

EXAMPLE 8-3.   The coil of Article 8–5 is completely submerged in an oil bath.* If the submerged surface is at t_1, find the general temperature, the mean temperature, and the ratio of general temperature above t_1 to maximum temperature above t_1.

Solution.   The boundary conditions are

$$F(\varphi) = a + bt_1 \quad \text{at } r = r_1 \text{ and } 0 < \varphi < 2\pi,$$

so that without difficulty we find the profile temperature as

$$t = \left(t_1 + \frac{1}{\alpha_0}\right)\frac{J_0(\sqrt{b}\,r)}{J_0(\sqrt{b}\,r_1)} - \frac{1}{\alpha_0}\cdot$$
(8–16)

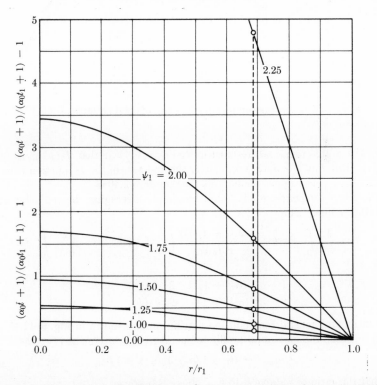

Fig. 8–11.   Temperature distribution and mean temperature in a coil of solid circular profile.

*This case has been investigated in detail by Jakob (2).

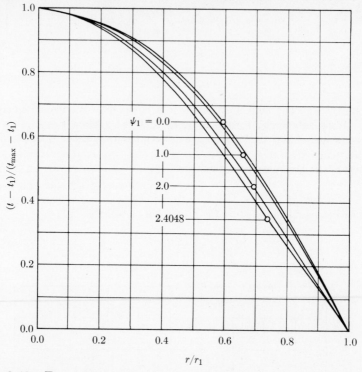

Fig. 8–12. Temperature uniformity in a coil of solid circular profile. (Courtesy of Professor Jakob.)

Since the profile temperature must exceed t_1, it is clear that $J_0(\psi)$ must exceed $J_0(\psi_1)$. But $J_0(\psi) > J_0(\psi_1)$ only up to the first zero of the J_0 function (Fig. 3–2) when $r < r_1$. The upper bound on ψ_1 is therefore 2.4048.*

The mean temperature t is found by simply averaging the temperature $t(r)$ over the profile. Thus

$$\bar{t} = \frac{1}{\pi r_1^2} \int_0^{r_1} 2\pi r t \, dr = \frac{2(t_1 + 1/\alpha_0)}{r_1^2 J_0(\psi_1)} \int_0^{r_1} r J_0(\sqrt{b}\, r) dr - \frac{2}{\alpha_0 r_1^2} \int_0^{r_1} r \, dr,$$

or

$$\frac{(\alpha_0 \bar{t} + 1)}{(\alpha_0 t_1 + 1)} = \frac{2}{\psi_1} \frac{J_1(\psi_1)}{J_0(\psi_1)}. \tag{8–17}$$

The mean and general temperature distribution are shown in Fig. 8–11.

In this case the maximum profile temperature t_{max} occurs at $r = 0$ as

$$t_{max} = (t_1 + 1/\alpha_0)/J_0(\psi_1) - 1/\alpha_0,$$

so that the ratio of t above t_1 to t_{max} above t_1 becomes

---

*It is to be understood that $\psi_1 = 2.4048$ ($t = \infty$) is only a theoretical limit which cannot actually exist, since the coil would overheat and thus change its thermal and electrical properties long before this limit was reached.

$$\frac{t - t_1}{t_{max} - t_1} = \frac{J_0(\psi) - J_0(\psi_1)}{1 - J_0(\psi_1)}. \tag{8-18}$$

Jakob (2) has computed the temperature uniformity (8–18) as shown in Fig. 8–12. This ratio is seen to be rather insensitive to maximum changes in the dimensionless parameter ψ_1, although Fig. 8–11 suggests that the temperature distribution itself is decidedly sensitive to ψ_1.

8-6 Case of unknown surface temperature. Consider a coil of solid circular profile dissipating heat to an ambient gas g. Here the coil surface temperature is unknown, and only the uniform gas temperature t_g and uniform unit surface conductance h are given.

If the coil is again of uniform thermal conductivity k, then the symmetrical temperature distribution $t(r)$ for this case is that which satisfies the total-differential equation

$$\frac{d^2t}{dr^2} + \frac{1}{r}\frac{dt}{dr} + \frac{q_0'''}{k}(1 + \alpha_0 t) = 0, \tag{8-19}$$

and the particular boundary condition

$$\frac{dt}{dr} = -\frac{h}{k}(t - t_g) \quad \text{at } r = r_1. \tag{8-20}$$

In terms of $T = a + bt$, (8–19) reappears in the Bessel form of zero order

$$r^2\frac{d^2T}{dr^2} + r\frac{dT}{dr} + br^2 T = 0,$$

whose general solution reads

$$T = C_1 J_0(\sqrt{b}\, r) + C_2 Y_0(\sqrt{b}\, r).$$

Again C_2 must be zero, and according to the condition (8–20),

$$\left(\frac{dt}{dr}\right)_1 = -\frac{C_1}{\sqrt{b}} J_1(\psi_1) = -\frac{h}{k}\left[\frac{C_1}{\sqrt{b}} J_0(\psi_1) - t_g - \frac{1}{\alpha_0}\right],$$

which puts us in possession of the first integration constant as

$$C_1 = \frac{\left(t_g + \dfrac{1}{\alpha_0}\right) b}{J_0(\psi_1) - \gamma J_1(\psi_1)},$$

wherein $\gamma = \sqrt{q_0''' \alpha_0 k}/h$. This gives the required solution as

$$\frac{\alpha_0 t + 1}{\alpha_0 t_g + 1} = \frac{J_0(\psi)}{J_0(\psi_1) - \gamma J_1(\psi_1)}, \tag{8-21}$$

which reduces, as it should, to (8–16) as $h \to \infty$ ($\gamma = 0$ and $t_g = t_1$). Corresponding to (8–17) and (8–18) we have

$$(\alpha_0\bar{t}+1)/(\alpha_0 t_g+1)=2J_1(\psi_1)/\psi_1[J_0(\psi_1)-\gamma J_1(\psi_1)]$$

and

$$(t-t_g)/(t_{max}-t_g)=[J_0(\psi)-J_0(\psi_1)+\gamma J_1(\psi_1)]/[1-J_0(\psi_1)+\gamma J_1(\psi_1)].$$

8–7 Coil of hollow circular profile.

Hollow profiles are a rather recent innovation for internally cooled coils of high-output generators (3). Consider such a coil with a hollow circular profile and of uniform thermal conductivity k, as in Fig. 8–13. The coil generates linear Joulean heat $q_t''' = q_0'''(1 + \alpha_0 t)$, and its surface temperatures $t(r_1,\varphi)$ and $t(r_2,\varphi)$ are arbitrary functions $t = f(\varphi)$ and $t = g(\varphi)$ respectively.

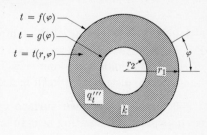

Fig. 8–13. Coil of hollow circular profile.

Again the appropriate partial-differential equation is (8–10), which was found to be satisfied by the primitive product solutions (8–11) and (8–12). Here Y_λ must be retained, and we take $T = R\Phi$ in the legitimate form

$$T = \sum_{\lambda=0}^{\infty} \{[A_\lambda J_\lambda(\sqrt{b}\,r) + B_\lambda Y_\lambda(\sqrt{b}\,r)]\sin\lambda\varphi$$
$$+ [C_\lambda J_\lambda(\sqrt{b}\,r) + D_\lambda Y_\lambda(\sqrt{b}\,r)]\cos\lambda\varphi\}. \quad (8\text{–}22)$$

Thus, in satisfying the boundary temperatures in T as

$$T = a + bf(\varphi) = F(\varphi) \quad \text{at } r = r_1 \text{ and } 0 < \varphi < 2\pi,$$
$$T = a + bg(\varphi) = G(\varphi) \quad \text{at } r = r_2 \text{ and } 0 < \varphi < 2\pi,$$

we obtain the Fourier expansions

$$F(\varphi) = \sum_{\lambda=0}^{\infty} \{[A_\lambda J_\lambda(\psi_1) + B_\lambda Y_\lambda(\psi_1)]\sin\lambda\varphi$$
$$+ [C_\lambda J_\lambda(\psi_1) + D_\lambda Y_\lambda(\psi_1)]\cos\lambda\varphi\},$$

$$G(\varphi) = \sum_{\lambda=0}^{\infty} \{[A_\lambda J_\lambda(\psi_2) + B_\lambda Y_\lambda(\psi_2)]\sin\lambda\varphi$$
$$+ [C_\lambda J_\lambda(\psi_2) + D_\lambda Y_\lambda(\psi_2)]\cos\lambda\varphi\}.$$

The constant coefficients in brackets, being the Fourier coefficients of these expansions, are then given by

$$A_\lambda J_\lambda(\psi_1) + B_\lambda Y_\lambda(\psi_1) = \frac{1}{\pi}\int_0^{2\pi} F(\varphi)\sin\lambda\varphi d\varphi,$$

$$A_\lambda J_\lambda(\psi_2) + B_\lambda Y_\lambda(\psi_2) = \frac{1}{\pi}\int_0^{2\pi} G(\varphi)\sin\lambda\varphi d\varphi,$$

$$C_\lambda J_\lambda(\psi_1) + D_\lambda Y_\lambda(\psi_1) = \frac{1}{\pi}\int_0^{2\pi} F(\varphi)\cos\lambda\varphi d\varphi,$$

$$C_\lambda J_\lambda(\psi_2) + D_\lambda Y_\lambda(\psi_2) = \frac{1}{\pi}\int_0^{2\pi} G(\varphi)\cos\lambda\varphi d\varphi,$$

$$(8\text{–}23)$$

wherein, according to previous notation, $\psi_1 = \sqrt{b}\, r_1$ and $\psi_2 = \sqrt{b}\, r_2$.

These four relations serve to evaluate the A_λ, B_λ, C_λ, and D_λ if the $F(\varphi)$ and $G(\varphi)$ can be represented in the 2π interval of φ. The final solution is determined when the A_λ, B_λ, C_λ, and D_λ in (8–22) are identified as those obtained through simultaneous solution of (8–23).

EXAMPLE 8–4. The coil of Article 8–7 has uniform boundary temperatures $f(\varphi) = t_1$ and $g(\varphi) = t_2$. Find $t(r)$.

Solution. In this elementary case,

$$F(\varphi) = a + bt_1 \quad \text{at } r = r_1 \text{ and } 0 < \varphi < 2\pi,$$
$$G(\varphi) = a + bt_2 \quad \text{at } r = r_2 \text{ and } 0 < \varphi < 2\pi,$$
(8–24)

whereby the $A_\lambda = B_\lambda = C_\lambda = D_\lambda = 0$, and only the leading coefficients for $\lambda = 0$ are nonvanishing, as

$$\frac{1}{2\pi}\int_0^{2\pi} F(\varphi)d\varphi = a + bt_1 \quad \text{and} \quad \frac{1}{2\pi}\int_0^{2\pi} G(\varphi)d\varphi = a + bt_2,$$

so that

$$C_0 = \frac{1}{\Psi}[(a + bt_2)Y_0(\psi_1) - (a + bt_1)Y_0(\psi_2)],$$

$$D_0 = \frac{1}{\Psi}[(a + bt_1)J_0(\psi_2) - (a + bt_2)J_0(\psi_1)],$$

in which

$$\Psi = J_0(\psi_2)Y_0(\psi_1) - J_0(\psi_1)Y_0(\psi_2).$$

With the arbitrary constants in (8–22) evaluated as such, the final solution $t(r)$ satisfying (8–10) and (8–24) reads

$$t = \frac{1}{\Psi}[(t_2 + 1/\alpha_0)Y_0(\psi_1) - (t_1 + 1/\alpha_0)Y_0(\psi_2)]J_0(\psi)$$

$$+ \frac{1}{\Psi}[(t_1 + 1/\alpha_0)J_0(\psi_2) - (t_2 + 1/\alpha_0)J_0(\psi_1)]Y_0(\psi) - \frac{1}{\alpha_0}. \quad (8–25)$$

8–8 Effect of nonuniform thermal conductivity. It is of interest to investigate a case where the thermal conductivity of a generating coil is not uniform but, say, varies linearly with local profile temperature as $k_t = k_0(1 + \beta_0 t) = A + Bt$. In particular, we consider a coil of hollow circular profile with uniform surface temperatures t_1 and t_2 and generating uniform Joulean heat q_0'''.

The temperature distribution in this case must evidently satisfy the total-differential equation

$$\frac{d}{dr}\left(k_t \frac{dt}{dr}\right) + \frac{1}{r}\frac{d}{dr}(k_t t) + q_0''' = 0, \quad (8–26)$$

and again we can use the Kirchhoff method of integration, as discussed in Article 2–7. Following the procedure outlined there, we introduce the Kirchhoff transformation (2–12) into (8–26) and arrive at the differential equation in u as

$$\frac{d^2u}{dr^2} + \frac{1}{r}\frac{du}{dr} + \frac{q_0'''}{k_c} = 0. \tag{8-27}$$

This result corresponds to (2–14).

The general solution of (8–27) is readily found to be

$$u = C_1 \ln r - \frac{q_0'''}{4k_c} r^2 + C_2,$$

and the integration constants are evaluated by application of the transformation boundary conditions (2–13). The particular solution satisfying these for the simplest case of $t_1 = t_2 = 0$ is

$$u = \frac{q_0'''}{4k_c}(r_1^2 - r^2) + \frac{q_0'''(r_1^2 - r_2^2)}{4k_c \ln \dfrac{r_1}{r_2}} \ln \frac{r}{r_1}. \tag{8-28}$$

In this case the semidefinite integration of du gives $t = t(u)$ for $t_1 = 0$ as

$$\frac{B}{2}t^2 + At - k_c u = 0, \tag{8-29}$$

a result corresponding to (2–16). By carrying through the integration of du to both limits, we determine the constant k_c for $t_1 = t_2 = 0$ as simply $k_c = A$. Then by solving the quadratic (8–29) and substituting therein the expression for u given by (8–28) along with $k_c = A$, we have

$$t = \frac{1}{\beta_0}(\sqrt{1 + 2\beta_0 \Omega} - 1), \tag{8-30}$$

in which

$$\Omega = \frac{q_0'''}{4k_0}\left[(r_1^2 - r^2) - \frac{(r_1^2 - r_2^2)}{\ln(r_1/r_2)}\ln\frac{r_1}{r}\right].$$

Note that $t = \Omega$ for $\beta_0 = 0$, and that for a positive conductivity $-\beta_0 \leq \frac{1}{2}\Omega_{\max}$.

The effects of a nonuniform thermal conductivity are best exhibited by way of a numerical example. Let $q_0''' = 10^6$ Btu/hr-ft^3, $k_0 = 10$ Btu/hr-ft-°F, $r_2 = \frac{1}{4}''$, and $r_1/r_2 = 4$. Computing with these values, we find the temperature distributions shown in Fig. 8–14 for exaggerated values of the temperature coefficient of thermal conductivity β_0.

When working with actual coils an equivalent thermal conductivity must be computed for the nonhomogeneous profile composed of, say, copper wires wound with silk insulation, or determined directly by experimental measurement. Jakob (2) has used an approximate analytical method for a special coil, and the results indicate that the equivalent conductivity is quite low. In the specific case of that reference, the

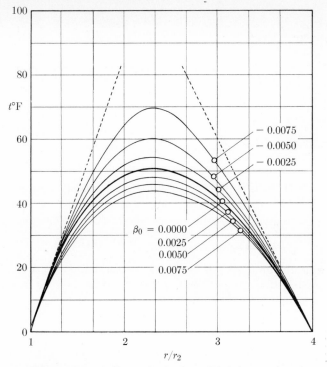

Fig. 8–14.   Effect of nonuniform thermal conductivity on the temperature distribution in a coil of hollow circular profile.

equivalent conductivity was only 3.7 times that of the silk insulation alone, even though the ratio of the conductivities for copper and silk is nearly 2400.   Copper in its pure state exhibits a negative temperature coefficient of $\beta_0 = -0.00023/°F$.   Silk apparently has little or no temperature dependency, and as such it appears that the equivalent thermal conductivity for the actual coil (predominately influenced by the insulation) is one which varies only slightly with temperature.   If this variation is an inverse one ($+\beta_0$), then maximum coil temperatures computed with k_0 will be overestimated, with the end result of underestimating the maximum admissible electrical loading for the coil.

8–9 Coil of solid rectangular profile.   We now examine the important case of a coil with a solid rectangular profile, as in Fig. 8–15.   Let the thermal conductivity be uniform as k, and once again assume linear heat generation $q_0''' (1 + \alpha_0 t)$.   The analytical treatment with arbitrary boundary temperatures is possible but prohibitively cumbersome.   Instead we develop the solution for the practical case investigated by Higgins (4) of uniform boundary temperature t_1 on all four edges, as in Fig. 8–15.

Following Higgins' analysis, we identify the temperature field $t(x,y)$ as that solution which satisfies the partial-differential equation

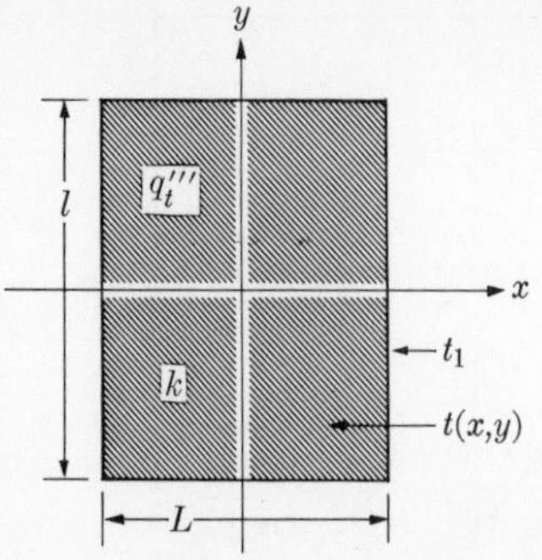

$$\frac{\partial^2 t}{\partial x^2} + \frac{\partial^2 t}{\partial y^2} + a + bt = 0, \quad (8\text{-}31)$$

and the boundary conditions

$$t = .t_1 \quad \text{at } x = \pm \frac{L}{2},$$

$$\qquad\qquad\qquad\qquad (8\text{-}32)$$

$$t = t_1 \quad \text{at } y = \pm \frac{l}{2}.$$

Fig. 8–15. Coil of solid rectangular profile.

Primitive product solutions $t = XY$ of (8–31), where $X = X(x)$ and $Y = Y(y)$, are easily found to be linear combinations of sines and cosines as

$$(\sin \mu x + \cos \mu x)(\sin \eta y + \cos \eta y).$$

However, due to the observed symmetry of the temperature field in this case as $t(x,y) = t(-x,-y)$, the required solution can be made up of even functions only, i.e., a double Fourier series in cosines alone (Article 5–5). The allowable form of the solution is therefore

$$t = C_0 + \sum_{i=1}^{\infty} \sum_{j=1}^{\infty} C_{ij} \cos \mu_i x \cos \eta_j y. \qquad (8\text{-}33)$$

Here the separation constants μ_i and η_j must be

$$\left.\begin{aligned} \mu_i &= \frac{\pi}{L}(2i - 1) \\[2mm] \eta_j &= \frac{\pi}{l}(2j - 1) \end{aligned}\right\} \quad i = j = 1, 2, 3, \cdots,$$

and evidently $C_0 = t_1$ if (8–33) is to satisfy (8–32). This exhausts our supply of boundary conditions, and we have yet to evaluate the coefficients C_{ij}.

In Article 5–5 we developed the coefficients in a double Fourier sine-series expansion of the arbitrary function $f(x,y)$ as (5–12), and we now employ the same method for evaluating the C_{ij} of the double Fourier cosine series contained in (8–33). In this case the function to be expanded is found by substituting (8–33) in (8–31). Thus with

$$\frac{\partial^2 t}{\partial x^2} = -\sum_{i=1}^{\infty} \sum_{j=1}^{\infty} C_{ij}\mu_i^2 \cos \mu_i x \cos \eta_j y,$$

and

$$\frac{\partial^2 t}{\partial y^2} = -\sum_{i=1}^{\infty} \sum_{j=1}^{\infty} C_{ij}\eta_j^2 \cos \mu_i x \cos \eta_j y,$$

we have

$$a + bt_1 = \sum_{i=1}^{\infty} \sum_{j=1}^{\infty} C_{ij}(\mu_i^2 + \eta_j^2 - b) \cos \mu_i x \cos \eta_j y.$$

Multiplying both sides of the above expansion by $\cos \mu_p x \cos \eta_q y$ and integrating between $x = L/2$ and $y = l/2$ leads to

$$(a + bt_1) \int_0^{L/2} \int_0^{l/2} \cos \mu_p x \cos \eta_q y \, dx dy$$

$$= \sum_{i=1}^{\infty} \sum_{j=1}^{\infty} C_{ij}(\mu_i^2 + \eta_j^2 - b) \int_0^{L/2} \int_0^{l/2} \cos \mu_i x \cos \mu_p x \cos \eta_i y \cos \eta_q y \, dx dy.$$

But if $p \neq i$ and $q \neq j$, all the integrals on the right side vanish (Article 5–5), and if $p = i$ and $q = j$, then for the double integral on the left side,

$$\int_0^{L/2} \cos \mu_i x \, dx = -\frac{1}{\mu_i} \sin \mu_i x \Big]_0^{L/2} = \frac{(-1)^i}{\mu_i}, \quad \int_0^{l/2} \cos \eta_j y \, dy = \frac{(-1)^j}{\eta_j},$$

and for the double integral on the right side,

$$\int_0^{L/2} \cos^2 \mu_i x \, dx = \frac{x}{2} + \frac{1}{4\mu_i} \sin 2\mu_i x \Big]_0^{L/2} = \frac{L}{4}, \quad \int_0^{l/2} \cos^2 \eta_j y \, dy = \frac{l}{4}.$$

This gives us the C_{ij} as

$$C_{ij} = \frac{16(a + bt_1)(-1)^{i+j}}{Ll\mu_i\eta_j(\mu_i^2 + \eta_j^2 - b)},$$

and therewith, according to (8–33), the final solution

$$\frac{t - t_1}{(1/\alpha_0) + t_1} = \frac{16b}{Ll} \sum_{i=1}^{\infty} \sum_{j=1}^{\infty} \frac{(-1)^{i+j}}{\mu_i\eta_j(\mu_i^2 + \eta_j^2 - b)} \cos \mu_i x \cos \eta_j y. \quad (8\text{–}34)$$

Higgins (4) determines an alternate form of (8–34) which is easier to compute by:

$$\frac{t - t_1}{(1/\alpha_0) + t_1} = \frac{\cos \sqrt{b}\, x}{\cos \sqrt{b}\, (L/2)} - \frac{4b}{L} \sum_{i=1}^{\infty} \frac{(-1)^{i-1} \cos \mu_i x \cosh \sqrt{\mu_i^2 - b}\, y}{\mu_i(\mu_i^2 - b) \cosh \sqrt{\mu_i^2 - b}\, (l/2)} - 1.$$

$$(8\text{–}35)$$

Then for the maximum temperature occurring at $x = y = 0$, we have

$$\frac{t_{max} - t_1}{(1/\alpha_0) + t_1} = \sec \frac{\psi_1}{2} - \frac{4}{\pi} \psi_1^2 \sum_{i=1}^{\infty}$$

$$\times \frac{(-1)^{i-1}}{(2i-1)[\pi^2(2i-1)^2 - \psi_1^2] \cosh(\psi_2/2) \sqrt{\dfrac{\pi^2}{\psi_1^2}(2i-1)^2 - 1}} - 1, \quad (8\text{–}36)$$

where now $\psi_1 = \sqrt{b}\, L$ and $\psi_2 = \sqrt{b}\, l$.

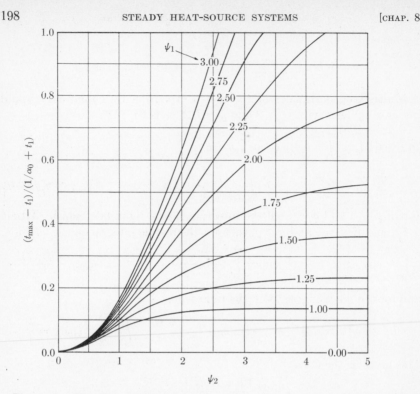

Fig. 8–16. First-term approximation to the maximum temperature in a coil of solid rectangular profile.

The maximum temperature in a rectangular coil is shown in Fig. 8–16, the calculation of these curves being based on the first term ($i = 1$) of the series solution (8–36). The convergence of this series is rapid enough to make this a fairly close approximation for $\psi < 1$ and a very close approximation for $\psi > 1$.

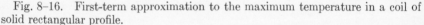

EXAMPLE 8–5. Jakob (2) and Higgins (4) give data from electrical-coil experiments by Rogowski and Vieweg. In one of these experiments, concerned with a toroidal coil of square profile 4.4×4.4 cm, the profile surface was essentially isothermal at a measured temperature of $t_1 = 76.1°C$, and the maximum profile temperature was recorded as $t_{max} = 122.4°C$. Higgins takes the Joulean heat generation as the linear function $q_0'''(1 + \alpha_0 t)$, and then computes the heat release at $t = 0$ as $q_0''' = 0.1207$ watt/cm^3 and selects the temperature coefficient $\alpha_0 = 0.00423/°C$. Jakob computes an equivalent uniform thermal conductivity (Article 8–8) as $k = 0.00531$ watt/cm-°C. Check the experimentally recorded t_{max} in this coil with an exact analytical solution.

Solution. In this case $\psi_1 = \psi_2 = L(q_0'''\alpha_0/k)^{1/2} = 4.4(0.1207 \times 0.00423/ 0.00531)^{1/2} = 1.363$, and entering Fig. 8–16 with these values, we find that

$$\frac{t_{\max} - t_1}{(1/\alpha_0) + t_1} \doteq 0.15.$$

This gives $t_{\max} = 0.15(236.2 + 76.1) + 76.1 = 122.9°C$, which is in close agreement with the recorded value of $t_{\max} = 122.4°C$.

8–10 Coil temperatures by the numerical method. The numerical method for distributed heat sources is similar to that illustrated for local sources in Article 8–3, except that now the network nodal points need not be located at predetermined points. Each subregion is now thought of as generating or absorbing the same quantity of heat, and therefore each nodal point will contain a generation or absorption term which may or may not be a function of local nodal temperature. Thus for a network of n nodal points

$$\bar{q}_1' = q_{t_1}'''V_1 + \sum_{\mathrm{I}} K_{\mathrm{I}1}(t_{\mathrm{I}} - t_1),$$

$$\bar{q}_2' = q_{t_2}'''V_2 + \sum_{\mathrm{II}} K_{\mathrm{II}2}(t_{\mathrm{II}} - t_2),$$

.

.

.

$$\bar{q}_n' = q_{t_n}'''V_n + \sum_{\sigma} K_{\sigma n}(t_{\sigma} - t_n). \tag{8–37}$$

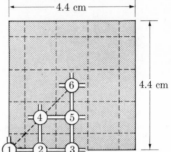

Fig. 8–17.   Numerical network for a coil of solid square profile.

EXAMPLE 8–6.   Obtain a corresponding numerical solution for $t_{\max}$ in the coil of Example 8–5.

Solution. Let the 4.4 cm² profile area be subdivided as in Fig. 8–17. With uniform surface temperatures we need consider only one-eighth of the square profile, and with the square network chosen, $K_{ji} = k$ and $q_0'''V_i = 0.1207(1.1)^2 = 0.146$ watt. Then $q_{t_i}'''V_i = 0.146(1 + 0.00423t_i)$, and a residual equation for a typical nodal point such as ④ reads

$$\bar{q}_4 = 2t_2 + 2t_5 + \frac{0.146}{0.00531} - \left(4 - \frac{0.146 \times 0.00423}{0.00531}\right)t_4.$$

In like manner, the three required residual equations appear as

$$\bar{q}_4 = 2t_2 \qquad + 2t_5 + 27.5 - 3.884t_4,$$

$$\bar{q}_5 = \quad t_3 + 2t_4 + \quad t_6 + 27.5 - 3.884t_5, \tag{8–38}$$

$$\bar{q}_6 = \qquad 4t_5 \qquad + 27.5 - 3.884t_6.$$

The relaxation of (8–38) is carried out in Table 8–3 to the nearest $\frac{1}{2}°C$.

TABLE 8–3

RELAXATION OF RESIDUAL EQUATIONS (8–38)

$\bar{q}_4$	t_4	$\bar{q}_5$	t_5	$\bar{q}_6$	t_6
179.7	0.0	103.6	0.0	27.5	0.0
−388.4	100.0	200.0			
−208.7	100.0	303.6			
220.0		−427.0	110.0	440.0	
11.3		−123.4	110.0	467.5	
		120.0		−466.0	120.0
		−3.4		1.5	120.0
−13.6	3.5	7.0			
−2.3	103.5	3.6			
3.0		−5.8	1.5	6.0	
0.7		−2.2	111.5	7.5	
		2.0		−7.8	2.0
		−0.2		−0.3	122.0

If the end temperatures in Table 8–3 are correct, then the heat generated in the internal subregions should just balance the heat transferred to all four edges:

$$\sum q_0'''(1 + \alpha_0 t) = \sum K\Delta t$$

$$
\begin{array}{l|l}
4 \times 0.146(1 + 0.00423 \times 103.5) & 8 \times 0.00531(103.5 - 76.1) \\
+ \, 4 \times 0.146(1 + 0.00423 \times 111.5) & + \, 4 \times 0.00531(111.5 - 76.1) \\
+ \, 1 \times 0.146(1 + 0.00423 \times 122.0) &
\end{array}
$$

$$1.920 \text{ watt} \doteq 1.917 \text{ watt.}$$

The maximum temperature in this coil, computed by the numerical method, is thus $t_{max} = 122.0°C$ to the nearest $\frac{1}{2}°C$. This result is in substantial agreement with the experimentally measured value of 122.4°C and the exact analytical value of 122.9°C, despite the relatively crude network chosen.

EXAMPLE 8–7. A coil of hollow square profile, 4″ on a side and with walls 1″ thick, is exposed to ambient air at 80°F and cooled internally by a forced gas flow at a mean temperature of 120°F. The outer unit surface conductance is 6 Btu/hr-ft²-°F, and the inner unit surface conductance is four times this value. Let $k = 1$ Btu/hr-ft-°F, $q_0''' = 86.4$ Btu/hr-ft³, and $\alpha_0 = 0.002/°F$, and then determine the temperature field in the coil by the numerical method.

Solution. We consider two cases. In Case (a) let a number of such coils be in contact with each other, as found in a high-output generator. With this arrangement the contact surfaces are to be considered as adiabatic. In Case (b) let the coils be separated so that all outer surfaces are exposed to ambient air.

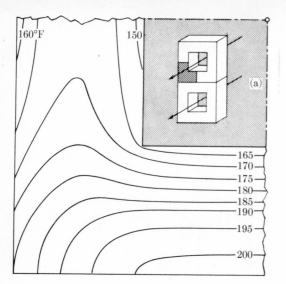

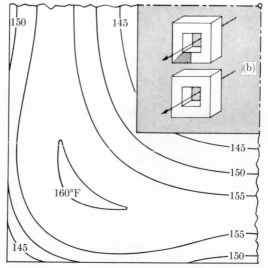

Fig. 8–18.   Temperature fields in internally cooled coils of hollow square profile.

The relaxation of these systems is left here as an exercise in problem 8–18, the results to be checked against the fields shown in Fig. 8–18. Note that the favorable effects of internal cooling are much more pronounced in Case (b), where the maximum coil temperature is depressed to somewhat over 160°F, while the maximum coil temperature in Case (a) is well over 200°F.

EXAMPLE 8–8. To compare numerical results with an exact solution for circular geometry, consider the coil of solid circular profile dissipating heat to an ambient gas, as in Article 8–6. Let $k = 1$ Btu/hr-ft-°F, $q_0''' = 10^4$ Btu/hr-ft³,

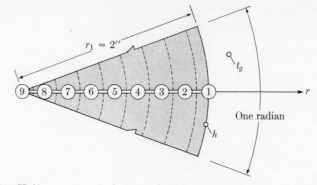

Fig. 8–19. Uniform numerical network for a coil of solid circular profile.

TABLE 8–4

TABULATION OF CONDUCTANCES AND VOLUMES

$K_{1g} = 2.5$	$144V_1 = 0.3347$
$K_{21} = 7.5$	$144V_2 = 0.4375$
$K_{32} = 6.5$	$144V_3 = 0.3750$
$K_{43} = 5.5$	$144V_4 = 0.3125$
$K_{54} = 4.5$	$144V_5 = 0.2500$
$K_{65} = 3.5$	$144V_6 = 0.1875$
$K_{76} = 2.5$	$144V_7 = 0.1250$
$K_{87} = 1.5$	$144V_8 = 0.0625$
$K_{98} = 0.5$	$144V_9 = 0.0781$

TABLE 8–5

EXACT AND NUMERICAL TEMPERATURES IN CIRCULAR COIL

r/r_1	Exact	Numerical	% Error
1	61.09	61	−0.15
$\frac{7}{8}$	79.05	79	−0.06
$\frac{6}{8}$	94.76	95	0.25
$\frac{5}{8}$	108.13	108	−0.12
$\frac{4}{8}$	119.20	119	−0.17
$\frac{3}{8}$	127.73	128	0.21
$\frac{2}{8}$	133.86	134	0.11
$\frac{1}{8}$	137.56	138	0.32
0	138.82	139	0.13

$\alpha_0 = 0.001/°F$, $h = 15$ Btu/hr-ft^2-°F, $t_g = 0°F$, and $r_1 = 2''$, and then compute the temperature distribution in the coil by the numerical method, checking the numerical results against a corresponding exact solution.

Solution. Suppose that temperatures at equal intervals of radius are desired, and then choose the natural subdivision shown in Fig. 8–19. Tabulating the conductances and volumes as in Table 8–4 leads to the nine required residual equations as

$$\bar{q}_1' = 2.5t_g + 7.5t_2 + 16.819 - 9.983t_1,$$

$$\bar{q}_2' = 7.5t_1 + 6.5t_3 + 30.382 - 13.970t_2,$$

$$\bar{q}_3' = 6.5t_2 + 5.5t_4 + 26.042 - 11.974t_3,$$

$$\bar{q}_4' = 5.5t_3 + 4.5t_5 + 21.702 - 9.978t_4,$$

$$\bar{q}_5' = 4.5t_4 + 3.5t_6 + 17.361 - 7.983t_5, \qquad (8\text{–}39)$$

$$\bar{q}_6' = 3.5t_5 + 2.5t_7 + 13.021 - 5.987t_6,$$

$$\bar{q}_7' = 2.5t_6 + 1.5t_8 + 8.681 - 3.991t_7,$$

$$\bar{q}_8' = 1.5t_7 + 0.5t_9 + 4.340 - 1.996t_8,$$

$$\bar{q}_9' = 0.5t_8 \qquad + 0.542 - 0.499t_9.$$

The exact solution for this case is given by (8–21) as

$$t = \frac{\left(t_g + \dfrac{1}{\alpha_0}\right)}{J_0(\psi_1) - \gamma J_1(\psi_1)} J_0(\psi) - \frac{1}{\alpha_0} = 1138.819 J_0(\psi) - 1000,$$

where $\gamma = \sqrt{q_0'''\alpha_0 k}/h$ and $\psi = \sqrt{q_0'''\alpha_0/k}\, r$. Table 8–5 lists the approximate numerical temperatures obtained through relaxation of the residual equations (8–39) to the nearest degree, and the corresponding exact temperatures computed from the above solution. It is apparent that these two solutions are nearly identical (5).

8–11 Method of successive numerical integration. In this article we consider the solution of the Poisson equation by direct numerical integration. With this method the characteristic differential equation is to be transformed into an equivalent *integral equation*, and the latter integrated by *successive numerical integration*. Such a technique is often useful when the differential equation in question cannot be integrated by formal means.

We illustrate by finding the temperature distribution in a plane plate of semithickness δ, and with uniform face temperatures t_1 at $x = \pm\delta$. If the plate generates linear nonuniform heat $q_t''' = q_0''' (1 + \alpha_0 t)$, then the exact solution (Problem 8–8) is given by

$$\frac{\alpha_0 t + 1}{\alpha_0 t_1 + 1} = \frac{\cos \sqrt{b}\, x}{\cos \sqrt{b}\, \delta}\,; \quad -\delta < x < \delta. \tag{8-40}$$

This solution satisfies the characteristic differential equation

$$\frac{d^2 T}{dx^2} + bT = 0, \tag{8-41}$$

where $T = a + bt$; $a = q_0'''/k$ and $b = q_0'''\alpha_0/k$.

Now consider the transformation of (8–41) into an equivalent integral equation. A first integration of (8–41) gives

$$\frac{dT}{dx} + b \int_0^x T\, dx + C_1 = 0,$$

and a second integration leads to

$$T = C_2 - \int_0^x \left(b \int_0^x T\, dx + C_1 \right) dx.$$

But in the present problem $dT/dx = 0$ at $x = 0$ because of temperature symmetry. Hence $C_1 = 0$, and the integral equation becomes

$$1 + \alpha_0 t = C_2 - \int_0^x \left[b \int_0^x (1 + \alpha_0 t)\, dx \right] dx. \tag{8-42}$$

The second integration constant C_2 can be adjusted so that $1 + \alpha_0 t = 1 + \alpha_0 t_1$ at $x = \delta$.

Since t appears on both sides of the integral equation (8–42), it is necessary to carry out the solution by *successive approximations*. This means that we can begin by selecting any function for t, and then numerically perform the indicated integration. This first *iteration* gives an improved function for t which we can then feed back into (8–42) for a second iteration, and so on. The successive solutions obtained in this way will usually converge after approximately three iterations.

The first numerical integration for this example is carried out with $q_0''' = 10^3$ Btu/hr-ft^3, $\alpha_0 = 10^{-3}/°$F, $k = 2$ Btu/hr-ft-°F, $\delta = 1$ ft, and $t_1 = 0°$F, so that $b = 0.5$. If we select an *initial trial function* of $^0t = t_1 = 0$, then the results for the first iteration, ^1t, are as shown in Table 8–6. The numerical integration is performed, in this case, by the simple *trapezoidal rule*, which approximates an area as a trapezoid:

$$\int_{x_i}^{x_j} f(x)\, dx = \frac{d}{2}\, (f_i + f_j); \quad d = (x_j - x_i).$$

Then with $1 + \alpha_0 t = 1$ at $x = \delta$, we have from Table 8–6, $1 = {}^1C_2 - 0.2500$, or $^1C_2 = 1.2500$. A second iteration $({}^2C_2 = 1.312)$, using the results of the first, is shown in Table 8–7, and in Fig. 8–20 we show how the successive approximations build up.   It is clear from Fig. 8–20 that a third iteration ($^3C_2 = 1.315$) very nearly converges to the exact solution.

TABLE 8–6

FIRST ITERATION FOR (8–42).

$$F_1 = \int_0^x (1 + \alpha_0 t)dx, \; F_2 = \int_0^x bF_1 dx$$

x	$(1 + \alpha_0^0 t)$	$^1F_1$	b^1F_1	$^1F_2$	$(1 + \alpha_0^1 t)$	^1t
0.0	1.0	0.0	0.00	0.0000	1.250	250
0.1	1.0	0.1	0.05	0.0025	1.248	248
0.2	1.0	0.2	0.10	0.0100	1.240	240
0.3	1.0	0.3	0.15	0.0225	1.228	228
0.4	1.0	0.4	0.20	0.0400	1.210	210
0.5	1.0	0.5	0.25	0.0625	1.188	188
0.6	1.0	0.6	0.30	0.0900	1.160	160
0.7	1.0	0.7	0.35	0.1225	1.128	128
0.8	1.0	0.8	0.40	0.1600	1.090	90
0.9	1.0	0.9	0.45	0.2025	1.048	48
1.0	1.0	1.0	0.50	0.2500	1.000	0

TABLE 8–7

SECOND ITERATION FOR (8–42).

x	$(1 + \alpha_0^1 t)$	$^2F_1$	b^2F_1	$^2F_2$	$(1 + \alpha_0^2 t)$	^2t
0.0	1.250	0.0000	0.0000	0.0000	1.312	312
0.1	1.248	0.1249	0.0624	0.0031	1.309	309
0.2	1.240	0.2493	0.1246	0.0125	1.300	300
0.3	1.228	0.3727	0.1864	0.0281	1.284	˙284
0.4	1.210	0.4946	0.2473	0.0498	1.262	262
0.5	1.188	0.6145	0.3072	0.0775	1.234	234
0.6	1.160	0.7319	0.3660	0.1112	1.201	201
0.7	1.128	0.8463	0.4232	0.1507	1.161	161
0.8	1.090	0.9572	0.4786	0.1958	1.116	116
0.9	1.048	1.0641	0.5320	0.2463	1.066	66
1.0	1.000	1.1665	0.5832	0.3121	1.000	0

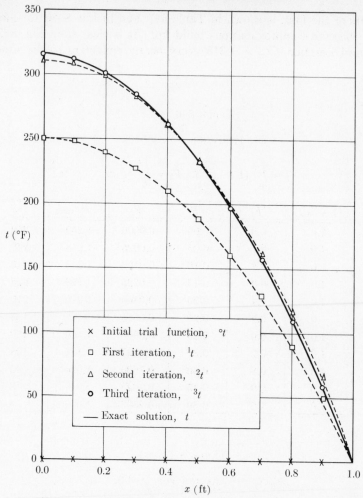

Fig. 8-20. Convergence of the successive numerical integrations.

The method of successive approximation is applicable in any case where the governing differential equation can be transformed into integral form. In a given case, more rapid convergence can be achieved by either selecting a better initial trial function or by predicting the course of succeeding iterations. The numerical integrations themselves are most conveniently handled by a desk calculator along with the trapezoidal rule and a subdivision interval of $d = 0.2$.

8–12 Temperature field in a nuclear reactor. As a second practical example of structures with distributed heat sources, we consider the modern system of an internally cooled nuclear reactor heated by fission and the

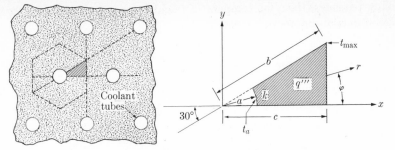

Fig. 8–21.   Distribution of cooling passages in a nuclear reactor.

radiation field within the reactor.   One of the important problems peculiar to such systems is the particularly high thermal stresses which result from large temperature gradients, and the study of these stresses depends, in turn, on knowledge of the temperature pattern within the solid portion of the reactor.

In some cases the heat development associated with fission can be regarded as a thermal source of uniform strength, while in all cases the mode of radiation heat generation represented by gamma-ray absorption must be considered as a complicated exponentially distributed source of heat.*

Consider, however, the fundamental case investigated by Fend $et\ al.$ (7), of a large, uniformly heated reactor having circular coolant holes distributed at the vertices of equilateral triangles, as in Fig. 8–21.   The uniform rate of heat generation in the solid is q''' Btu/hr-ft^3, and the conducting material is assumed to be of uniform thermal conductivity k.   Since the region has 30° symmetry, in Fig. 8–21 we need consider only the shaded area bounded by the adiabatic planes $\varphi = 0°$, $\varphi = 30°$, and $x = c$.   If, in addition, we consider only small coolant tubes, i.e., high-solidity systems for which $a \ll c$, then the temperature of the cooled walls $r = a$ can be taken as a uniform t_a, and this would correspond to the bulk temperature of the cooling fluid for zero inner-surface thermal resistance.

$Approximate\ solution\ in\ circular\ harmonics.$ No exact solution can be found for the temperature field in this region because all of the required boundary conditions cannot be simultaneously satisfied in both rectangular and circular coordinates.   For this reason we can obtain only an approximate solution in circular coordinates by first satisfying the isothermal boundary condition at $r = a$ and the adiabatic conditions at $\varphi = 0$ and 30°, and then attempting to satisfy the remaining adiabatic condition at $x = c$ by fixing $(\partial t / \partial x)_c = 0$ at several values of φ and assuming this condition for all other φ along $x = c$.

If the temperature gradient is zero along the reactor axis parallel to the

*The exponential absorption case has been investigated by Durham (6). (See problem 8–23.)

cooling passages, then the temperature field in question must satisfy the Poisson partial-differential equation

$$\frac{\partial^2 t}{\partial r^2} + \frac{1}{r}\frac{\partial t}{\partial r} + \frac{1}{r^2}\frac{\partial^2 t}{\partial \varphi^2} + \frac{q'''}{k} = 0,$$

which can be reduced, when in this form, to the convenient Laplace equation by the substitution $T = t + q'''r^2/4k$ as

$$\frac{\partial^2 T}{\partial r^2} + \frac{1}{r}\frac{\partial T}{\partial r} + \frac{1}{r^2}\frac{\partial^2 T}{\partial \varphi^2} = 0.$$

Now it was shown in Article 6–5 that this cylindrical form of Laplace's equation could be separated into the total-differential equations

$$r^2\frac{d^2 R}{dr^2} + r\frac{dR}{dr} - n^2 R = 0, \quad \text{and} \quad \frac{d^2 \Phi}{d\varphi^2} + n^2 \Phi = 0,$$

whose general solutions can be written down directly for both $n \neq 0$ and $n = 0$ as

$$R = C_1 r^n + C_2 r^{-n}; \qquad n \neq 0,$$

$$R = C_3 + C_4 \ln r; \qquad n = 0,$$

and

$$\Phi = C_5 \cos n\varphi + C_6 \sin n\varphi; \quad n \neq 0,$$

$$\Phi = C_7 \varphi + C_8; \qquad n = 0.$$

But as in all of our problems of temperature potential, t must be single-valued throughout the field. This means that n is integral and that C_7 must be zero if t is to remain the same when φ is increased by any multiple of 2π. An alternate form of (6–23) for the general solution of the Laplace equation in terms on nth-degree circular harmonics is therefore

$$T = (A_0 + B_0 \ln r) + \sum_{n=1}^{\infty} (A_n r^n + B_n r^{-n})(C_n \cos n\varphi + D_n \sin n\varphi).$$

$$(8\text{--}43)$$

The adiabatic conditions along the radial boundaries $\varphi = 0$ and $30°$ can now be satisfied by modifying the general solution (8–43) for conditions of symmetry. In this connection, note first that t must be periodic in each $\pi/3$; that is to say, the temperature must repeat itself in each $60°$ segment, and permissible eigenvalues are therefore $n = 0, 6, 12, \cdots$. Since t must also be an even function of φ, only the cosines are appropriate to the solution, whereby

$$t = A_0 + B_0 \ln r - \frac{q'''}{4k} r^2 + \sum_{n=1}^{\infty} (A_{6n} r^{6n} + B_{6n} r^{-6n}) \cos 6n\varphi;$$

$$n = 1, 2, 3, \cdots.$$

The constant B_0 can be evaluated by observing that the total heat generated in the 30° volume, $(3\sqrt{3}\, b^2/2 - \pi a^2)/12$, must leave this volume through the cylindrical surface $r = a$ between $\varphi = 0$ and 30°. Thus

$$\frac{q'''}{12}(3\sqrt{3}\, b^2/2 - \pi a^2) = \int_0^{\pi/6} k(ad\varphi)(\partial t/\partial r)_a = \frac{\pi}{6}(B_0 k - q'''a^2/2),$$

from which $B_0 = 3\sqrt{3}\, q'''b^2/4\pi k$. Then by observing the isothermal condition that $t = t_a$ at $r = a$, we can choose $A_{6n} = -B_{6n}a^{-12n}$ if we set $A_0 = t_a + q'''a^2/4k - B_0 \ln a$.

This puts the solution in the form

$$t = t_a + \frac{3\sqrt{3}\, q'''b^2}{4\pi k}\ln\frac{r}{a} - \frac{q'''}{4k}(r^2 - a^2) + \sum_{n=1}^{\infty} A_{6n}\left(\frac{r^{12n} - a^{12n}}{r^{6n}}\right)\cos 6n\varphi.$$

We now consider just two terms of this series solution and therewith satisfy the adiabatic condition along $x = c$ at only two points, φ_1 and φ_2. To do this we have to compute $\partial t/\partial x$ with $t = t(x,y)$ and in cylindrical coordinates $x = r\cos\varphi$ and $y = r\sin\varphi$. The partial derivatives (Article 1–4) of this composite function $t(x,y)$ are

$$\frac{\partial t}{\partial r} = \frac{\partial t}{\partial x}\frac{\partial x}{\partial r} + \frac{\partial t}{\partial y}\frac{\partial y}{\partial r} = \frac{\partial t}{\partial x}\cos\varphi + \frac{\partial t}{\partial y}\sin\varphi,$$

and

$$\frac{\partial t}{\partial\varphi} = \frac{\partial t}{\partial x}\frac{\partial x}{\partial\varphi} + \frac{\partial t}{\partial y}\frac{\partial y}{\partial\varphi} = \frac{\partial t}{\partial x}(-r\sin\varphi) + \frac{\partial t}{\partial y}r\cos\varphi.$$

Then by solving one of these for $\partial t/\partial y$ and substituting it in the other, we have for $\partial t/\partial x$

$$\frac{\partial t}{\partial x} = \cos\varphi\,\frac{\partial t}{\partial r} - \frac{\sin\varphi}{r}\frac{\partial t}{\partial\varphi}. \tag{8–44}$$

Thus, for the present case of $a \ll c$,

$$\frac{\partial t}{\partial x} = 6\sum_{n=1}^{\infty} nA_{6n}\left(\frac{\sqrt{3}\, b}{2\cos\varphi}\right)^{6n-1}\cos(6n-1)\varphi + \frac{q'''b}{2k}\left(\frac{3}{\pi}\cos^2\varphi - \frac{\sqrt{3}}{2}\right).$$

The values of A_6 and A_{12} are found from this by setting $\partial t/\partial x = 0$ at φ_1 and φ_2. Since the best choices of φ_1 and φ_2 are not known, we are at liberty to select arbitrarily, say, $\varphi_1 = 12°$ and $\varphi_2 = 30°$. Then from the two resulting equations,

$$6A_6\left(\frac{\sqrt{3}\, b}{2\cos 12°}\right)^5\cos 60° + 12A_{12}\left(\frac{\sqrt{3}\, b}{2\cos 12°}\right)^{11}\cos 132°$$

$$+ \frac{q'''b}{2k}\left(\frac{3}{\pi}\cos^2 12° - \frac{\sqrt{3}}{2}\right) = 0,$$

$$6A_6 \left(\frac{\sqrt{3}\,b}{2\cos 30°} \right)^5 \cos 150° + 12A_{12} \left(\frac{\sqrt{3}\,b}{2\cos 30°} \right)^{11} \cos 330°$$

$$+ \frac{q'''b}{2k} \left(\frac{3}{\pi} \cos^2 30° - \frac{\sqrt{3}}{2} \right) = 0,$$

we find the two unknowns A_6 and A_{12} as

$$A_6 = -0.02968\,(q'''/2kb^4) \quad \text{and} \quad A_{12} = -0.00042\,(q'''/2kb^{10}).$$

It is clear here that we might just as well have selected several other points, or even three or four such points. The selection of just two points means that we are using only two terms of the series solution, and that if we consider more points φ on $x = c$ then we are not only approaching the true adiabatic condition along $x = c$ but retaining a larger number of terms in the series solution as well.

The final approximate solution is therefore given by

$$\frac{t - t_a}{q'''b^2/k} = \frac{1}{4} \left[\frac{3\sqrt{3}}{\pi} \ln \left(\frac{r}{a} \right) - \left(\frac{r}{a} \right)^2 + \left(\frac{a}{b} \right)^2 \right] - 0.01484 \left(\frac{r}{b} \right)^6 \cos 6\varphi$$

$$- 0.00021 \left(\frac{r}{b} \right)^{12} \cos 12\varphi. \quad (8\text{--}45)$$

Note here that the cosine functions in this solution are simply correction terms for the corresponding solution $t = t(r)$ in a hollow cylinder of cross-sectional area equal to the actual hexagonal area in question, the outer radius of this approximating cylinder being $c = (3\sqrt{3}/2\pi)^{1/2}b$. This is shown in Fig. 8–22, along with the approximation obtained by taking either $c = b$ or $c = c$.

We now want to investigate just how closely the approximate solution (8–45) satisfies the adiabatic condition at points $x = c$ other than φ_1 and φ_2. Here, again, there is no criterion which tells us how small the gradient $\partial t/\partial x$ must be for this condition to be reasonably well satisfied. About the best we can do is to simply compare this gradient with the maximum temperature gradient in the segment given by (8–45) as $(k/q'''b)[(t_{\max} - t_a)/b]$. Thus, by computing $\partial t/\partial x$ in (8–44) from (8–45) as

$$\frac{k}{q'''b} \left(\frac{\partial t}{\partial x} \right) = \left(\frac{b}{r} \right) \cos\varphi \left[0.41348 - 0.5 \left(\frac{r}{b} \right)^2 - 0.08904 \left(\frac{r}{b} \right)^6 \cos 6\varphi \right.$$

$$\left. - 0.00252 \left(\frac{r}{b} \right)^{12} \cos 12\varphi \right] - \left(\frac{b}{r} \right) \sin\varphi \left[0.08904 \left(\frac{r}{b} \right)^6 \sin 6\varphi \right.$$

$$\left. + 0.00252 \left(\frac{r}{b} \right)^{12} \sin 12\varphi \right],$$

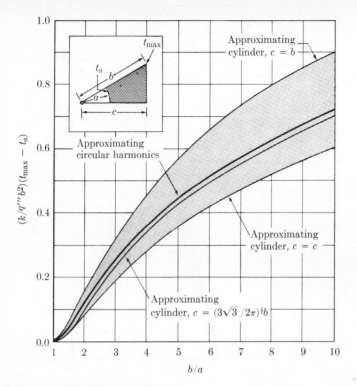

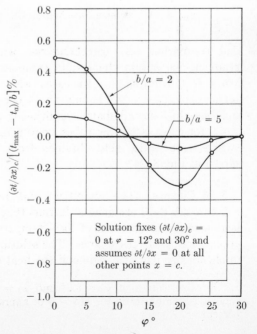

Fig. 8–22. Maximum temperature difference by various approximations.

Fig. 8–23. Percent error in series solution attempt to satisfy adiabatic condition at $x = c$.

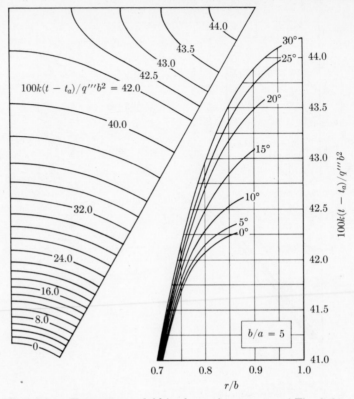

Fig. 8–24. Temperature field in the nuclear reactor of Fig. 8–21.

and comparing this percentagewise with the maximum temperature gradient, we obtain the results exhibited in Fig. 8–23. Evidently for $b/a = 5$ (corresponding to cases where $a \ll c$), the maximum ratio $(\partial t/\partial x)_c/[(t_{max} - t_a)/b]$ is only about one-tenth of one percent,* and this suggests that the adiabatic condition is quite well satisfied along all of $x = c$ for cases of cooling tubes small compared with tube spacing.

The temperature field obtained from an auxiliary plot of (8–45) is shown in Fig. 8–24.

8–13 Closure. The analytical and numerical solutions in Articles 8–5 through 8–10 are general in that they hold for any region developing heat as a linear function of local temperature as well as for the specific application to electrical coils. The solutions are appropriate, for instance, in chemically reacting regions if the heat of exothermic reaction increases

---

*Choosing values of $\varphi_1 = 8.2°$ and $\varphi_2 = 18°$, Fend (7) finds a somewhat smaller maximum ratio for $b/a = 5$ of approximately three-hundredths of one percent.

linearly with temperature. Cases of endothermic reactions involve the simple extension of replacing q_0''' by $-q_0'''$. Also of interest are cases where the temperature coefficient is negative $(-\alpha_0)$, and several such solutions are considered in problems 8–10 and 8–11. It is apparent that the form of the solution for distributed sources with $-\alpha_0$ will be the same as the form for distributed sinks with $+\alpha_0$. Likewise, the solution for sources with $+\alpha_0$ will have the same form as that for sinks with $-\alpha_0$.

The method of direct numerical integration used in Article 8–11 is especially valuable for finding particular solutions which must satisfy either linear or nonlinear differential equations. The method can be applied successfully in any case for which the differential equation is easily reducible to integral form.

The general problem of thermal stresses and shocks (transient state) in heat-generating plates has been studied in detail by Manson (8).

The method of approximately satisfying required boundary conditions, as used in the nuclear-reactor problem of Article 8–12, is one which has only recently come into wider use; it has general application to systems having both rectangular and circular boundaries.

REFERENCES

1. L. M. K. Boelter, F. E. Romie, A. G. Guibert, and M. A. Miller, "An Investigation of Aircraft Heaters, XXVII—Equations for Steady-State Temperature Distribution Caused by Thermal Sources in Flat Plates Applied to Calculation of Thermocouple Errors, Heat-Meter Corrections, and Heat Transfer by Pin-Fin Plates" (Univ. of Calif.), *NACA TN* No. 1452. Washington: August, 1948.

2. M. Jakob, "Influence of Nonuniform Development of Heat Upon the Temperature Distribution in Electrical Coils and Similar Heat Sources of Simple Form," *Trans. ASME*, Vol. 65, 1943, pp. 593–605.

3. C. M. Laffon, "Generator Coils Cooled Internally," *Westinghouse Engineer*, November, 1951.

4. T. J. Higgins, "Formulas for Calculating the Temperature Distribution in Electrical Coils of General Rectangular Cross Section," *Trans. ASME*, Vol. 66, 1944, pp. 665–670.

5. P. J. Schneider, "Temperature Fields in Electrical Coils—Numerical Solutions," *AIEE Communication and Electronics*, Jan., 1954.

6. F. P. Durham, "Optimum Heat Transfer for Minimum Thermal Stress in Nuclear-Reactor Shells," *ASME Preprint No. 54-A-126*, August, 1954.

7. F. A. Fend, E. M. Boroody, and J. C. Bell, "An Approximate Calculation of the Temperature Distribution Surrounding Coolant Holes in a Heat Generating Solid," *BMI-T-42*, USAEC Reference Branch, Technical Information Service, Oak Ridge.

8. S. V. Manson, "Temperatures, Thermal Stress, and Shock in Heat-Generating Plates of Constant Conductivity and of Conductivity that Varies Linearly with Temperature," *NACA TN* No. 2988. Washington: July, 1953.

PROBLEMS

8-1. A plane plate 0.15″ thick, and of thermal conductivity 20 Btu/hr-ft-°F, is exposed to an 1800°F gas on one face where the unit surface conductance is 20 Btu/hr-ft²-°F, and a 100°F gas on the other face where the unit surface conductance is estimated to be 10 Btu/hr-ft²-°F. The plate temperature is to be measured by a thermocouple fitted to the high-temperature face. Thermocouple lead wires are both #28 gage and of separate thermal conductivity 35.7 and 14.6 Btu/hr-ft-°F. The unit surface conductance over each lead wire wound with insulation 0.006″ thick, and of thermal conductivity 0.01 Btu/hr-ft-°F, is estimated to be 200 Btu/hr-ft²-°F. (a) Show that the ratio of plate to thermocouple conductance is 112. (b) Show that the conductance ratio K_1^t/K_2^t is 129. (c) Show that in the absence of the thermocouple the plate temperature would be 1233°F. (d) Show that the thermocouple overestimates the plate temperature by approximately 4°F.

8-2. Repeat problem 8-1 for an uninsulated thermocuple, assuming that the unit surface conductance for the bare wires is the same as for the insulated wires.

8-3. Plot a family of dimensionless curves on semilogarithmic coordinates for the simplified solution (8-7).

8-4. A local heat source in a thin infinite plate generates 1000 Btu/hr. If $\delta = 0.2''$, $k = 20$ Btu/hr-ft-°F, $h_1 = h_2 = 20$ Btu/hr-ft²-°F, and $t_1 = t_2 = 1000$°F, determine the temperature distribution in the plate by the numerical method, and check with temperatures computed by the exact solution (8-3).

8-5. An electrical coil of solid circular profile is partially submerged in an oil bath such that its boundary temperatures are

$$f(\varphi) = t_0 \quad \text{at } r = r_1 \text{ and } 45° < \varphi < 135°,$$

$$f(\varphi) = t_1 \quad \text{at } r = r_1 \text{ and } 135° < \varphi < 45°.$$

Find $t = t(r,\varphi)$.

8-6. A coil of solid circular profile has a uniform boundary temperature $t_1 = 100$°F. If $q_0''' = 5 \times 10^5$ Btu/hr-ft³, $\alpha_0 = 10^{-3}/$°F, $k = 10$ Btu/hr-ft-°F, and $r_1 = 1.2''$, show that (a) the maximum profile temperature is 252°F, (b) the profile temperature at $r/r_1 = 0.35$ is 231°F, and (c) the mean profile temperature is 175°F.

8-7. Show that the maximum temperature in the coil of Article 8-6 can be expressed dimensionlessly as

$$\frac{\alpha_0 t_{max} + 1}{\alpha_0 t_g + 1} = \frac{1}{J_0(\psi_1) - \gamma J_1(\psi_1)},$$

and graph a family of dimensionless maximum-temperature curves by this solution.

8-8. A plane plate of *semi*thickness δ and with uniform face temperatures t_1 generates linear nonuniform heat. If x is measured from the mid-plane of the plate, and if the plate is of infinite extent in the y- and z-directions, then show that the general temperature distribution within the plate is given by

$$\frac{\alpha_0 t + 1}{\alpha_0 t_1 + 1} = \frac{\cos \psi}{\cos \psi_1}.$$

8-9. With reference to the infinite plate in problem 8-8, (a) show that its mean temperature is given by

$$\frac{\alpha_0 \bar{t} + 1}{\alpha_0 t_1 + 1} = \frac{1}{\psi_1} \tan \psi_1.$$

(b) Show that its ratio of t above t_1 to t_{max} above t_1 is given by

$$\frac{t - t_1}{t_{max} - t_1} = \frac{\cos \psi - \cos \psi_1}{1 - \cos \psi_1}.$$

(c) Plot graphs of its general temperature given in problem 8-8, its mean temperature given in (a), and its temperature uniformity given in (b).

8-10. If the temperature coefficient in the infinite plate of problem 8-8 is negative $(-\alpha_0)$, then show that

(a) $(\alpha_0 t - 1)/(\alpha_0 t_1 - 1) = \cosh \psi / \cosh \psi_1$.

(b) $(\alpha_0 t - 1)/(\alpha_0 t_1 - 1) = \dfrac{1}{\psi_1} \tanh \psi_1$.

(c) $(t - t_1)/(t_{max} - t_1) = (\cosh \psi - \cosh \psi_1)/(1 - \cosh \psi_1)$.

8-11. If the temperature coefficient in the coil of solid circular profile in Example 8-3 is negative $(-\alpha_0)$, then show that

(a) $(\alpha_0 t - 1)/(\alpha_0 t_1 - 1) = I_0(\psi)/I_0(\psi_1)$.

(b) $(\alpha_0 \bar{t} - 1)/(\alpha_0 t_1 - 1) = \dfrac{2}{\psi_1} \dfrac{I_1(\psi_1)}{I_0(\psi_1)}$.

(c) $(t - t_1)/(t_{max} - t_1) = [I_0(\psi) - I_0(\psi_1)]/[1 - I_0(\psi_1)]$.

8-12. Show that changing the sign of the temperature coefficient α_0 for the coil in problem 8-6 has the effect of decreasing its maximum profile temperature by 19.4%, decreasing its mean temperature by 13.7%, and decreasing its temperature at $r/r_1 = 0.35$ by 17.8%.

8-13. Plot dimensionless graphs of the solutions obtained in problems 8-10 and 8-11.

8-14. A coil of hollow circular profile with $r_1 = 0.2'$ and $r_2 = r_1/2$ has uniform boundary temperatures $t_1 = 70°F$ and $t_2 = 110°F$. The coil is of uniform thermal conductivity $k = 10$ Btu/hr-ft-°F, and generates nonuniform Joulean heat $q''' = 10^6(1 + 10^{-3}t)$ Btu/hr-ft³. (a) Show that the temperature of a point halfway through the profile is 241°F. (b) Derive an expression for the mean profile temperature in a coil of hollow circular profile with uniform surface temperatures. (c) Show that the mean profile temperature in this coil is 186°F.

8-15. The coil in problem 8-14 develops uniform heat $q_0''' = 10^6$ Btu/hr-ft³, and surface temperatures are $t_1 = t_2 = 0°F$. (a) Show that the temperature of a point halfway through the profile is 63.5°F. (b) If this coil is of nonuniform thermal conductivity with $k_0 = 10$ Btu/hr-ft-°F and $\beta_0 = -0.005/°F$, then show that the halfway temperature in (a) is increased by 24.7%.

8-16. A coil of solid rectangular profile with $L = 3''$ and $l = 2''$ is of uniform

thermal conductivity $k = 10$ Btu/hr-ft-°F and has a uniform surface temperature of $t_1 = 100$°F. If the coil generates linear heat $q_t''' = 10^6(1 + 10^{-3}t)$ Btu/
hr-ft³, then show that its maximum profile temperature would be 484°F.

8–17. A coil of hollow rectangular profile has $k = 1$ Btu/hr-ft-°F, $q_0''' = 10^5$
Btu/hr-ft³, $\alpha_0 = 0.0025/$°F, and $t_1 = t_2 = 0$°F. Find t by the numerical method
for each nodal point shown in the network of Fig. 8–25, and compare with
the numerical results listed in Table 8–8.

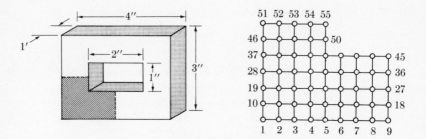

Fig. 8–25.   Numerical network for a coil of hollow rectangular profile.

TABLE 8–8

NUMERICAL TEMPERATURES IN HOLLOW RECTANGULAR COIL

i	t_i	i	t_i	i	t_i
11	48.0	23	116.5	35	79.5
12	72.5	24	111.5	36	79.0
13	82.0	25	109.0	38	82.5
14	82.5	26	107.0	39	115.5
15	81.5	27	106.5	40	93.5
16	80.8	29	81.5	47	81.5
17	79.5	30	121.0	48	112.0
18	79.5	31	121.0	49	85.5
20	72.5	32	94.0	52	81.0
21	110.5	33	86.5	53	110.5
22	121.5	34	81.5	54	83.5

8–18. Carry out the complete numerical solutions for the coil in Example
8–7, and check numerical temperatures against the fields plotted in Fig. 8–18.

8–19. Develop a numerical solution for the coil in problem 8–14, and compare
with the mid-point analytical temperature of 241°F.

8–20. Develop a numerical solution for the coil in (b) of problem 8–15, and
compare with the mid-point analytical temperature of 79.2°F.

8–21.   Calculate the temperature profile in the plate of Article 8–11 for the case
where $q_t''' = q_0''' (1 + \alpha_0 t^2)$.   Use the method of successive numerical integration.

8–22. Develop a numerical solution for the nuclear reactor in Article 8–12, and check numerical temperatures against the approximate analytical solution (8–45).

8–23. Consider the shell of a nuclear reactor as being a large plate of thickness δ and of uniform thermal conductivity k. The gamma-ray heating within the plate is assumed to vary exponentially with x as

$$q_x''' = q''\gamma e^{-\gamma x},$$

where q'' is the rate of heat liberation per unit area (Btu/hr-ft^2) and γ is defined as the mean radiation absorption coefficient (ft^{-1}). (a) Show that the general temperature distribution within the plate is given by

$$\frac{t - t_1}{q''/k\gamma} = 1 - \gamma x e^{-\gamma a} - e^{-\gamma x},$$

where t_1 is the face temperature at $x = 0$ and a is the distance from this face to the plane of zero temperature gradient within the plate. (b) If the tensile surface stress for the plate is a minimum when the face temperatures at $x = 0$ and $x = \delta$ are equal, then show that the value of a for this *optimum* condition is

$$a_{\text{opt}} = \frac{1}{\gamma} \ln\left(\frac{\gamma\delta}{1 - e^{-\gamma\delta}}\right).$$

(c) Show that the heat which must be removed from each A ft^2 of the plate faces for the minimum thermal stress condition is

$$\frac{q_{\text{opt}_0}}{q''A} = \frac{1}{\gamma\delta}(\gamma\delta + e^{-\gamma\delta} - 1),$$

and

$$\frac{q_{\text{opt}_\delta}}{q''A} = \frac{1}{\gamma\delta}[1 - (\gamma\delta + 1)e^{-\gamma\delta}].$$

(d) Plot the solutions in (c) for a range of the absorption parameter, $\gamma\delta$, from 0 to 10.

8–24. The normal thermal stress, σ_t (lb/ft^2), associated with an asymmetric one-dimensional temperature profile in a plate is given by

$$\frac{(1 - \gamma)}{E\epsilon}\sigma_t = -t + \frac{1}{\delta}\int_{-\delta/2}^{\delta/2} t\,dx + \frac{12x}{\delta^3}\int_{-\delta/2}^{\delta/2} tx\,dx; \quad \frac{-\delta}{2} < x < \frac{\delta}{2},$$

where γ is Poisson's ratio, E is the modulus of elasticity (lb/ft^2), and ϵ is the coefficient of linear thermal expansion (ft/ft $-$ °f) for the plate material. Calculate and plot the inner-surface (tensile), midplane (compressive), and outer-surface (tensile) thermal stress in the plate of problem 8–23, for a range of $\gamma\delta$ from 0 to 10.

CHAPTER 9

STEADY POROUS SYSTEMS

In this chapter we consider a few structures which are constructed of porous materials and cooled by forcing a liquid or gas through the pores of the solid material.

9–1 Introduction. Porous materials have become increasingly attractive for application in such structures as high-temperature heat exchangers, conduits for transporting high-temperature fluids, turbine blades, rocket nozzles, and the like. These applications are chiefly stimulated by the lack of commercially available materials suitable for sustained operation at elevated temperatures, and the general inadequacy of the more familiar types of cooling in which a solid is in contact with a cooling fluid on only one or more of its face surfaces. In practice, the cooling of porous structures is accomplished by forcing a liquid or gas through the capillary passages of the solid material. With this type of solid-fluid heat exchange, which we shall refer to here as *porous cooling*, the specimen is maintained at a low temperature because it is essentially flooded with the coolant, and therefore a larger proportion of the cooling fluid is in wetted contact with the solid than is possible when the coolant is in contact with only the face or free surfaces of the structure.

The process of solid-fluid heat transfer represented by porous cooling is understandably complex. For purposes of analysis we replace the actual heterogeneous network of pores by a simple equivalent system consisting of identical and parallel cylindrical passages or channels which serve to transport the coolant through the porous structure. We also assume that all heat conducted in the interior of the specimen takes place in the solid portion only. Weinbaum and Wheller (1) have demonstrated on the basis of these assumptions that solid and coolant temperatures are nearly indistinguishable throughout the porous structure. This is a very important result, in that the analysis considered here is greatly simplified if solid and coolant temperatures within the specimen are assumed equal.

9–2 Porous-cooled plate. Consider a plane nongenerating plate of uniform thermal conductivity k_w, as in Fig. 9–1. Here the high-temperature face at $x = \delta$ is at a known temperature t_2, and the coolant forced through the plate in the positive x-direction is at a known temperature t_0' at $x = -\infty$. The mass velocity of fluid coolant (product of its specific weight in lb/ft^3 and its velocity in ft/hr) approaching the plate is taken as

G lb/hr-ft^2, its uniform thermal capacity as C Btu/lb-°F, and its uniform thermal conductivity as k_f. With a plate of large dimensions in the y- and z-directions, the temperature within the plate is effectively one-dimensional as $t(x)$, $0 \le x \le \delta$, as is the temperature in the approaching fluid as $t'(x)$, $-\infty \le x \le 0$.

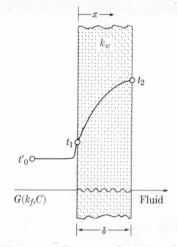

Fig. 9–1.　Porous cooling of a plane plate.

The *porosity P* of a porous specimen is defined as the ratio of pore volume to total volume of material. This is equivalent to saying that if we consider a unit area of the plate normal to the flow, then the area for fluid flow within the plate is $A_f = P$, and the solid area for heat conduction is $A_c = 1 - A_f = 1 - P$. Note also that if the mass velocity of the approaching fluid is G, then the mass velocity within the plate is G/P.

The mechanism of porous heat exchange is now identified as being made up of two components. The first component is conduction within the solid as $-k_w A_c dt/dx$, or in terms of a differential unit-area increment of the plate,

$$q_x = -k_w(1 - P)\frac{dt}{dx},$$

and

$$q_{x+dx} = -k_w(1 - P)\frac{d}{dx}\left(t + \frac{dt}{dx}dx\right).$$

The second component is the solid-fluid heat exchange which raises the coolant temperature by $dt = dq/(G/P)A_f C$. This heat exchange is thus $dq = GCdt$, and since this must be supplied by the difference in conducted heat $q_x - q_{x+dx}$, we have

$$-k_w(1 - P)\frac{dt}{dx} + k_w(1 - P)\left(\frac{dt}{dx} + \frac{d^2t}{dx^2}dx\right) = GCdt.$$

The differential equation which must be satisfied by the plate temperature t is therefore

$$\frac{d^2t}{dx^2} - \xi_w\frac{dt}{dx} = 0; \quad 0 \le x \le \delta, \tag{9–1}$$

if the parameter $\xi_w(1/\text{ft})$ is defined by

$$\xi_w = \frac{GC}{k_w(1 - P)} \cdot$$

A similar heat balance in the region $-\infty \le x \le 0$ gives the differential equation which must be satisfied by the temperature t' of the approaching fluid as

$$\frac{d^2t'}{dx^2} - \xi_f \frac{dt'}{dx} = 0, \tag{9-2}$$

where

$$\xi_f = \frac{GC}{k_f} \cdot$$

The general solution of (9–1) is

$$t = C_1 e^{\xi_w x} + C_2,$$

from which the particular plate solution satisfying the boundary conditions

$$t = t_1 \quad \text{at } x = 0, \qquad t = t_2 \quad \text{at } x = \delta,$$

follows directly as

$$t = t_1 + \frac{(t_2 - t_1)}{(e^{\xi_w \delta} - 1)} (e^{\xi_w x} - 1); \quad 0 \le x \le \delta. \tag{9-3}$$

In like manner, the general solution of (9–2) is

$$t' = C_3 e^{\xi_f x} + C_4,$$

and this is to satisfy the fluid boundary conditions

$$t' = t_0' \qquad \qquad \text{at } x = -\infty,$$

$$k_f \frac{dt'}{dx} = k_w(1 - P)\frac{dt}{dx} \quad \text{at } x = 0,$$

the latter condition requiring that the heat gained by the fluid at $x = 0$ must equal that lost by the plate at its free surface $x = 0$. The particular fluid solution is therefore

$$t' = t_0' + \frac{(t_2 - t_1)}{(e^{\xi_w \delta} - 1)} e^{\xi_f x}; \quad -\infty \le x \le 0. \tag{9-4}$$

The boundary temperature t_1 can now be eliminated from (9–3) by noting its value from (9–4) as $t_1 = t_1' = t_0' + (t_2 - t_0')e^{-\xi_w \delta}$. This gives the final solution for the temperature distribution in the porous plate as

$$\frac{t - t_0'}{t_2 - t_0'} = e^{-\xi_w \delta(1 - x/\delta)}; \quad 0 \le x \le \delta. \tag{9-5}$$

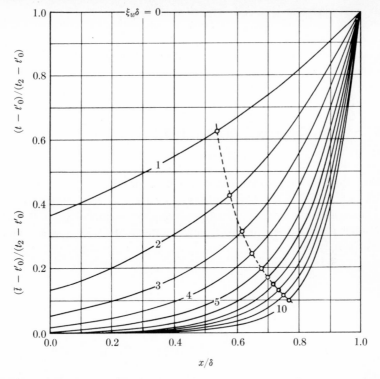

Fig. 9–2.   Temperature distribution and mean temperature in a porous plate.

The mean temperature in the plate is calculated from the integral $\bar{t} = \dfrac{1}{\delta} \displaystyle\int_0^\delta t\, dx$ as

$$\frac{\bar{t} - t_0'}{t_2 - t_0'} = \frac{1}{\xi_w \delta}\,(1 - e^{-\xi_w \delta}); \quad 0 \le x \le \delta. \tag{9–6}$$

The general temperature profile according to (9–5) and mean temperature according to (9–6) in a porous-cooled plate are displayed in Fig. 9–2.

9–3 Generating porous-cooled plate.   As an extension of the non-generating plate in Article 9–2, we now consider a plane semi-infinite porous plate which generates uniform distributed heat in amount q''' Btu/hr-ft^3,* the plate being insulated at $x = \delta$. In this case only the differential equation for the plate temperature is altered, since in a differential unit-area increment we have heat generated in amount $q'''(1 - P)dx$. Thus

---

*This case has been investigated by Green (2).

$$\frac{d^2t}{dx^2} - \xi_w \frac{dt}{dx} + \frac{q'''}{k_w} = 0, \qquad (9\text{--}7)$$

and again (9–2) for the approaching fluid. The general solution of (9–7) becomes

$$t = C_1 e^{\xi_w x} + \frac{q'''(1 - P)}{GC} x + C_2, \qquad (9\text{--}8)$$

and, as before, the general solution of (9–2) is

$$t' = C_3 e^{\xi_f x} + C_4. \qquad (9\text{--}9)$$

Now the total temperature rise which the fluid experiences is evidently $q'''(1 - P)\delta/GC = \zeta$. The fluid temperature at $x = \delta$ is therefore $t_0' + \zeta$, and since the fluid and plate temperatures are assumed equal, $0 \le x \le \delta$, this must also be the unknown plate temperature t_2 at $x = \delta$. Then for $t(x)$ to satisfy

$$t = t_1 \qquad \text{at } x = 0,$$

$$t = t_2 = t_0' + \zeta \quad \text{at } x = \delta,$$

the plate temperature by (9–8) must read

$$t = t_1 + \frac{(t_1 - t_0')}{(1 - e^{\xi_w \delta})} (e^{\xi_w x} - 1) + \zeta \frac{x}{\delta}; \quad 0 \le x \le \delta, \qquad (9\text{--}10)$$

and for $t'(x)$ to satisfy

$$t' = t_0' \qquad \text{at } x = -\infty,$$

$$k_f \frac{dt'}{dx} = k_w 1 - P \frac{dt}{dx} \quad \text{at } x = 0,$$

the fluid temperature by (9–9) must read

$$t' = t_0' + \left[\frac{t_1 - t_0'}{1 - e^{\xi_w \delta}} + \frac{q''' k_w (1 - P)^2}{(GC)^2} \right] e^{\xi_f x}; \quad -\infty \le x \le 0. \quad (9\text{--}11)$$

Finally, by eliminating t_1 from both (9–10) and (9–11), we have for the plate and fluid temperature solutions

$$\frac{t - t_0'}{\zeta} = \frac{1}{\xi_w \delta} [1 - e^{-\xi_w \delta(1 - x/\delta)}] + \frac{x}{\delta}; \quad 0 \le x \le \delta, \qquad (9\text{--}12)$$

and

$$\frac{t' - t_0'}{\zeta} = \frac{1}{\xi_w \delta} (1 - e^{\xi_w \delta}) e^{\xi_f \delta (x/\delta)}; \quad -\infty \le x \le 0, \qquad (9\text{--}13)$$

where $\zeta = q'''(1 - P)\delta/GC$.

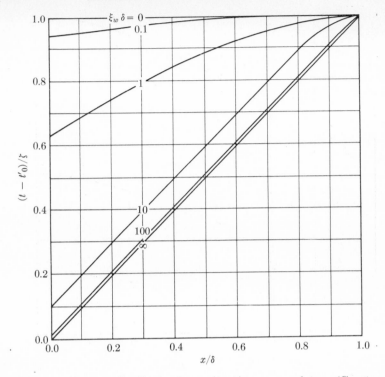

Fig. 9–3.   Temperature distribution in a generating porous plate.   (Courtesy of L. Green, Jr.)

The solution (9–12) predicts that for large mass velocities $G \to \infty$, the plate temperature approaches the upstream coolant temperature t'_0, as expected. This is also seen to occur for large thermal capacities $C \to \infty$ and small rates of heat generation $q''' \to 0$. It is also of interest to note that under the single condition of small plate thermal conductivity $k_w \to 0$, the plate temperature t approaches the simple linear function $(t - t'_0)/\zeta = x/\delta$. This is graphically illustrated in the temperatures curves of Fig. 9–3, as computed by Green (2). The actual temperature profiles in both the cooling fluid and porous generating plate can only be visualized by way of example. Figure 9–4 shows such representative temperature profiles as computed by Green (2) for a $\frac{1}{2}''$ thick porous graphite plate of thermal conductivity $k_w = 9.3 \times 10^{-4}$ Btu/sec-in.-°F, and generating $q''' = 10$ Btu/sec-in.^{3}. The plate is cooled by helium gas for which $k_f = 1.89 \times 10^{-4}$ Btu/sec-in.-°F and $C = 1.25$ Btu/lb-°F.

Since the exit surface temperature t_2 need not be specified in the case of a generating porous plate, it is of interest to determine the conditions under which the temperature difference across the plate is a maximum. This temperature difference,

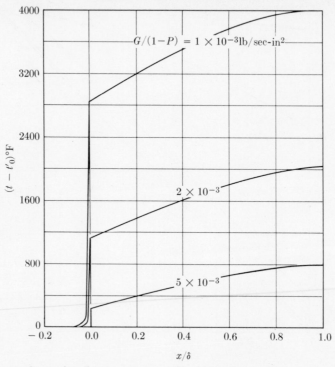

Fig. 9–4.   Gas and wall temperature-profiles in a helium-cooled generating porous plate.   (Courtesy of L. Green, Jr.)

$$t_2 - t_1 = \zeta \left[1 - \frac{1}{\xi_w \delta} (1 - e^{-\xi_w \delta}) \right] = \frac{F(G)}{f(G)},$$

is evidently a maximum when $G = 0$, and since the limiting value of $F(G)/f(G)$ as $G \to 0$ is

$$\lim_{G \to 0} \frac{F(G)}{f(G)} = \lim_{G \to 0} \frac{d^2 F(G)/dG^2}{d^2 f(G)/dG^2} = \lim_{G \to 0} \frac{q''' \delta^2}{2k_w} e^{-\frac{C\delta}{k_w(1-P)} G},$$

the maximum temperature difference must be

$$(t_2 - t_1)_{\max} = \frac{q''' \delta^2}{2k_w} .   \tag{9–14}$$

In the case of a generating porous plate, the mean temperature is found from (9–12) to be

$$t = \frac{1}{\delta} \int_0^\delta t\, dx = t_0' + \frac{\zeta}{\xi_w \delta} - \frac{\zeta}{(\xi_w \delta)^2} (1 - e^{-\xi_w \delta}) + \frac{\zeta}{2},$$

or

$$\frac{\bar{t} - t_0'}{\zeta} = \frac{1}{(\xi_w \delta)^2} (\xi_w \delta + e^{-\xi_w \delta} - 1) + \tfrac{1}{2},   \tag{9–15}$$

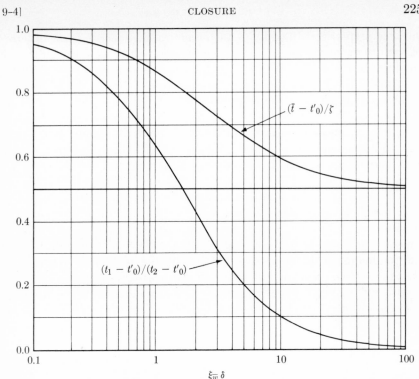

Fig. 9–5. Mean temperature and temperature uniformity in a generating porous plate.

and uniformity of the plate temperature follows directly as

$$\frac{t_1 - t'_0}{t_2 - t'_0} = \frac{1}{\xi_w \delta} \left(1 - e^{-\xi_w \delta}\right). \tag{9–16}$$

The mean temperature (9–15) and temperature uniformity (9–16) are shown in Fig. 9–5.

9–4 Closure. The method of porous cooling, or what is frequently referred to as *sweat cooling*, is being intensively studied for application in high-temperature, high-pressure ducts in nuclear reactors, and for use in thermal jets and components of high-speed missiles. One of the principal advantages of the method is the possibility of achieving efficient heat removal without large temperature gradients occurring within the solid.

Temperature solutions for a generating or nongenerating tube are more difficult to obtain than those for the plate. Although the numerical approach is not particularly adaptable to porous systems, the method does provide a means of obtaining approximate solutions for the practical case of a tube, and for those cases where the exact approach is not useful because of the presence of such nonuniformities as variable heat development and variable properties. In applying the numerical method, we think in terms of a tube replacing the usual conducting rod, where now the tube wall conducts heat and the pipe itself serves to transport the coolant between each nodal point with the same pressure drop as would occur between corresponding points in the original system.

This chapter concludes our study of steady conduction heat transfer except for a special class of problems which we shall examine later under the heading of transient systems. These problems have to do with a moving heat source such as occurs, for instance, in welding and machining operations, firing of guns, sliding contacts, and so on. The analytical device used in treating such problems is to change to a moving coordinate system whose origin follows the moving source. The temperature field with respect to this moving coordinate system is stationary, and hence this might be classified as a steady-state system. On the other hand, the diffusivity of the conducting material (Article 1–3) enters the analytical solution, and thus the system might be classified as a transient-state system.

Although moving-source systems are generally classified in the literature as "quasi-steady," we shall nevertheless examine them as transient systems, as the actual phenomenon suggests.

REFERENCES

1. S. Weinbaum and H. L. Wheller, Jr., "Heat Transfer in Sweat-Cooled Metals," *Journal of Applied Physics*, Vol. 20, No. 1, Jan., 1949, pp. 113–122.

2. L. Green, Jr., "Gas Cooling of a Porous Heat Source," *Journal of Applied Mechanics*, Trans. ASME, Vol. 19, No. 2, June, 1952, pp. 173–178.

PROBLEMS

9–1. Show that the fluid temperature for a porous-cooled plate is

$$\frac{t' - t_0'}{t_2 - t_0'} = e^{\xi_f \delta(x/\delta) - \xi_w \delta}.$$

9–2. A graphite wall $2.41''$ thick of porosity 0.4 is to be cooled by air with an upstream mass velocity of 500 lb/hr-ft^2. The air is at 0°F away from the wall, and the high-temperature face of the wall is at 500°F. Show that the upstream face temperature is 184°F, and that the mean wall temperature is 316°F.

9–3. The wall in problem 9–2 generates uniform heat in amount 0.1 Btu/sec-in^3. Show that the high- and low-temperature faces are at 625°F and 395°F respectively, and that the mean wall temperature is 542°F.

9–4. A porous-cooled wall generates linear nonuniform heat $q_t''' = q_0'''(1 + \alpha_0 t)$. Show that the general solution for the wall temperature $t(x)$, $0 \leq x \leq \delta$, is

$$t = C_1 e^{D_1 x} + C_2 e^{D_2 x} - \frac{1}{\alpha_0},$$

where the D_1 and D_2 are given by $\xi_w/2 \pm [(\xi_w/2)^2 - q_0''' \alpha_0/k_w]^{1/2}$.

9–5. Show that the particular solution in terms of t_2 for the wall temperature in problem 9–4 is

$$t = \frac{1}{E}(T_1 e^{D_2 \delta} - T_2)e^{D_1 x} + \frac{1}{E}(T_2 - T_1 e^{D_1 \delta})e^{D_2 x} - \frac{1}{\alpha_0},$$

where $E = e^{D_2 \delta} - e^{D_1 \delta}$, $T_1 = t_1 + 1/\alpha_0$, $T_2 = t_2 + 1/\alpha_0$, and where the t_1 is given by

$$t_1 = \frac{(D_1 - D_2)T_2 - E t_0' \xi_w - \bar{E}/\alpha_0}{\bar{E} - E \xi_w},$$

in which $\bar{E} = D_1 e^{D_2 \delta} - D_2 e^{D_1 \delta}$.

9–6. A porous wall 2.41″ thick generates linear heat for which $q_0''' = 1$ Btu/sec-in.³ and $\alpha_0 = 10^{-3}/°F$. The wall is of porosity 0.2 and thermal conductivity 9.3×10^{-4} Btu/sec-in.-°F, and is cooled by air at an upstream temperature of 60°F and an upstream mass velocity of 1000 lb/hr-ft². If the high-temperature face of the wall is maintained at 1000°F, then show that the low-temperature face is at 344°F, and that the temperature of a point halfway through the wall is 1376°F.

9–7. Show that the temperature distribution $t(r)$ in a porous-cooled tube must satisfy the differential equation

$$r^2 \frac{d^2 t}{dr^2} + (1 - \xi_w r)r \frac{dt}{dr} - \xi_w r t = 0.$$

Is this an equivalent form of Bessel's differential equation (3–1)?

9–8. Show that the second-order differential equation derived in problem 9–7 can be transformed into

$$u \frac{d^2 t}{du^2} + (1 - u) \frac{dt}{du} - t = 0,$$

by changing the independent variable to $u = \xi_w r$. This result is equivalent to *Kummer's first confluent hypergeometric differential equation*

$$u \frac{d^2 v}{du^2} + (c_1 - u) \frac{dv}{du} - c_2 v = 0,$$

which has a solution

$$v_{\mathrm{I}} = 1 + \frac{c_2}{1!c_1} u + \frac{c_2(c_2 + 1)}{2!c_1(c_1 + 1)} u^2 + \cdots.$$

From this result show that one solution of the differential equation in problem 9–7 is

$$t_{\mathrm{I}} = e^{\xi_w r}.$$

Since one solution of the differential equation in problem 9–7 is known as t_{I}, a second independent solution t_{II} can be found by setting

$$t(r) = t_{\mathrm{I}}(r)t_{\mathrm{II}}(r) = e^{\xi_w r}t_{\mathrm{II}}(r) = y e^{\xi_w r}.$$

Differentiating this and substituting it into the differential equation of problem 9–7, show that a new equation is obtained as

$$r \frac{d^2 y}{dr^2} + (1 + \xi_w r) \frac{dy}{dr} = 0,$$

and obtain its general solution

$$y = C_1 \int_\infty^r \frac{1}{r} e^{-\xi_w r} dr + C_2 = C_1 F(r) + C_2,$$

where the lower integration limit is chosen at will as ∞. This integral cannot be evaluated in terms of the elementary functions; it is called the *exponential integral function*, and is tabulated. The general solution for the temperature profile in a porous-cooled tube is therefore

$$t = e^{\xi_w r} [C_1 F(r) + C_2].$$

CHAPTER 10

TRANSIENT SYSTEMS. HEATING AND COOLING

In this chapter we take up the study of conduction heat-transfer for nongenerating systems in which the temperature varies not only from point to point in the structure, but undergoes a continuous change with time at any local point as well. In particular, we consider the practical process of heating or cooling in which the local internal temperature of the structure varies as some general nonperiodic function of time. We consider first systems for which the internal thermal resistance is small compared with the surface thermal resistance, then go on to systems for which the surface resistance is small compared with the internal resistance, and finally consider the most realistic type of system for which both of these thermal resistances must be taken into account.

10–1 Transient states. In preceding chapters we considered various systems in which the temperature distribution was always steadily or permanently located, and we now turn to cases where these temperature distributions are no longer stationary but change with *time*. These remaining cases can be roughly divided into two other distinct transient states, namely, those which we shall refer to as *nonperiodic* and *periodic*. In the nonperiodic transient state, the temperature at any point within the structure changes as some general nonlinear function of time, while in the periodic transient state, temperatures within the structure undergo a periodic change which is either *regular* or *irregular* but definitely cyclic. A regular periodic variation is characterized by a harmonic sinusoidal or cosinusoidal function, and irregular periodic variations by any function which is cyclic but not necessarily harmonic.

10–2 Nonperiodic heating and cooling. A large class of important industrial problems have to do with the prediction of temperature uniformities, equilibrium temperatures, and instantaneous and cumulative heat rates in a solid structure being heated or cooled by immersion in a large mass of fluid. Such problems are of frequent occurrence in, for example, metallurgical processes, where it is necessary to estimate heating and cooling rates of long cylindrical or rectangular bar stock, either solid or hollow, and ingots of such various shapes as short cylinders, parallelepipeds, cubes, and spheres. This information is then used to predict the time required for such objects to attain prescribed temperature levels for purposes of melting, hot-working, heat-treatment, and the like. Heating and cooling rates are also of extreme practical interest in the canning industry, where perishable canned foods are chilled by immersion, in the paper industry where wood logs are immersed in steam baths preparatory to pulping and vernier cutting, in the manufacture of bricks, glass, and rubber products, in the prediction of allowable combustion times in rocket-engine nozzles, in the calculation of allowable acceleration rates for air-borne vehicles subject to high-speed transient aerodynamic heating, and so on. In all such examples, either the surface temperature of the structure is suddenly changed, without surface resistance, to the temperature of the ambient medium, or the surface temperature changes gradually after sudden exposure, with finite surface resistance, to an ambient medium at some higher or lower temperature.

In any case of heating or cooling, the heat-transfer process is influenced by both the internal and surface resistance, the limiting cases being represented by a zero internal resistance as the one extreme and a zero surface resistance as the other. In practice, these extremes are never actually reached as $R = L/kA = 0$ or $R_1 = 1/hA_1 = 0$, although the ratio of R to R_1 may be so small or so large as to allow us to ignore R or R_1.

Negligible Internal Resistance

10-3 Newtonian heating or cooling. Consider an object being heated from some *initial* uniform temperature state t_i. If the object is of high thermal conductivity k, then its internal thermal resistance can be ignored, and we can regard the heat-transfer process as being controlled solely by surface resistance. Under these conditions there are no temperature gradients within the object at any instant θ, and we refer to such a process as *Newtonian heating or cooling*.

The rate of heat gain from the surroundings for $\theta > 0$ is given by (1–4) and independently by (1–20) as

$$q = CwV \frac{dt}{d\theta} = hA_1(t_f - t),$$

where C, w, V, and A_1 are the thermal capacity, specific weight, total volume, and surface area of the object, t is its uniform temperature at the instant θ, and h and t_f are uniform values of the unit surface conductance and ambient fluid temperature. To determine $t(\theta)$, we find the general solution of the total differential equation

$$\frac{dt}{d\theta} - \frac{hA_1}{CwV}(t_f - t) = 0$$

as

$$\ln(t - t_f) = -\frac{hA_1}{CwV}\theta + C_1,$$

where the constant of integration must be $C_1 = \ln (t_i - t_f)$ in order to satisfy the initial condition that

$$t = t_i \quad \text{at } \theta = 0.$$

The particular solution for either heating, $t_f > t_i$, or cooling, $t_f < t_i$, is therefore

$$\frac{t - t_f}{t_i - t_f} = e^{-(hA_1/CwV)\theta}. \tag{10-1}$$

The solution (10–1) indicates that under the simplest condition of Newtonian heating or cooling, the uniform temperature of the object rises or falls exponentially with time, and that the time interval required for the object to experience a given temperature change is directly proportional to its surface resistivity $1/h$, to its thermal capacity C and specific weight w, and to its volume-to-surface-area ratio V/A_1. The solution also suggests that it would take an infinite time for the object to attain the steady-state condition of being in thermal equilibrium with its surroundings as $t = t_f$. This should not cause concern, since we have only to appreciate that this is a mathematical necessity, and that the difference between t and t_f will be extremely small after only a short interval of time compared with $\theta = \infty$. The essential point to keep in mind whenever this question arises is that the analytical solution tells us that we are approaching something which our experience informs us we have already reached for all practical purposes.

10–4 Plates, cylinders, rods, cubes, and spheres. If we introduce a *Nusselt number* N_u and a *Fourier modulus* Θ defined by

$$N_u = \frac{h\delta_1}{k},$$

$$\Theta = \frac{\alpha\theta}{\delta_1^2} = \frac{k\theta}{Cw\delta_1^2}, \tag{10-2}$$

where δ_1 is *either a semithickness or a surface radius*, then the solution (10–1) takes the form

$$\frac{t - t_f}{t_i - t_f} = e^{-(A_1\delta_1/V)N_u\Theta}. \tag{10-3}$$

Note that this expression is still independent of the thermal conductivity, since k is not contained in the product $N_u\Theta$. In the alternate solution (10–3) the constant $G = A_1\delta_1/V$ depends only on the geometry of the object, and on closer examination we find that for

Infinite plates, $G = 1$,
Infinite cylinders, $G = 2$,

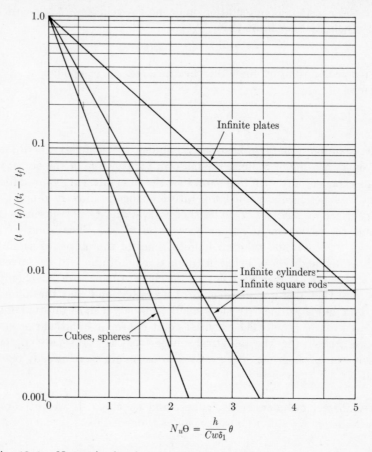

Fig. 10–1. Newtonian heating or cooling from initial temperature t_i to ambient fluid temperature t_f.

$$
\begin{aligned}
\text{Infinite square rods,} \quad & G = 2, \\
\text{Cubes,} \quad & G = 3, \\
\text{Spheres,} \quad & G = 3.
\end{aligned}
$$

The temperature history of these objects during Newtonian heating or cooling is illustrated graphically in Fig. 10–1. Here we see that for the same unit surface conductance, the time required for an infinite cylinder (or infinite square rod) of high conductivity to heat or cool to within, say, 1% of thermal equilibrium with its surroundings is $(2.25 - 1.50)/1.50 = 50\%$ longer than for a cube (or sphere) of the same material and same diameter. An infinite plate of the same material and of thickness equal to the diameter of the cylinder would require $(4.56 - 1.50)/1.50 = 204\%$ more time.

EXAMPLE 10–1.   To rapidly estimate the unit surface conductance between copper cylinders and a water bath, a solid copper cylinder $2''$ in diameter was dropped into ice water after recording its temperature as 82°F.   After 3 minutes the temperature of the cylinder was again measured and recorded as 37°F. With these data make a rough estimate of the average unit surface conductance h.

Solution.   Assuming that the surface resistance is much higher than the internal resistance of the high-conductivity copper cylinder, we can apply the temperature-time solution for Newtonian cooling.   Solving for h in (10–1) and computing directly (Table 1–2), we find that

$$h = \left(\frac{V}{A_1}\right)\frac{Cw}{\theta}\ln\left(\frac{t_i - t_f}{t - t_f}\right) = \left(\frac{\pi \times 1 \times L}{2\pi \times 12 \times L}\right)\frac{0.092 \times 558}{3/60}\ln\left(\frac{82 - 32}{37 - 32}\right)$$

$$= 98.5 \text{ Btu/hr-ft}^2\text{-°F.}$$

It is frequently of more interest to compute, rather than the temperature history, the rate of heat exchange and the total heat exchanged during a given time interval.   The *instantaneous heat rate* q (Btu/hr) at any time θ is calculated by

$$q = CwV\frac{dt}{d\theta}$$

and (10–1) as

$$\frac{q}{hA_1(t_f - t_i)} = e^{-GN_u\theta}, \tag{10–4}$$

and the *cumulative heat rate* Q (Btu) after time θ from $\theta = 0$ is calculated by

$$Q = \int_{\theta=0}^{\theta} qd\theta,$$

and (10–4) as

$$\frac{Q}{CwV(t_f - t_i)} = 1 - e^{-GN_u\theta}. \tag{10–5}$$

Hence, values of the instantaneous and cumulative heat rates can be obtained directly from Fig. 10–1 by interpreting the ordinates as $q/hA_1(t_f - t_i)$ and $1 - Q/CwV(t_f - t_i)$ respectively.   For Newtonian cooling we simply replace $(t_f - t_i)$ by $(t_i - t_f)$.

NEGLIGIBLE SURFACE RESISTANCE

We now consider a class of problems having to do with the heating and cooling of objects which have an appreciable internal thermal resistance. In these problems we shall simply assign a temperature for the surface of the object, as t_1 for $\theta > 0$.   This is to imply that in the practical situation either t_1 is known from actual measurement, or the surface thermal resistance is negligible $(1/hA_1 = 0)$, so that t_1 is actually the ambient temperature t_f.

10–5 Infinite plate.   Consider the heating or cooling of a large plate of uniform thickness $L = 2\delta_1$. The temperature distribution through the plate, $t(x,\theta)$, is initially $(\theta = 0)$ some arbitrary function of x as $t(x,0) = t_i(x)$, whereupon both face surfaces $x = 0$ and L are suddenly changed to and maintained at a uniform temperature t_1 for all $\theta > 0$.

The solution for the temperature history $t(x,\theta)$ must satisfy the characteristic partial-differential equation of Fourier, (1–8), as

$$\frac{\partial^2 T}{\partial x^2} = \frac{1}{\alpha} \frac{\partial T}{\partial \theta}, \qquad (10\text{–}6)$$

and the initial and boundary conditions

$$T = T_i(x) \quad \text{at } \theta = 0; \quad 0 \le x \le L,$$
$$T = 0 \cdot \quad \text{at } x = 0; \quad \theta > 0,$$
$$T = 0 \quad \text{at } x = L; \quad \theta > 0,$$

where, for convenience, we let $T = t - t_1$ so that $T_i(x) = t_i(x) - t_1$. Integrating (10–6) by the separation of variables method (Article 5–8) leads to product solutions of the form

$$T_\lambda = e^{-\lambda^2 \alpha \theta}(C_1 \cos \lambda x + C_2 \sin \lambda x),$$

if the separation constant is chosen as $-\lambda^2$. In these solutions $C_1 = 0$ if T is to vanish at $x = 0$ for all $\theta > 0$. If T is also to vanish at $x = L$ for all $\theta > 0$, then $\sin \lambda L = 0$, so that $\lambda = n\pi/L$. This requires that the eigenvalues be integral as $n = 1, 2, 3, \cdots$. The solution, which now takes the form

$$T = \sum_{n=1}^{\infty} C_n e^{-(n\pi/L)^2 \alpha \theta} \sin \frac{n\pi}{L} x,$$

is to finally satisfy the initial condition that

$$T_i(x) = \sum_{n=1}^{\infty} C_n \sin \frac{n\pi}{L} x.$$

This result is recognized as a Fourier sine-series expansion of the arbitrary function $T_i(x)$, for which the constant amplitudes C_n are given by

$$C_n = \frac{2}{L} \int_0^L T_i(x) \sin \frac{n\pi}{L} x dx.$$

The complete solution is therefore

$$T = \frac{2}{L} \sum_{n=1}^{\infty} e^{-(n\pi/2)^2 \Theta} \sin \frac{n\pi}{L} x \int_0^L T_i(x) \sin \frac{n\pi}{L} x dx, \qquad (10\text{–}7)$$

where Θ is the Fourier modulus in (10–2) with $\delta_1 = L/2$. The solution (10–7) is also that for an insulated rod of length L with end temperatures maintained at t_1, the rod heating or cooling from an initial temperature state $t_i(x)$.

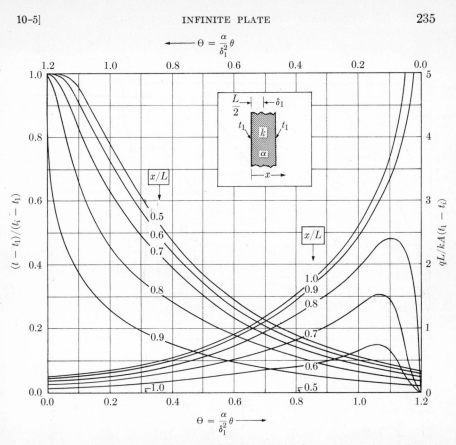

Fig. 10-2. Temperature history and instantaneous heat rate as a function of the Fourier modulus Θ for an infinite plate with negligible surface resistance.

Consider the special case represented by a uniform initial temperature $t_i(x) = t_i$. This is a practical case where $T_i(x) = t_i - t_1$, and for which (10-7) reappears in the particular form

$$\frac{t - t_1}{t_i - t_1} = \frac{4}{\pi} \sum_{n=1}^{\infty} \frac{1}{n} e^{-(n\pi/2)^2 \Theta} \sin \frac{n\pi}{L} x; \quad n = 1, 3, 5, \cdots. \quad (10\text{-}8)$$

Then the instantaneous rate at which heat is conducted across any plane of area A in the wall is $q = -kA \partial t/\partial x$, or

$$q(x,\theta) = 4 \left(\frac{kA}{L} \right) (t_1 - t_i) \sum_{n=1}^{\infty} e^{-(n\pi/2)^2 \Theta} \cos \frac{n\pi}{L} x; \quad n = 1, 3, 5, \cdots.$$

$$(10\text{-}9)$$

Notice that the heat flow is initially infinite at the two surfaces. The temperature history (10-8) and instantaneous heat rate (10-9) are shown in Fig. 10-2 for various stations in the plate.

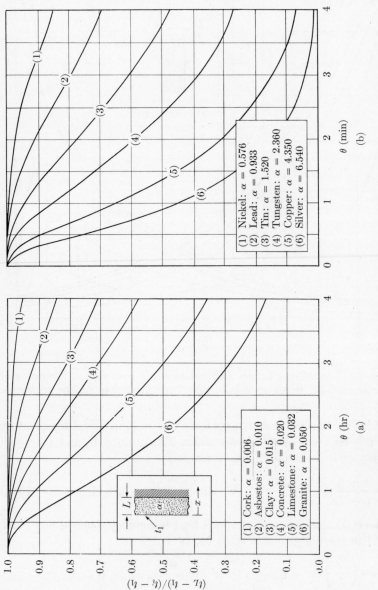

Fig. 10-3. Temperature rise at the insulated rear face of a plane wall 6″ thick, for various building materials (a) and pure metals (b).

Integration of (10–9) with respect to θ from $\theta = 0$ to θ gives for the cumulative heat rate in the plate

$$Q(x,\theta) = \frac{4}{\pi^2}\left(\frac{kAL}{\alpha}\right)(t_1 - t_i)\sum_{n=1}^{\infty}\frac{1}{n^2}[1 - e^{-(n\pi/2)^2\theta}]\cos\frac{n\pi}{L}x;$$

$$n = 1, 3, 5, \cdots. \quad (10\text{–}10)$$

The series (10–8) has been accurately computed by Olson and Schultz (1) for the mid-plane temperature history at $x = L/2$ as given by

$$\frac{t(L/2,\theta) - t_1}{t_i - t_1} = \frac{4}{\pi} = [e^{-(1/4)\pi^2\theta} - \tfrac{1}{3}e^{-(9/4)\pi^2\theta} + \tfrac{1}{5}e^{-(25/4)\pi^2\theta} - \cdots] = P(\Theta).$$

$$(10\text{–}11)$$

Values of $P(\Theta)$ for the plate are listed in Table A–8 of the Appendix, and later on we shall show how this particular series can be combined with an analogous series for the cylinder and semi-infinite solid to obtain solutions for a variety of other cases of practical interest.

EXAMPLE 10–2. As an example in the use of the plate series $P(\Theta)$, suppose that a large mass of combustible material is piled up against the 6″-thick wall of a large room. If a flash fire suddenly raises and maintains the temperature of the outside wall surface at t_1, how long will it take for the inside surface to reach the ignition temperature of the combustible material?

Solution. If the dimensions of the room are large compared with the wall thickness, then its walls can be approximated by an infinite plate 6″ thick and at a uniform temperature t_i preceding its exposure to fire at the face surface $x = 0$. Suppose further that the combustible material is of low thermal conductivity; the face surface at $x = L$ is then considered to be adiabatic.

A solution to the problem of the infinite plate with one insulated face is also encompassed in (10–8), for if we consider a plate of double thickness $2L$ with each face at t_1, then its mid-plane (around which the temperature is symmetrical) can be taken as the adiabatic face of the original plate. The temperature history at this adiabatic face is given by (10–11).

Values of $P(\Theta)$ with $L = 1$ are taken from Table A–8 and plotted in Fig. 10–3 for walls of various building materials in (a), and for large pure-metal walls in (b). Note that the units of time in (a) and (b) are hours and minutes respectively.

From these results we see that the walls of higher diffusivity have shorter allowable heating times, the duration being comparatively short for the metal walls. For example, if the ignition temperature of the stored material is 140°F, and the fire raises the outside surface temperature of the walls (initially at 80°F) to 380°F, then it would take a 6″ clay wall over three hours to reach $(t_L - t_1)/(t_i - t_1) = (140 - 380)/(80 - 380) = 0.8$, as compared with just three minutes for a 6″ lead wall.

10–6 Infinite cylinder. Let the initial temperature throughout an infinitely long solid cylinder be some arbitrary function of the radius, $t_i(r)$, and imagine the temperature of its surface $r = r_1$ to be suddenly raised or lowered to t_1 and maintained at this value for all $\theta > 0$.

In this case the solution for $t(r,\theta)$ must satisfy (10–6) expressed in cylindrical coordinates as

$$\frac{\partial^2 T}{\partial r^2} + \frac{1}{r}\frac{\partial T}{\partial r} = \frac{1}{\alpha}\frac{\partial T}{\partial \theta}, \tag{10–12}$$

and the initial and boundary conditions

$$T = T_i(r) \quad \text{at } \theta = 0; \quad 0 \le r \le r_1,$$

$$T = 0 \quad \text{at } r = r_1; \quad \theta > 0,$$

where again $T = t - t_1$. The partial-differential equation (10–12) is now separated into the assumed product solutions

$$T_\lambda = \left[C_1 J_0\left(\frac{\lambda}{\sqrt{\alpha}}r\right) + C_2 Y_0\left(\frac{\lambda}{\sqrt{\alpha}}r\right) \right] e^{-\lambda^2\theta},$$

in which one of the two integration constants is immediately determined by observing that the temperature $t(r,\theta)$ must remain finite as $r \to 0$. Hence $C_2 = 0$, and the boundary condition $T = 0$ at $r = r_1$ is evidently satisfied only if

$$J_0\left(\frac{\lambda}{\sqrt{\alpha}}r_1\right) = 0 = J_0(M_n). \tag{10–13}$$

Each value of M_n for which this eigenfunction is zero represents a root of the zero-order Bessel function (Fig. 3–2) which determines the permissible eigenvalues λ_n. The first five consecutive roots ($n = 1, 2, 3, 4, 5$) of $J_0(M_n)$ are contained in Table A–11 of the Appendix.

With $\lambda_n/\sqrt{\alpha} = M_n/r_1$, the solution now takes the series form

$$T = \sum_{n=1}^{\infty} C_n e^{-\lambda_n^2\theta} J_0\left(M_n \frac{r}{r_1}\right). \tag{10–14}$$

If this is also to satisfy the initial condition $T = T_i(r)$ at $\theta = 0$, then the constants C_n must be the consecutive coefficients in a zero-order Bessel expansion of the arbitrary function $T_i(r)$:

$$T_i(r) = \sum_{n=1}^{\infty} C_n J_0\left(M_n \frac{r}{r_1}\right), \tag{10–15}$$

in which the M_n are positive roots of (10–13). It was shown in Article 3–7 that these consecutive coefficients could be determined by a method similar to that used in evaluating the amplitudes of a Fourier expansion.

Multiplying both sides of (10–15) by $rJ_0(M_mr/r_1)dr$ and integrating over the circular cross section, we have

$$\int_0^{r_1} rT_i(r)J_0\left(M_m\frac{r}{r_1}\right)dr = \sum_{n=1}^{\infty} C_n \int_0^{r_1} rJ_0\left(M_m\frac{r}{r_1}\right)J_0\left(M_n\frac{r}{r_1}\right)dr.$$

But by (3–28), if $m \neq n$

$$\int_0^{r_1} rJ_0\left(M_m\frac{r}{r_1}\right)J_0\left(M_n\frac{r}{r_1}\right)dr = 0,$$

while if $m = n$, then the right-hand integral reduces to

$$\int_0^{r_1} rJ_0^2\left(M_n\frac{r}{r_1}\right)dr = \frac{r_1^2}{2}[J_0^2(M_n) + J_1^2(M_n)].$$

The general coefficient C_n must therefore be given by

$$C_n = \frac{2}{r_1^2[J_0^2(M_n) + J_1^2(M_n)]}\int_0^{r_1} rT_i(r)J_0\left(M_n\frac{r}{r_1}\right)dr. \quad (10\text{--}16)$$

Substituting (10–16), with $J_0(M_n) = 0$ as required by (10–13), in (10–14) gives the final solution

$$T = \frac{2}{r_1^2}\sum_{n=1}^{\infty} e^{-(M_n/r_1)^2\alpha\theta}\frac{J_0\left(M_n\frac{r}{r_1}\right)}{J_1^2(M_n)}\int_0^{r_1} rT_i(r)J_0\left(M_n\frac{r}{r_1}\right)dr. \quad (10\text{--}17)$$

For the special case of a uniform initial temperature distribution $t_i(r) = t_i$ or $T_i(r) = t_i - t_1$, we evaluate the integral as

$$\int_0^{r_1} rT_i(r)J_0\left(M_n\frac{r}{r_1}\right)dr = (t_i - t_1)\frac{r_1^2}{M_n}J_1(M_n),$$

and therewith reduce (10–17) to the particular solution

$$\frac{t - t_1}{t_i - t_1} = 2\sum_{n=1}^{\infty}\frac{1}{M_n}e^{-M_n^2\theta}\frac{J_0\left(M_n\frac{r}{r_1}\right)}{J_1(M_n)}. \quad (10\text{--}18)$$

The instantaneous heat rate for a unit length of the cylinder is

$$q = k(2\pi r)\partial t/\partial r.$$

Evaluating the derivative of $J_0(M_nr/r_1)$,

$$\frac{\partial}{\partial r}J_0\left(M_n\frac{r}{r_1}\right) = -\frac{M_n}{r_1}J_1\left(M_n\frac{r}{r_1}\right),$$

we have

$$q(r,\theta) = 4\pi k(t_1 - t_i) \left(\frac{r}{r_1}\right) \sum_{n=1}^{\infty} e^{-M_n^2\theta} \frac{J_1\left(M_n \dfrac{r}{r_1}\right)}{J_1(M_n)}, \quad (10\text{--}19)$$

and therewith the cumulative heat rate $Q = \int_0^\theta q\,d\theta$ as

$$Q(r,\theta) = \frac{4\pi k}{\alpha}(t_1 - t_i)r_1 r \sum_{n=1}^{\infty} \frac{1}{M_n^2}[1 - e^{-M_n^2\theta}] \frac{J_1\left(M_n \dfrac{r}{r_1}\right)}{J_0(M_n)}. \quad (10\text{--}20)$$

The series (10–18) has also been computed (1) for the axial temperature history at $r = 0$ as given by

$$\frac{t(0,\theta) - t_1}{t_i - t_1} = 2\left(\frac{e^{-M_1^2\theta}}{M_1 J_1(M_1)} + \frac{e^{-M_2^2\theta}}{M_2 J_1(M_2)} + \cdots\right) = C(\theta). \quad (10\text{--}21)$$

Values of $C(\theta)$ for the cylinder are listed in Table A–9 of the Appendix.

10–7 Sphere. A solid sphere initially at t_i and with its surface $r = r_1$ suddenly changed to, and maintained at, t_1 for $\theta > 0$ is considered in the Problems. In this case the general and central temperature history and the instantaneous and cumulative heat rates are found to be

$$\frac{t - t_1}{t_i - t_1} = \frac{2}{\pi}\left(\frac{r_1}{r}\right) \sum_{n=1}^{\infty} \frac{(-1)^{n+1}}{n} e^{-(n\pi)^2\theta} \sin n\pi \frac{r}{r_1}, \quad (10\text{--}22)$$

$$\frac{t_0 - t_1}{t_i - t_1} = 2 \sum_{n=1}^{\infty} (-1)^{n+1} e^{-(n\pi)^2\theta}, \quad (10\text{--}23)$$

$$q(r,\theta) = 8k(t_1 - t_i)r_1 r^2 \sum_{n=1}^{\infty} \frac{(-1)^{n+1}}{n} e^{-(n\pi)^2\theta}\left(\frac{1}{r^2}\sin n\pi \frac{r}{r_1} - \frac{n\pi}{r_1 r}\cos n\pi \frac{r}{r_1}\right),$$
$$(10\text{--}24)$$

and

$$Q(r,\theta) = \frac{8k}{\pi^2\alpha}(t_1 - t_i)r_1^3 r^2 \sum_{n=1}^{\infty} \frac{(-1)^{n+1}}{n^3}[1 - e^{-(n\pi)^2\theta}]$$
$$\times \left(\frac{1}{r^2}\sin n\pi \frac{r}{r_1} - \frac{n\pi}{r_1 r}\cos n\pi \frac{r}{r_1}\right). \quad (10\text{--}25)$$

10–8 Semi-infinite solid. We now consider a case whose solution requires the use of Fourier's integral, namely, a semi-infinite solid bounded by the yz-plane only and extending to infinity in the positive x-direction. The initial temperature distribution in the solid is given as $T_i(x) = t_i(x) - t_1$, and at time $\theta = 0$ the temperature of its surface $x = 0$ is suddenly changed to, and maintained at, t_1 for all $\theta > 0$.

Since the solution $t(x,\theta)$ must satisfy (10–6), we can use the product solutions found in Article 10–5 as

$$T_\lambda = e^{-\lambda^2\alpha\theta}(C_1 \cos \lambda x + C_2 \sin \lambda x).$$

Here again $C_1 = 0$ if T is to vanish at the boundary for all $\theta > 0$. But no other boundary exists for the determination of the λ's. This forces us to consider all solutions corresponding to all possible values of λ, nonintegral as well as integral. In this case, then, the usual series passes over into the integral form

$$T = \int_{\lambda=0}^{\infty} C(\lambda)e^{-\lambda^2\alpha\theta} \sin \lambda x d\lambda. \tag{10–26}$$

If the solution (10–26) is to satisfy the initial condition that $T = T_i(x)$ at $\theta = 0$, then

$$T_i(x) = \int_{\lambda=0}^{\infty} C(\lambda) \sin \lambda x d\lambda.$$

On comparing this with the Fourier sine integral (5–20),

$$T_i(x) = \frac{2}{\pi} \int_0^{\infty} T_i(x')dx' \int_0^{\infty} \sin \lambda x \sin \lambda x' d\lambda$$

$$= \frac{2}{\pi} \int_{\lambda=0}^{\infty} \left[\int_{x'=0}^{\infty} T_i(x') \sin \lambda x' dx' \right] \sin \lambda x d\lambda,$$

we have

$$C(\lambda) = \frac{2}{\pi} \int_{x'=0}^{\infty} T_i(x') \sin \lambda x' dx',$$

so that by (10–26),

$$T = \int_{\lambda=0}^{\infty} \left[\frac{2}{\pi} \int_{x'=0}^{\infty} T_i(x') \sin \lambda x' dx' \right] e^{-\lambda^2\alpha\theta} \sin \lambda x d\lambda,$$

or equivalently,

$$T = \frac{2}{\pi} \int_{x'=0}^{\infty} T_i(x') \left[\int_{\lambda=0}^{\infty} e^{-\lambda^2\alpha\theta} \sin \lambda x' \sin \lambda x d\lambda \right] dx'.$$

Evaluating the integral in λ,

$$\int_{\lambda=0}^{\infty} e^{-\lambda^2\alpha\theta} \sin \lambda x' \sin \lambda x d\lambda = \frac{1}{2} \int_{\lambda=0}^{\infty} e^{-\lambda^2\alpha\theta} \cos \lambda(x' - x)d\lambda$$

$$- \frac{1}{2} \int_{\lambda=0}^{\infty} e^{-\lambda^2\alpha\theta} \cos \lambda(x' + x)d\lambda$$

$$= \frac{1}{4}\sqrt{\frac{\pi}{\alpha\theta}} [e^{-(x'-x)^2/4\alpha\theta} - e^{-(x'+x)^2/4\alpha\theta}],$$

serves to reduce T to the final form

$$T = \frac{1}{2\sqrt{\pi\alpha\theta}} \int_{x'=0}^{\infty} T_i(x') \, [e^{-(x'-x)^2/4\alpha\theta} - e^{-(x'+x)^2/4\alpha\theta}]dx'. \quad (10\text{--}27)$$

Consider the special case represented by a uniform initial temperature distribution $T_i(x) = t_i - t_1$. If we let $\lambda = (x' \mp x)/2\sqrt{\alpha\theta}$, so that $x' = 2\sqrt{\alpha\theta}\,\lambda \pm x$ and $dx' = 2\sqrt{\alpha\theta}\,d\lambda$, then the lower integration limit corresponding to $x' = 0$ becomes $\lambda = \mp x/2\sqrt{\alpha\theta}$, and the upper limit for $x' = \infty$ becomes $\lambda = \infty$. The solution (10–27) is then given by

$$T = \frac{T_i}{\sqrt{\pi}}\left[\int_{-x/2\sqrt{\alpha\theta}}^{\infty} e^{-\lambda^2}d\lambda - \int_{x/2\sqrt{\alpha\theta}}^{\infty} e^{-\lambda^2}d\lambda\right] = \frac{T_i}{\sqrt{\pi}}\int_{-x/2\sqrt{\alpha\theta}}^{x/2\sqrt{\alpha\theta}} e^{-\lambda^2}d\lambda,$$

or simply

$$\frac{t - t_1}{t_i - t_1} = \frac{2}{\sqrt{\pi}}\int_0^{x/2\sqrt{\alpha\theta}} e^{-\lambda^2}d\lambda = \frac{2}{\sqrt{\pi}}\int_0^{X} e^{-\lambda^2}d\lambda = \text{erf}\,(X) = S(X),$$

$$(10\text{--}28)$$

where

$$X = \frac{x}{2\sqrt{\alpha\theta}}.$$

This integral is known as either the *error function* or *probability integral*, and we list its values as a function of X in Table A–10 of the Appendix.

The instantaneous heat rate at the surface of the semi-infinite solid is readily calculated to be [see (10-31) below]

$$q_1(0,\theta) = \frac{kA\,(t_1 - t_i)}{\sqrt{\pi\alpha\theta}} \quad (10\text{--}29)$$

for surface area A, and the surface cumulative heat rate becomes

$$Q_1(0,\theta) = 2kA\,\sqrt{\frac{\theta}{\pi\alpha}}\,(t_1 - t_i). \quad (10\text{--}30)$$

To find the temperature gradient at time θ and at any point x in the semi-infinite solid, we must differentiate (10–28) with respect to x. Recalling the general differentiation formula

$$\frac{d}{dv}\int_o^{v} f(w)dw = f(v),$$

we have

$$\frac{\partial T}{\partial x} = \frac{\partial T}{\partial(x/2\sqrt{\alpha\theta})}\frac{\partial(x/2\sqrt{\alpha\theta})}{\partial x} = \frac{2T_i}{\sqrt{\pi}}\,(e^{-x^2/4\alpha\theta})(1/2\sqrt{\alpha\theta}) = \frac{T_i}{\sqrt{\pi\alpha\theta}}\,e^{-x^2/4\alpha\theta},$$

$$(10\text{--}31)$$

or, in dimensionless form,*

$$\frac{x}{(t_i - t_1)} \frac{\partial t}{\partial x} = \frac{2}{\sqrt{\pi}} X e^{-X^2}.$$

By differentiating (10–28) with respect to θ, we can find the rate of heating or cooling at time θ and at any point x in the semi-infinite solid:

$$\frac{\partial T}{\partial \theta} = \frac{\partial T}{\partial (x/2\sqrt{\alpha\theta})} \frac{\partial (x/2\sqrt{\alpha\theta})}{\partial \theta} = \frac{2T_i}{\sqrt{\pi}} (e^{-x^2/4\alpha\theta}) \left(\frac{-x}{4\sqrt{\alpha}\,\theta^{3/2}}\right)$$

$$= \frac{-T_i x}{2\sqrt{\pi\alpha}\,\theta^{3/2}} e^{-x^2/4\alpha\theta}, \qquad (10\text{--}32)$$

or in dimensionless form,

$$\frac{-\sqrt{\pi}\,\theta}{(t_i - t_1)} \frac{\partial t}{\partial \theta} = X e^{-X^2}.$$

Note that both (10–31) and (10–32) have maximum values, since by differentiating with respect to x

$$X e^{-X^2}(-2X) + e^{-X^2} = 0,$$

and taking the positive root, we find that

$$(X)_{\max} = \frac{x_{\max}}{2\sqrt{\alpha\theta}} = \frac{1}{\sqrt{2}} = 0.707.$$

Since this maximum value is the same for both functions, we have for the corresponding maximum temperature gradient and heating or cooling rate

$$\frac{x}{(t_i - t_1)} \left(\frac{\partial t}{\partial x}\right)_{\max} = \sqrt{\frac{2}{\pi e}} = 0.484,$$

and

$$\frac{-\pi\theta}{(t_i - t_1)} \left(\frac{\partial t}{\partial \theta}\right)_{\max} = \sqrt{\frac{1}{2e}} = 0.429.$$

The temperature history (10–28), temperature gradient (10–31), and heating or cooling rate (10–32) are illustrated in Fig. 10–4.

---

*It is interesting to note that Kelvin was the first to use (10–31) for estimates of the earth's age. Disregarding the curvature of the earth, the effects of radioactivity on the cooling process, and assuming an average value of the diffusivity as $\alpha = 0.0456$ ft^2/hr, a surface temperature of $t_1 = 0°$F, an initial temperature of $t_i = 7000°$F, and an average temperature gradient at the surface $(\partial t/\partial x)_1 = 0.02°$F/ft, we have

$$\theta = T_i^2/\pi\alpha(\partial t/\partial x)_1^2 = (7000)^2/3.14 \times 0.0456(0.02)^2(24 \times 365) = 97,500,000,$$

or nearly 100 million years. This figure, however, is far short of more recent and independent estimates.

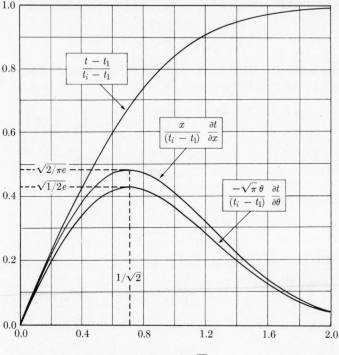

$$X = x/2\sqrt{\alpha\theta}$$

Fig. 10–4. Temperature history, temperature gradient, and cooling rate in a semi-infinite solid with steady surface temperature t_1.

EXAMPLE 10–3.   A large mass of copper ($\alpha = 4.35$ ft^2/hr), which is initially at 100°F throughout, has its surface temperature suddenly lowered to 0°F and maintained at this value for all $\theta > 0$.   (a) What is its temperature $\frac{1}{2}''$ below the surface after 2 sec?   (b) How many seconds would it take for its temperature to drop down to 41°F at a point $1''$ below the surface?   (c) How long would it take for the temperature gradient at its surface to be 20°F/in.?   (d) At what depth will the rate of cooling be a maximum after 1 sec?

Solution.   (a) Computing first the value of X as

$$X = x/2\sqrt{\alpha\theta} = 0.5/12 \times 2\sqrt{4.35 \times 2/3600} = 0.419,$$

and then referring to Fig. 10–4 (or Table A–10), we find $S(X) = 0.44$, so that $t = 44°$F.

(b) In this case $S(X) = 0.41$, and from Fig. 10–4 (or Table A–10), $X = 0.38$. This value corresponds to a time of

$$\theta = \frac{(1/12)^2 \times 3600}{4 \times 4.35 \times (0.38)^2} = 10 \text{ sec.}$$

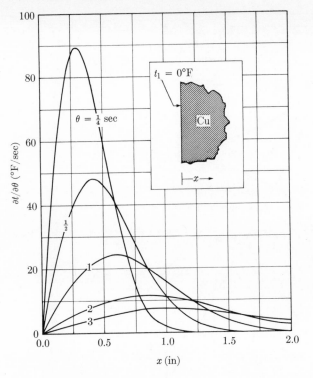

Fig. 10–5. Instantaneous cooling rates in a large mass of copper initially at 100°F.

(c) To find the time corresponding to a temperature gradient of 20°F/in., we solve (10–31) for θ and compute directly as

$$\theta = \frac{(100)^2 \times 3600}{3.14 \times 4.35(20 \times 12)^2} = 45.8 \text{ sec}.$$

(d) The maximum cooling rate after 1 sec occurs at a depth below the surface of

$$x = \sqrt{2\alpha\theta} = 12\sqrt{2 \times 4.35 \times 1/3600} = 0.59 \text{ in.},$$

as in Fig. 10–5. From this figure we see that the maximum cooling rates not only diminish with time, but that these maximum values are located at higher values of depth as time progresses. These are important considerations in the heat treatment of metals, in welding operations, in the theories of contact-surface temperatures and shrink fittings, and so on.

10–9 Summary of heat rates. For purposes of comparison, the instantaneous and cumulative surface heat rates for the infinite plate, infinite cylinder, sphere, and semi-infinite solid can all be reduced to analogous

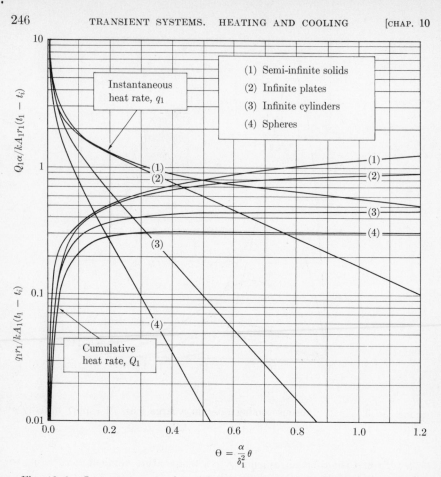

Fig. 10–6.   Instantaneous and cumulative surface heat rates under the condition of negligible surface resistance.

forms in terms of the Fourier modulus in (10–2).   Let the thickness of the infinite plate be $2r_1$, and set $x = 0$ in (10–9) and (10–10); for the infinite cylinder set $r = r_1$ in (10–19) and (10–20), and likewise for the sphere in (10–24) and (10–25); for the semi-infinite solid, simply multiply the numerator of both sides in (10–29) by r_1, and the denominator of both sides in (10–30) by r_1, and therewith introduce Θ.   The solutions representing the surface heat rates q_1 and Q_1 for surface areas A_1 are obtained in this way as:

Infinite plate:

$$\frac{q_1 r_1}{kA_1(t_1 - t_i)} = 2 \sum_{n=1}^{\infty} e^{-(n\pi/2)\Theta} \qquad \frac{Q_1\alpha}{kA_1 r_1(t_1 - t_i)} = \frac{8}{\pi^2} \sum_{n=1}^{\infty} \frac{1}{n^2}[1 - e^{-(n\pi/2)^2\Theta}],$$

$$(n = 1, 3, 5, \cdots) \qquad\qquad (n = 1, 3, 5, \cdots)$$

Infinite cylinder:

$$\frac{q_1 r_1}{k A_1(t_1 - t_i)} = 2 \sum_{n=1}^{\infty} e^{-(M_n)^2 \Theta} \qquad \frac{Q_1 \alpha}{k A_1 r_1(t_1 - t_i)} = 2 \sum_{n=1}^{\infty} \frac{1}{M_n^2} [1 - e^{-(M_n)^2 \Theta}],$$

Sphere:

$$\frac{q_1 r_1}{k A_1(t_1 - t_i)} = 2 \sum_{n=1}^{\infty} e^{-(n\pi)^2 \Theta} \qquad \frac{Q_1 \alpha}{k A_1 r_1(t_1 - t_i)} = \frac{2}{\pi^2} \sum_{n=1}^{\infty} \frac{1}{n^2} [1 - e^{-(n\pi)^2 \Theta}],$$

Semi-infinite solid:

$$\frac{q_1 r_1}{k A_1(t_1 - t_i)} = \frac{1}{\sqrt{\pi \Theta}} \qquad \frac{Q_1 \alpha}{k A_1 r_1(t_1 - t_i)} = 2 \sqrt{\frac{\Theta}{\pi}}.$$

These are plotted in Fig. 10–6. Note that the instantaneous rates tend to infinity, while the cumulative rates tend to zero as $\Theta \to 0$.

10–10 Central temperatures in various solids. Instead of deriving separate temperature-time solutions for other important solid shapes such as the short cylinder, cube, and so on, we can obtain these solutions directly by simply combining solutions for the infinite plate, the infinite cylinder, and the semi-infinite solid.

As an example, let $T = X$ be the solution for the temperature history in the semi-infinite plate, where $X = X(x,\theta)$ satisfies $\partial^2 X/\partial x^2 = (1/\alpha)(\partial X/\partial \theta)$. If the y-coordinate were chosen normal to the plate, then $T = Y$ would also be a solution, where $Y = Y(y,\theta)$ satisfies $\partial^2 Y/\partial y^2 = (1/\alpha)(\partial Y/\partial \theta)$. Now we know that $T(x,y,\theta)$ in an infinite rectangular bar must satisfy the partial-differential equation

$$\frac{\partial^2 T}{\partial x^2} + \frac{\partial^2 T}{\partial y^2} = \frac{1}{\alpha} \frac{\partial T}{\partial \theta},$$

and we can prove that $T(x,y,\theta)$ is the simple product

$$T(x,y,\theta) = X(x,\theta) Y(y,\theta),$$

since by differentiating

$$\frac{\partial^2 T}{\partial x^2} = Y \frac{\partial^2 X}{\partial x^2}, \qquad \frac{\partial^2 T}{\partial y^2} = X \frac{\partial^2 Y}{\partial y^2},$$

$$\frac{\partial T}{\partial \theta} = X \frac{\partial Y}{\partial \theta} + Y \frac{\partial X}{\partial \theta} = \alpha X \frac{\partial^2 Y}{\partial y^2} + \alpha Y \frac{\partial^2 X}{\partial x^2},$$

and substituting in the above partial-differential equation, we get the identity

$$Y \frac{\partial^2 X}{\partial x^2} + X \frac{\partial^2 Y}{\partial y^2} = X \frac{\partial^2 Y}{\partial y^2} + Y \frac{\partial^2 X}{\partial x^2}.$$

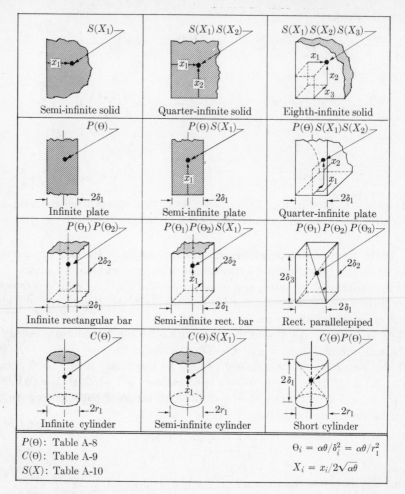

Fig. 10–7. Product solutions for central temperature history in solids, plates, bars, and cylinders with steady surface temperature t_1.

In this way, for example, the temperature at any point on the axis of the infinite rectangular bar is $P(\Theta_1)P(\Theta_2)$ and, similarly, the temperature at the geometric center of a rectangular parallelepiped is $P(\Theta_1)P(\Theta_2)P(\Theta_3)$. If one of the dimensions is unlimited, then we combine the solution for the totally infinite case with the solution for the semi-infinite solid. Thus, the temperature at any point on the axis of a semi-infinite cylinder being $C(\Theta)$, the temperature at a point on the axis of a semi-infinite cylinder and at a point x_1 from its end is $P(\Theta)S(X_1)$. Central temperatures can therefore be computed from $P(\Theta)$, $C(\Theta)$, and $S(X)$ for the twelve solids (1) shown in Fig. 10–7.

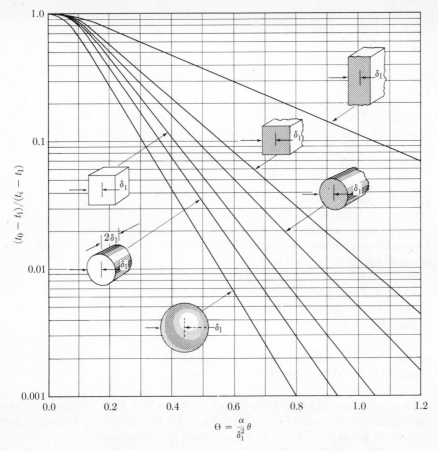

$$\Theta = \frac{\alpha}{\delta_1^2}\theta$$

Fig. 10–8. Central temperature history in an infinite plate, an infinite square rod, an infinite cylinder, a cube, a finite cylinder of length equal to its diameter, and a sphere, with all surfaces at t_1.

EXAMPLE 10–4. A very large cast-iron plate 4″ thick ($\alpha = 0.520$ ft²/hr) which is initially at 500°F throughout has its face and edge surfaces suddenly chilled to, and maintained at, 32°F. After 2 minutes of cooling, what is the temperature at a point halfway through the plate and 6″ in from each of the two perpendicular edges forming a corner?

Solution. We can treat this system as a quarter-infinite plate. Computing first the values of Θ and X:

$$\Theta = \frac{\alpha\theta}{\delta_1^2} = \frac{0.520 \times 2}{60(2/12)^2} = 0.624,$$

$$X_1 = X_2 = \frac{x}{2\sqrt{\alpha\theta}} = \frac{0.5}{2\sqrt{0.520 \times 2/60}} = 1.90,$$

we find in Table A–8 that $P(\Theta) = 0.2730$, and in Table A–10 that $S(X_1) = 0.9928$.

Then

$$T_0 = \frac{t_0 - t_1}{t_i - t_1} = \frac{t_0 - 32}{500 - 32} = P(\Theta)S(X_1)S(X_2) = (0.2730)(0.9928)^2 = 0.269,$$

or $t_0 = 158°F$.

Central temperatures computed in this way are shown in Fig. 10–8 for an infinite plate, an infinite square bar, an infinite cylinder, a cube, a finite cylinder of length equal to its diameter, and finally a sphere.

FINITE INTERNAL AND SURFACE RESISTANCE

We now consider the most realistic cases of heating and cooling in which both the internal and surface resistance of the object must be considered. In these problems the temperature of the ambient medium with which heat is being exchanged is assumed to be uniform, as is the known value of the unit surface conductance h.

10–11 Infinite plate. Consider the convective heating or cooling of a large plate of uniform thickness $2\delta_1$. The plate is initially at a uniform temperature t_i throughout, and at time $\theta = 0$ the plate is suddenly exposed to, or immersed in, a large mass of fluid at t_f. The plate is exposed to these surroundings for all $\theta > 0$, with t_f and the unit surface conductance h remaining uniform throughout the entire heating $(t_f > t)$ or cooling $(t_f < t)$ period.

In an effort to simplify the problem, we select the origin of the x-axis at the center of the plate and therewith take advantage of temperature symmetry about $x = 0$. In this case, then, the temperature history $t(x,\theta)$ must satisfy (10–6) and the initial, symmetry, and convective boundary conditions

$$T = T_i \quad \text{at } \theta = 0,$$

$$\frac{\partial T}{\partial x} = 0 \quad \text{at } x = 0,$$

$$\mp \frac{\partial T}{\partial x} = \frac{h}{k} T \quad \text{at } x = \pm \delta_1,$$

where now $T = t - t_f$. The single boundary condition refers here to a heating process in which $t_f > t_1$, and expresses the fact that the heat given up by the fluid is equal to that gained by the plate at its surfaces $x = \pm\delta$.

The product solutions obtained by separation of (10–6) in Article 10–5 are more conveniently used in this case if expressed in the form

$$T_\lambda = \left(C_1 \cos \frac{\lambda}{\sqrt{\alpha}} x + C_2 \sin \frac{\lambda}{\sqrt{\alpha}} x \right) e^{-\lambda^2\theta}, \tag{10–33}$$

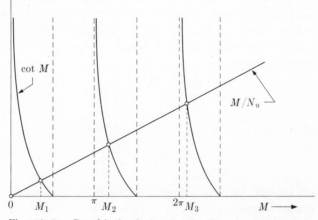

Fig. 10–9.   Graphical solution for the M_n roots of (10–34).

which is easily obtained by simply substituting $\lambda/\sqrt{\alpha}$ for λ.   Then from
the partial derivative of T with respect to x,

$$\frac{\partial T}{\partial x} = \frac{\lambda}{\sqrt{\alpha}} \left(C_2 \cos \frac{\lambda}{\sqrt{\alpha}} x - C_1 \sin \frac{\lambda}{\sqrt{\alpha}} x \right) e^{-\lambda^2 \theta},$$

we see that for temperature symmetry about $x = 0$, $C_2 = 0$, and for T to
satisfy the convective condition at $x = \delta_1$,

$$\frac{\lambda}{\sqrt{\alpha}} e^{-\lambda^2 \theta} C_1 \sin \frac{\lambda}{\sqrt{\alpha}} \delta_1 = \frac{h}{k} e^{-\lambda^2 \theta} C_1 \cos \frac{\lambda}{\sqrt{\alpha}} \delta_1.$$

Multiplying both sides of this equation by $\delta_1/\cos (\lambda \delta_1/\sqrt{\alpha})$, recalling from
(10–13) that we define $M_n = \lambda r_1/\sqrt{\alpha} = \lambda \delta_1/\sqrt{\alpha}$, and introducing the
Nusselt number given in (10–2) as $N_u = h\delta_1/k$, we have

$$M_n \tan M_n = N_u. \qquad (10\text{–}34)$$

This result is analogous to (10–13), where now instead of determining the
eigenvalues M_n as roots of a Bessel equation, the present eigenvalues are
roots of a transcendental equation.   Each value of the Nusselt number N_u
determines an infinite number of real roots M_n, $n = 1, 2, 3, \cdots$.   Even
though these roots cannot be evaluated by ordinary algebraic means, a
graphical determination is possible.   In Fig. 10–9 we indicate the procedure
to be followed.   First graph cot M (only positive values shown), and then
superimpose on this graph the equivalent of cot M, that is, M/N_u.   The
slope of M/N_u is determined by N_u; for $N_u = \infty$ we get the infinite set of
intersections $\pi/2, 3\pi/2, \cdots$ corresponding to the required roots $M_1, M_2, \cdots$.

For any other N_u the slope of the intersecting line M/N_u changes, and we get other infinite sets of roots M_n. The first five roots of (10–34) for selected values of N_u are contained in Table A–12 of the Appendix.

It is now clear that for each eigenvalue λ_n contained in M_n we have a different undetermined constant C_1 as C_n. Then, since the required solution is also the sum of any number of solutions (here one for each n), we can build up the solution

$$T = \sum_{n=1}^{\infty} C_n e^{-\lambda^2 \theta} \cos \frac{\lambda_n}{\sqrt{\alpha}} x,$$

which is yet to satisfy the initial condition as required by

$$T_i = \sum_{n=1}^{\infty} C_n \cos \frac{M_n}{\delta_1} x. \tag{10–35}$$

The result (10–35) presents a new problem in series expansions. If the M_n were simple integers 1, 2, 3, $\cdots$, then (10–35) would represent the usual Fourier cosine expansion of the constant T_i in which the amplitudes C_n would be given by (5–2). In the present problem, however, the M_n are not simple integers but roots of the trigonometric equation (10–34).

To determine the constants C_n in this case, we use the familiar method of multiplying both sides of (10–35) by $\cos (M_m/\delta_1) x dx$, where $m \neq n$, and integrating over the interval in which the expansion of T_i is to hold, i.e.,

$$T_i \int_0^{\delta_1} \cos \frac{M_m}{\delta_1} x dx = \sum_{n=1}^{\infty} C_n \int_0^{\delta_1} \cos \frac{M_m}{\delta_1} x \cos \frac{M_n}{\delta_1} x dx.$$

The integral on the left leads to

$$\int_0^{\delta_1} \cos \frac{M_m}{\delta_1} x dx = \frac{\delta_1}{M_m} \sin M_m,$$

and that on the right to

$$\int_0^{\delta_1} \cos \frac{M_m}{\delta_1} x \cos \frac{M_n}{\delta_1} x dx = \frac{M_m \sin M_m \cos M_n - M_n \sin M_n \cos M_m}{M_m^2 - M_n^2}.$$

But by (10–34),

$$M_m \tan M_m = N_u = M_n \tan M_n,$$

or

$$M_m \sin M_m \cos M_n = M_n \sin M_n \cos M_m.$$

From this we see that if $m \neq n$, then the integral on the right vanishes, and if $m = n$, then the left- and right-hand integrals are, respectively,

$$\frac{\delta_1}{M_n} \sin M_n$$

and

$$\frac{\delta_1}{2} + \frac{\sin 2M_n}{4M_n/\delta_1} \;.$$

The constants C_n must therefore be given by

$$C_n = 4T_i \sin M_n / (2M_n + \sin 2M_n),$$

and this serves to complete the final solution:

$$\frac{t - t_f}{t_i - t_f} = 4 \sum_{n=1}^{\infty} \left(\frac{\sin M_n}{2M_n + \sin 2M_n} \right) e^{-M_n^2 \Theta} \cos M_n \frac{x}{\delta_1} \;. \qquad (10\text{--}36)$$

Note that the temperature-position solution is now a function of two parameters rather than one as in the case of negligible surface resistance, namely, the Fourier modulus $\Theta = \alpha\theta/\delta_1^2$ and the Nusselt number $N_u = h\delta_1/k$ (contained implicitly in M_n) which describes the ratio of surface to internal conductance.

EXAMPLE 10–5.   A rocket-engine nozzle is constructed from a piece of high-temperature steel $\frac{1}{4}''$ thick having a uniform thermal conductivity of 18 Btu/hr-ft-°F and a uniform thermal diffusivity of 0.25 ft²/hr. The flameside unit surface conductance is 1500 Btu/hr-ft²-°F, and the uniform flame temperature during firing is 4000°F. If the nozzle temperature is initially 80°F throughout, and the maximum allowable operating temperature for this particular steel is specified as $t_a = 2000$°F, then what is the permissible combustion duration time θ_D?

Solution.   Since the nozzle diameter is probably large compared with the $\frac{1}{4}''$ thickness of its walls, we can assume that its behavior is close to that of a plane plate of the same thickness. If the nozzle is insulated against heat loss from its outside surface, then we can take $x = 0$ at this outside surface and consider a plate of double thickness $L = \frac{1}{2}''$ with the flameside at $x = \delta_1 = \frac{1}{4}''$.

From the given data,

$$\frac{t_a - t_f}{t_i - t_f} = \frac{2000 - 4000}{80 - 4000} = 0.51, \quad N_u = \frac{h\delta_1}{k} = \frac{1500(0.25/12)}{18} = 1.74.$$

We limit the computation to just the first two terms of the open solution, so that only the first two eigenvalues M_1 and M_2 corresponding to $N_u = 1.74$ are required. From Table A–12, $M_1 = 1.06$ and $M_2 = 3.56$. The maximum allowable temperature t_a will first be reached at the flameside $x = \delta_1$, where the solution (10–36) is

$$\frac{t_1 - t_f}{t_i - t_f} = 2 \sum_{n=1}^{\infty} \left(\frac{1}{1 + 2M_n/\sin 2M_n} \right) e^{-M_n^2 \Theta}.$$

Computing the trigonometric functions

$$\frac{1}{1 + 2M_1/\sin 2M_1} = 1/(1 + 2 \times 1.06/\sin 121.2°) = 0.288,$$

$$\frac{1}{1 + 2M_2/\sin 2M_2} = 1/(1 + 2 \times 3.56/\sin 408°) = 0.094,$$

and the exponential coefficients

$$(\alpha/\delta_1^2)M_1^2 = 0.25(48)^2(1.06)^2 = 646,$$

$$(\alpha/\delta_1^2)M_2^2 = 0.25(48)^2(3.56)^2 = 7295,$$

reduces the solution to the form

$$0.51 = 0.576e^{-646\theta D} + 0.188e^{-7295\theta D},$$

which is found to be satisfied by $\theta_D = 1$ sec. This is to say that one second after firing, the nozzle wall will reach its maximum permissible operating temperature of 2000°F on the exposed surface. Allowable combustion duration times are extended, in practice, by providing the flameside of the nozzle wall with a layer of insulating refractory material.

10–12 Infinite cylinder. Let the initial temperature throughout an infinitely long cylinder be uniform as t_i, and at time $\theta = 0$ let the cylinder be suddenly exposed to convective heating from an ambient fluid at t_f, the unit surface conductance at $r = r_1$ being a uniform h for all $\theta > 0$.

In this case we use the assumed product solutions of Article 10–6,

$$T_\lambda = \left[C_1 J_0\left(\frac{\lambda}{\sqrt{\alpha}}r\right) + C_2 Y_0\left(\frac{\lambda}{\sqrt{\alpha}}r\right)\right]e^{-\lambda^2\theta},$$

or, since Y_0 cannot be present,

$$T_\lambda = C_1 e^{-\lambda^2\theta} J_0\left(\frac{\lambda}{\sqrt{\alpha}}r\right).$$

With the partial derivative with respect to r evaluated as

$$\frac{\partial T}{\partial r} = -C_1 \frac{\lambda}{\sqrt{\alpha}} e^{-\lambda^2\theta} J_1\left(\frac{\lambda}{\sqrt{\alpha}}r\right),$$

we find that for T to satisfy the convective boundary condition $-\partial T/\partial r = hT/k$ at $r = r_1$,

$$C_1 \frac{\lambda}{\sqrt{\alpha}} e^{-\lambda^2\theta} J_1\left(\frac{\lambda r_1}{\sqrt{\alpha}}\right) = C_1 \frac{h}{k} e^{-\lambda^2\theta} J_0\left(\frac{\lambda r_1}{\sqrt{\alpha}}\right),$$

or

$$M_n \frac{J_1(M_n)}{J_0(M_n)} = N_u. \tag{10–37}$$

The first five roots of the eigenfunction Bessel equation (10–37) are contained in Table A–13 of the Appendix.

The solution now takes the form of an infinite series with undetermined coefficients C_n corresponding to the infinite set of eigenvalues for each value of the Nusselt number N_u in (10–37). Thus

$$T = \sum_{n=1}^{\infty} C_n e^{-\lambda^2 \theta} J_0 \left(\frac{M_n}{r_1} r \right),$$

and on applying the initial condition, we have

$$T_i = \sum_{n=1}^{\infty} C_n J_0 \left(M_n \frac{r}{r_1} \right),$$

in which the M_n are roots of (10–37). But this is the same expansion as obtained in Article 10–6 as (10–15). The C_n are therefore given by (10–16), where now $J_0(M_n) \neq 0$ and $T_i(r) = T_i$. Thus

$$C_n = \frac{2T_i}{M_n} \frac{J_1(M_n)}{J_0^2(M_n) + J_1^2(M_n)},$$

and in this way the complete solution becomes

$$\frac{t - t_f}{t_i - t_f} = 2 \sum_{n=1}^{\infty} \frac{1}{M_n} \frac{J_1(M_n)}{J_0^2(M_n) + J_1^2(M_n)} e^{-M_n^2 \theta} J_0 \left(M_n \frac{r}{r_1} \right). \quad (10\text{–}38)$$

10–13 Sphere. A sphere initially at t_i and suddenly exposed to convective heating or cooling is considered in the Problems. In this case the temperature history $t(r, \theta)$ is found to be

$$\frac{t - t_f}{t_i - t_f} = 4 \left(\frac{r_1}{r} \right) \sum_{n=1}^{\infty} \frac{\sin M_n - M_n \cos M_n}{2M_n - \sin 2M_n} e^{-M_n^2 \theta} \sin \left(M_n \frac{r}{r_1} \right), \quad (10\text{–}39)$$

where the M_n are now roots of the transcendental equation

$$1 - M_n \cot M_n = N_u, \quad (10\text{–}40)$$

as tabulated in Table A–14 of the Appendix.*

Solutions for the instantaneous and cumulative surface heat rates for the plate, cylinder, and sphere are derived in the Problems.

Mean temperatures. To compute the mean temperature $\bar{t}(\theta)$ within objects during convective heating or cooling, we simply average the local instantaneous temperatures. Thus, for the infinite plate, infinite cylinder, and sphere, respectively,

$$\frac{\bar{T}}{T_i} = \frac{1}{\delta_1} \int_0^{\delta_1} T \, dx, \quad \frac{\bar{T}}{T_i} = \frac{1}{\pi r_1^2} \int_0^{r_1} 2\pi r T \, dr, \quad \frac{\bar{T}}{T_i} = \frac{1}{\frac{4}{3} \pi r_1^3} \int_0^{r_1} 4\pi r^2 T \, dr,$$

wherewith by (10–36), (10–38), and (10–39):

---

*The reader should keep in mind that the notation M_n has been used here for four different systems. Thus, for an infinite cylinder with zero boundary resistance the M_n are roots of (10–13), and for systems with finite boundary resistance the M_n are roots of (10–34) for the infinite plate, roots of (10–37) for the infinite cylinder, and roots of (10–40) for the sphere.

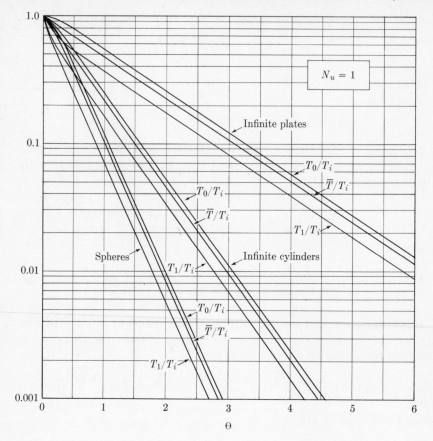

Fig. 10–10. Central, mean, and surface temperature histories for an internal-to-surface resistance ratio equal to one.

Infinite plate:

$$\frac{\bar{t} - t_f}{t_i - t_f} = 2 \sum_{n=1}^{\infty} \frac{1}{M_n} \left[\frac{\sin^2 M_n}{M_n + \sin M_n \cos M_n} \right] e^{-M_n{}^2 \theta}, \qquad (10\text{–}41)$$

Infinite cylinder:

$$\frac{\bar{t} - t_f}{t_i - t_f} = 4 \sum_{n=1}^{\infty} \frac{1}{M_n^2} \left[\frac{1}{1 + J_0^2(M_n)/J_1^2(M_n)} \right] e^{-M_n{}^2 \theta}, \qquad (10\text{–}42)$$

Sphere:

$$\frac{\bar{t} - t_f}{t_i - t_f} = 6 \sum_{n=1}^{\infty} \frac{1}{M_n^2} \left[\frac{(\sin M_n - M_n \cos M_n)^2}{M_n - \sin M_n \cos M_n} \right] e^{-M_n{}^2 \theta}. \quad (10\text{–}43)$$

In Fig. 10–10 we plot, according to (10–41), (10–42), and (10–43), the mean temperature history in an infinite plate, infinite cylinder, and sphere for a particular value of $N_u = 1$, along with central and surface temperature histories for comparison. Since $\ln (\bar{T}/T_i)$ is linear nearly all the way to 1.0, we conclude that the average temperature behaves much like the temperature history during Newtonian heating or cooling, as in Fig. 10–1. For the process represented here, however, temperatures near the center of the object lag behind the temperatures near the surface, the larger the value of N_u the more T_0 and T_1 spread from $\bar{T}$. By decreasing $N_u = h\delta_1/k$, the various position curves converge to $\bar{T}$, this condition corresponding to increasing (for a given δ_1) the surface resistance (decreasing the surface conductance) or decreasing the internal resistance (increasing the internal conductance) as in conditions exemplified by Newtonian heating or cooling.

The time interval between which the same temperature is reached at two different points in the object is called the *transfer lag*. In Newtonian heating or cooling, the transfer lag is zero, i.e., all points reach the same temperature at the same time. On the other hand, the rate of response of an object to temperature change is proportional to the slope of the curves in Fig. 10–10, the response time being in decreasing order from plates, to cylinders, to spheres. Since the slope of the Newtonian curves in Fig. 10–1 are given by (10–1) as $\ln (T/T_i) = (hA_1/CwV)\theta$, it follows that under the condition of Newtonian heating or cooling the response time is $(hA_1/CwV)\theta_c = 1$, or $\theta_c = (CwV)/(hA_1)$, i.e., the product of the total heat capacity and surface resistance. This is called the *capacity lag*. The heating and cooling time of any system is therefore increased or decreased if either its total thermal capacity or surface resistance is increased or decreased, while the difference in rate of response between different points in the system is increased or decreased by decreasing or increasing, respectively, its thermal conductivity.

10–14 Temperature-time charts. Graphical evaluations of (10-36), (10–38), and (10–39) have been presented in a wide variety of forms for practical use. Some of these charts are plotted as T/T_i vs. N_u with Θ as the parameter, while others are plotted as temperature-time charts with the Fourier modulus as the independent variable and the Nusselt number as the parameter. The earliest "Gurney-Lurie" charts are restricted to central and surface temperature histories, and are limited to a rather small range of Θ and N_u. Additional charts have appeared over the years which not only encompass a larger range of conditions but include central, surface, and mean temperatures for the infinite plate, infinite cylinder, and sphere.

Heisler (2) has developed temperature-time charts of the Gurney-Lurie type for a large range of the Nusselt parameter from $N_u = 0.01$ to ∞, and a large range of Θ. The Heisler charts shown in Fig. 10–11(a) are for the central temperature history T_0/T_i in infinite plates and infinite cylinders as a function of the Fourier modulus Θ and reciprocal Nusselt number $1/N_u$.

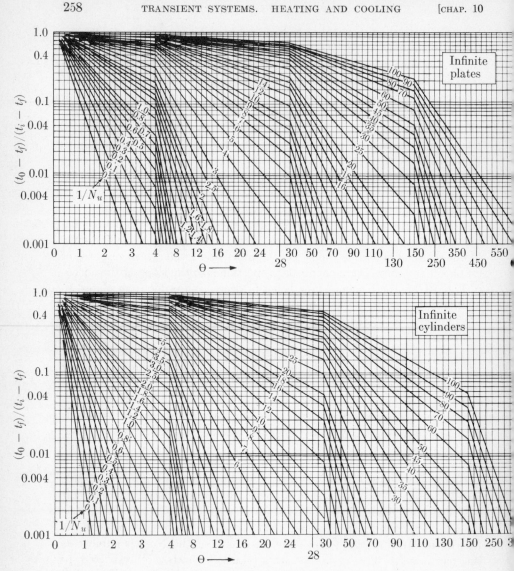

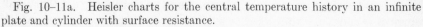

Fig. 10–11a. Heisler charts for the central temperature history in an infinite plate and cylinder with surface resistance.

Figure 10–11(b) shows a companion Heisler "position-correction" chart with $T'_{x,r}/T_0$ plotted against $1/N_u$ and with the relative position x/δ_1 for the plate or r/r_1 for the cylinder as parameters. The temperature at any point within the plate or cylinder, T/T_i, is determined by multiplying the values of T_0/T_i for particular values of Θ and $1/N_u$ from Fig. 10–11(a) by the value of T'_x/T_0 or T'_r/T_0 at the corresponding value of $1/N_u$ in Fig. 10–11(b).

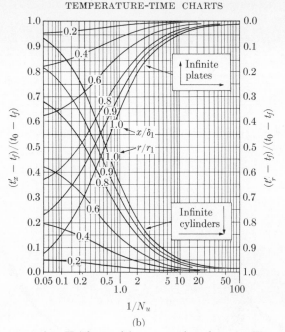

(b)

Fig. 10–11b.   Heisler position-correction chart for Fig. 10–11a.

From Fig. 10–11(b) we see that the temperature distribution through the plate or cylinder is nearly uniform for values of $1/N_u = k/h\delta_1$ greater than, say, 10. It is therefore permissible, as a first approximation, to consider the heating or cooling process for such cases as being controlled solely by surface resistance, the uniform temperature then being given by (10–3) for Newtonian heating or cooling.

EXAMPLE 10–6.   A long piece of cylindrical iron bar stock 5″ in diameter is heated in a furnace to a uniform temperature of 400°F, after which it is removed and left to cool in a forced-air cooler. If the unit surface conductance between its surface and ambient air at 80°F is estimated to be 29 Btu/hr-ft²-°F, then: (a) How long would it take for the center of the stock to cool down to 100°F? (b) What would be its mid-radius and surface temperatures at this time? (c) What would be the error in the answer to (a) if the cooling process were assumed to be Newtonian?

Solution.   (a) From Table 1–2, $k = 36$ Btu/hr-ft-°F and $1/\alpha = 1.280$ hr/ft². Then with the temperature ratio T_0/T_i and reciprocal Nusselt number computed as

$$\frac{t_0 - t_f}{t_i - t_f} = \frac{100 - 80}{400 - 80} = 0.0625, \quad \frac{1}{N_u} = \frac{k}{hr_1} = \frac{36 \times 12}{29 \times 2.5} = 5.96,$$

we enter the lower chart of Fig. 10–11(a) and find $\Theta = 8.5$, from which

$$\theta = \frac{\Theta r_1^2}{\alpha} = \frac{8.5(2.5)^2 1.280}{144} = 0.472,$$

or $\theta = 28$ min, 21 sec.

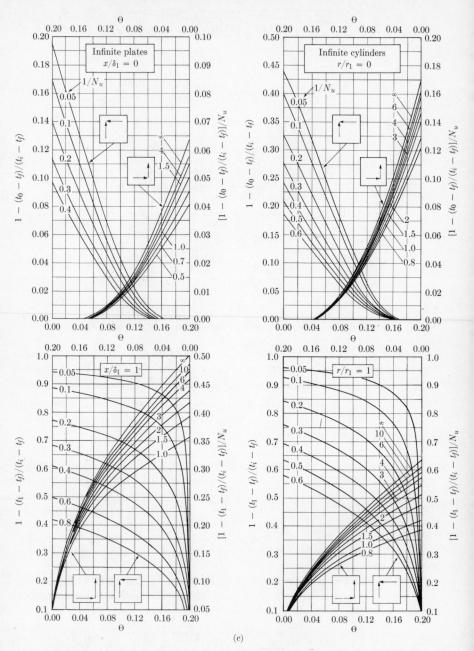

Fig. 10–11c.   Heisler short-time charts for the central and surface temperature histories in an infinite plate and cylinder with surface resistance.

(b) Entering Fig. 10–11(b) with $1/N_u = 5.96$ and $r/r_1 = 0.5$, we find a mid-radius position correction of $T'_{1/2}/T_0 = 0.965$, so that

$$\frac{T'_{1/2}}{T_0}\frac{T_0}{T_i} = 0.965 \times 0.0625 = \frac{t_{1/2} - 80}{400 - 80},$$

or $t_{1/2} = 99.3°F$. A position correction for the surface $r/r_1 = 1$ is found in Fig. 10–11(b) to be $T'_1/T_0 = 0.920$, whereby

$$\frac{t_1 - 80}{400 - 80} = 0.920 \times 0.0625,$$

or $t_1 = 98.4°F$.

(c) If the cooling process were assumed to be Newtonian, then by (10–3) with $A_1 r_1/V = 2$,

$$\ln \frac{T_0}{T_i} = -2N_u \Theta,$$

wherewith

$$\Theta = \frac{1}{2N_u} \ln \frac{T_i}{T_0} = \frac{5.96}{2} \ln \frac{1}{0.0625} = 8.3 = \frac{\alpha\theta}{r_1^2}.$$

This gives an estimated cooling time of $\theta = 8.3(2.5)^2 1.280/144 = 0.461$, or $\theta = 27$ min, 39 sec, an error of approximately $-0.70/28.35 = -2.5\%$.

The temperatures at this approximate time would all be

$$\frac{t - 80}{400 - 80} = e^{-2N_u\Theta} = e^{-2.78} = 0.062,$$

or $t = 99.8°F$.

It is apparent that the charts of Figs. 10–11(a) and (b) are not useful in the lower range of $1/N_u$ and Θ, as might be required for short heating or cooling periods which occur, for example, in the heat treatment of metals by quenching. The series solutions in this range converge very slowly, and hence detailed temperature calculations for small Θ are tedious and inaccurate unless a great many terms are computed. For these reasons, Heisler (2) has also developed "short-time" charts for values of $1/N_u$ from 0.05 to ∞ and a range of small Θ from 0 to 0.2. The complete charts for central and surface temperatures in an infinite plate and infinite cylinder are shown in Fig. 10–11(c). The short-time curves for the plate surface temperature at $x/\delta_1 = 1$ were computed, while the other charts were obtained by "electrical analogy" (Article 13–9) with the Heat and Mass-Flow Analyzer at Columbia University. Charts similar to Figs. 10–11(a), (b), and (c) have also been developed for the sphere (2).

EXAMPLE 10–7. A long metal bar of rectangular cross section $4'' \times 2''$ ($x_1 = \delta_1 = 2''$, $y_1 = \delta_2 = 1''$) is heated to a uniform temperature of 500°F, and then suddenly quenched in a large mass of fluid at 100°F. The bar material is anisotropic, with thermal conductivities in the x- and y-directions of $k_x = 20$ and $k_y = 5$ Btu/hr-ft-°F, and thermal diffusivities of $\alpha_x = 5.55$ and $\alpha_y = 1.00$ ft^2/hr. If the unit surface conductance during the quenching process is estimated to be a uniform 240 Btu/hr-ft^2-°F, then: (a) What is the central temperature in the bar after 3 sec of quenching? (b) What is the surface temperature t_1 at the center of its short face ($x = \delta_1$, $y = 0$), the center of its long face ($x = 0$, $y = \delta_2$), and at its edge ($x = \delta_1$, $y = \delta_2$)?

Solution. In this case the two-dimensional temperatures are computed as products of one-dimensional solutions, as in Article 10–10, and the anisotropic property dealt with by computing separate Nusselt numbers and Fourier moduli in the two directions as

$$(1/N_u)_x = \frac{k_x}{h\delta_1} = \frac{20 \times 12}{240 \times 2} = 0.50,$$

$$(1/N_u)_y = \frac{k_y}{h\delta_2} = \frac{5 \times 12}{240 \times 1} = 0.25,$$

and

$$\Theta_x = \frac{\alpha_x \theta}{\delta_1^2} = \frac{5.55(3/3600)}{(2/12)^2} = 0.166,$$

$$\Theta_y = \frac{\alpha_y \theta}{\delta_2^2} = \frac{1.00(3/3600)}{(1/12)^2} = 0.120.$$

(a) Since the Θ's are less than 0.2, we will have to use the short-time charts. Entering the infinite-plate curves of Fig. 10–11(c), we find that the central temperature for an infinite plate in the y-direction from the ordinate corresponding to $(1/N_u)_x$ and Θ_x

$$\left(\frac{T_0}{T_i}\right)_x = 1 - 0.028N_{v_x} = 0.944,$$

and in like fashion for an infinite plate in the x-direction,

$$\left(\frac{T_0}{T_i}\right)_y = 1 - 0.042 = 0.958.$$

In this way

$$\frac{t_0 - 100}{500 - 100} = 0.944 \times 0.958 = 0.904,$$

or $t_0 = 462$°F.

(b) For the surface temperature $t_{x,y} = t_{\delta_1,0}$, we use the product of T_1/T_i for an infinite plate in the y-direction and T_0/T_i for an infinite plate in the x-direction. Entering the curves for $x/\delta_1 = 1$ in Fig. 10–11(c), we find

$$\left(\frac{T_1}{T_i}\right)_x = 1 - 0.530 = 0.470,$$

so that

$$\frac{t_{\delta_1,0} - 100}{500 - 100} = 0.470 \times 0.958 = 0.450,$$

or $t_{\delta_1,0} = 280$°F.

By the same procedure for the surface temperature $t_{x,y} = t_{0,\delta_2}$, we find

$$\left(\frac{T_1}{T_i}\right)_y = 1 - 0.670 = 0.330$$

so that

$$\frac{t_{0,\delta_2} - 100}{500 - 100} = 0.944 \times 0.330 = 0.312,$$

or $t_{0,\delta_2} = 225°F$.

For the edge temperature $t_{x,y} = t_{\delta_1,\delta_2}$, we use the product of the surface solutions,

$$\frac{t_{\delta_1,\delta_2} - 100}{500 - 100} = 0.470 \times 0.330 = 0.155,$$

whereby $t_{\delta_1,\delta_2} = 162°F$.

10–15 Semi-infinite solid. We consider the same semi-infinite solid as in Article 10–8, except that here a surface resistance $1/hA$ at the face $x = 0$ is to be taken into account. With a convection boundary condition, only uniform values of the unit surface conductance h and ambient fluid temperature t_f are known. Then if the initial temperature state of the solid is uniform, we have to find a solution $t(x,\theta)$ of

$$\frac{\partial^2 t}{\partial x^2} = \frac{1}{\alpha}\frac{\partial t}{\partial \theta},$$

which will satisfy the initial and boundary conditions

$$t = t_i \qquad\qquad \text{at } \theta = 0; \quad x \geq 0,$$

$$\frac{\partial t}{\partial x} = \frac{h}{k}(t - t_f) \quad \text{at } x = 0; \quad \theta > 0.$$

Since the solution of this particular problem is not as easily determined by the use of the Fourier integral (Article 10–8) as it is by use of the *Laplace transformation*, we shall use the latter method as described in Articles 5–9 and 5–10. With this in mind, let $T = t - t_i$, so that $T_i = 0$ and $(t - t_f) = T - (t_f - t_i) = T - T_f$. In this way the partial-differential equation, along with the required initial and boundary conditions, is transformed into

$$\frac{\partial^2 T}{\partial x^2} = \frac{1}{\alpha}\frac{\partial T}{\partial \theta}, \qquad\qquad (10\text{–}44)$$

and

$$T = 0 \qquad\qquad \text{at } \theta = 0; \quad x \geq 0,$$

$$\frac{\partial T}{\partial x} = \frac{h}{k}(T - T_f) \quad \text{at } x = 0; \quad \theta > 0.$$

The *subsidiary equation* of (10–44) is derived, as in Article 5–10, by applying the Laplace transformation $\mathcal{L}(u)$ [(5–24)] with respect to θ on both sides of (10–44) according to

$$\int_0^\infty e^{-u\theta} \frac{\partial^2 T}{\partial x^2}\, d\theta = \frac{1}{\alpha} \int_0^\infty e^{-u\theta} \frac{\partial T}{\partial \theta}\, d\theta.$$

After interchanging the order of integration and differentiation on the left side, and expressing the right side in terms of its algebraic *transform* (5–25), we have

$$\frac{\partial^2}{\partial x^2} \int_0^\infty e^{-u\theta} T(x,\theta)\, d\theta = \frac{1}{\alpha} [u\mathcal{L}(u) - T(x,0)].$$

The left side is now a function of x alone, and in this case $T(x,0) = T_i = 0$. The subsidiary total-differential equation is therefore

$$\frac{d^2 \bar{u}}{dx^2} = \frac{u}{\alpha}\, \bar{u}, \tag{10–45}$$

where $\bar{u}$ is the abbreviation in (5–30) as $\bar{u} = \mathcal{L}(u)$. The boundary condition for the subsidiary equation (10–45) is a subsidiary equation corresponding to the boundary condition for (10–44). Since the transform of a constant is $1/u$ (Table 5–1), we have as the boundary condition to be satisfied by the general solution of (10–45)

$$\frac{d\bar{u}}{dx} = \frac{h}{k}\, \bar{u} - \frac{hT_f}{k} \frac{1}{u} \quad \text{at } x = 0,\ \theta > 0\cdot \tag{10–46}$$

Now the general solution of (10–45) is evidently given by

$$\bar{u} = C_1 e^{\sqrt{u/\alpha}\, x} + C_2 e^{-\sqrt{u/\alpha}\, x}.$$

But if T, and therefore u, is to remain finite as $x \to \infty$, then $C_1 = 0$ and

$$\bar{u} = C e^{-\sqrt{u/\alpha}\, x}.$$

The value of the integration constant C for which this general solution satisfies (10–46) is determined as

$$C = \frac{hT_f}{ku(h/k + \sqrt{u/\alpha})},$$

and hence

$$\bar{u} = \frac{hT_f}{ku(h/k + \sqrt{u/\alpha})} e^{-\sqrt{u/\alpha}\, x}. \tag{10–47}$$

The *inverse transform* of (10–47) can be determined directly from a table of transform pairs. Carslaw and Jaeger (3), for example, list* the trans-

---

*No. 14 of Appendix V, p. 380, (3).

form of

$$\frac{e^{-\sqrt{u/\alpha}\,x}}{u(h/k + \sqrt{u/\alpha})}$$

as

$$\frac{k}{h}\,\mathrm{erfc}\left(\frac{x}{2\sqrt{\alpha\theta}}\right) - \frac{k}{h}\,e^{(h/k)x+(h^2\alpha/k^2)\theta}\,\mathrm{erfc}\left(\frac{x}{2\sqrt{\alpha\theta}} + \frac{h}{k}\,\sqrt{\alpha\theta}\right),$$

where *erfc*, which is known as the *complementary error function*, is defined in terms of *erf* (Table A–10) as the difference*

$$\mathrm{erfc}\,(X) = 1 - \mathrm{erf}\,(X) = \frac{2}{\sqrt{\pi}}\int_X^\infty e^{-\lambda^2}d\lambda. \qquad (10\text{–}48)$$

The inverse transform of (10–47) is therefore, by comparison,

$$\frac{T}{T_f} = \mathrm{erfc}\left(\frac{x}{2\sqrt{\alpha\theta}}\right) - e^{h\sqrt{\alpha\theta}/k\,(x/\sqrt{\alpha\theta}+h\sqrt{\alpha\theta}/k)}\,\mathrm{erfc}\left(\frac{x}{2\sqrt{\alpha\theta}} + \frac{h}{k}\,\sqrt{\alpha\theta}\right),$$

or, in terms of $X = x/2\sqrt{\alpha\theta}$ and $N_u\sqrt{\Theta} = (h/k)\sqrt{\alpha\theta}$,

$$\frac{t - t_i}{t_f - t_i} = \mathrm{erfc}\,(X) - e^{N_u\sqrt{\Theta}\,(2X+N_u\sqrt{\Theta})}\,\mathrm{erfc}\,(X + N_u\sqrt{\Theta}). \quad (10\text{–}49)$$

The final solution represented by (10–49) is shown in Fig. 10–12.

EXAMPLE 10–8. During a late Fall day, a sudden cold wave reduces the ambient air temperature to $-10°F$. If the earth was at a uniform temperature of 60°F before the onset of the cold wave, then what is the surface temperature after 3 hours, and to what depth in the earth will the freezing temperature have penetrated in this time?

Solution. We neglect latent-heat effects, consider the upper layers of the earth to have been at a substantially uniform temperature of 60°F, and assume that the air temperature was suddenly reduced to, and maintained at, $-10°F$. Then, by selecting $\alpha = 0.0456$ ft^2/hr, $k = 1.5$ Btu/hr-ft-°F, and $h = 5$ Btu/hr-ft^2-°F, we can compute the parameter $N_u\,\Theta$ as

$$\frac{h}{k}\,\sqrt{\alpha\theta} = \frac{5}{1.5}\,\sqrt{0.0456 \times 3} = \frac{5}{1.5} \times 0.370 = 1.233$$

and enter Fig. 10–12 at $X = 0$. The surface temperature ratio is found to be

$$\frac{t_1 - 60}{-10 - 60} = 0.625,$$

from which $t_1 = 16.2°F$.

---

*This can be shown by integrating from 0 to ∞ and subtracting an integration from X to ∞. Thus from (10–28) with erf (0) = 0 and erf (∞) = 1, we have

$$\mathrm{erf}\,(X) = \int_0^X = \int_0^\infty - \int_X^\infty = 1 - 0 - \int_X^\infty = 1 - \mathrm{erfc}\,(X).$$

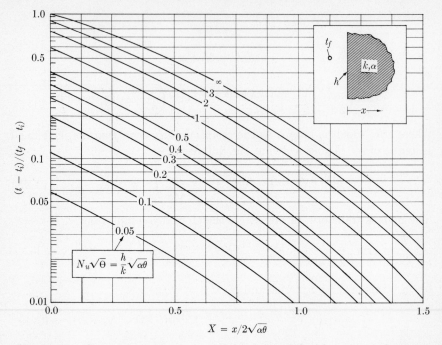

$$X = x/2\sqrt{\alpha\theta}$$

Fig. 10–12.   Temperature history in a semi-infinite solid with surface resistance.

To locate the freezing temperature we enter Fig. 10–12 with a temperature ratio of $(32 - 60)/(-10 - 60) = 0.4$, and read from the interpolated curve for $N_u\sqrt{\Theta} = 1.233$ the abscissa

$$X = \frac{x}{2\sqrt{\alpha\theta}} = 0.197.$$

The freezing temperature has therefore penetrated after 3 hours to a depth of approximately $x = 0.197 \times 2 \times 0.370 = 0.146$, or $1\frac{3}{4}$ inches.

EXAMPLE 10–9.   A large mass of aluminum cools by radiation from an initial uniform temperature of 1200°F to the temperature of surrounding air, at 100°F. The radiation unit surface conductance at the free face $x = 0$ is a function of temperature according to

$$h_R = \frac{14 \times 10^{-10}(t_{a_1}^4 - t_{a_f}^4)}{(t_1 - t_f)},$$

where t_{a_1} is the *absolute* temperature (Rankine) of the radiating surface, and t_{a_f} is the absolute temperature of the receiver.   What is the surface temperature of the aluminum mass after a 10-hour period of cooling?

Solution.   Since the solution (10–49) for the semi-infinite solid is based on a uniform surface conductance, we shall have to assume a mean surface temperature for the calculation of h_R, and subsequently recompute h_R on the basis of new mean temperatures until the surface temperatures obtained finally converge.

Based on $t_{1_1} = 1200°F$, the calculated value of h_R is

$$h_R = \frac{14 \times 10^{-10}[(1200 + 460)^4 - (100 + 460)^4]}{(1200 - 100)} = 9.54.$$

From Table 1–2, $1/\alpha = 0.262$ hr/ft^2 and $k = 117$ Btu/hr-ft-°F. Then $\sqrt{\alpha\theta}/k$ $= \sqrt{10/0.262}/117 = 0.0528$, and $N_u\sqrt{\Theta} = (h_R/k)\sqrt{\alpha\theta} = 9.54 \times 0.0528 = 0.504$. From the solution (10–49) with $X = 0$ (Table A–10),

$$\frac{T_1}{T_f} = 1 - e^{\overline{0.504}^2} \text{ erfc } (0.504) = \frac{t_1 - 1200}{100 - 1200},$$

whereby $t_1 = 766°F$.

The actual value of t_1 must be higher than 766°F because h_R is not as high as 9.54 through the entire cooling interval. A recalculated value of h_R, based this time on a mean radiating temperature of $t_{1_2} = (1200 + 766)/2 = 983°F$, becomes

$$h_R = \frac{14 \times 10^{-10}[(983 + 460)^4 - (100 + 460)^4]}{(983 - 100)} = 6.74.$$

Then $(h_R/k)\sqrt{\alpha\theta} = 6.74 \times 0.0528 = 0.356$, and

$$\frac{T_1}{T_f} = 1 - e^{\overline{0.356}^2} \text{ erfc } (0.356) = \frac{t_1 - 1200}{100 - 1200}.$$

This gives the second estimate of the surface temperature as $t_1 = 860°F$, or nearly 100°F higher than the first approximation.

A second recalculation of h_R based on a mean radiating temperature of $t_{1_3} = (1200 + 860)/2 = 1030$ gives $h_R = 7.26$, $(h_R/k)\sqrt{\alpha\theta} = 0.384$, $T_1/T_f = 0.316$, and finally $t_1 = 852°F$.

A fourth estimate based on a mean of $t_{1_4} = 1026°F$ gives a surface temperature of $t_1 = 850°F$. Since the fifth approximation would be based on $t_{1_5} = 1025°F$, which differs by only one degree from the fourth estimate, we stop here and take $t_1 = 850°F$ as the final answer for the surface temperature after 10 hours of cooling.

10–16 Closure. In addition to the problems considered in this chapter, there are still other systems within the special class of heating and cooling which have important technical and industrial applications. Carslaw and Jaeger (3) present a large number of analytical solutions in this class, many of which are obtained by the Laplace transform method. Ingersoll and Zobel (4) illustrate a wide variety of interesting applications for solutions of the infinite and semi-infinite solid such as the cooling of concrete, welding, contact-surface temperatures, thawing, shrink fittings, heat-treatment of metals, and a variety of important geological calculations.

There are several additional analytical devices which we shall mention here as being occasionally helpful in obtaining solutions of this sort. Suppose, for example, that we wish to find a solution for the temperature history in a quarter-infinite solid with steady but arbitrary surface temperatures $t(x,0)$ along $y = 0$ and $t(0,y)$ along $x = 0$ for all $\theta > 0$. The solution $t(x,y,\theta)$ must then satisfy

$$\frac{\partial^2 t}{\partial x^2} + \frac{\partial^2 t}{\partial y^2} = \frac{1}{\alpha} \frac{\partial t}{\partial \theta},$$

and if the initial temperature is also nonuniform,

$$t = t(x,y) \quad \text{at } \theta = 0,$$
$$t = t(x) \quad \text{at } y = 0, \theta > 0,$$
$$t = t(y) \quad \text{at } x = 0, \theta > 0.$$

But if we let

$$t = u + v; \quad u = u(x,y), v = v(x,y,\theta),$$

then it can be shown that u must satisfy

$$\frac{\partial^2 u}{\partial x^2} + \frac{\partial^2 u}{\partial y^2} = 0,$$

and the boundary conditions

$$u = t(x) \quad \text{at } y = 0,$$
$$u = t(y) \quad \text{at } x = 0,$$

which represents the steady-state solution, and that v must satisfy

$$\frac{\partial^2 v}{\partial x^2} + \frac{\partial^2 v}{\partial y^2} = \frac{1}{\alpha} \frac{\partial v}{\partial \theta},$$

and the boundary conditions

$$v = t(x,y) - u \quad \text{at } \theta = 0,$$
$$v = 0 \quad \text{at } x = 0, y = 0.$$

Difficulties which might arise with a convection boundary condition can also be avoided in some cases by treating the system as one with a homogeneous boundary condition. Suppose that we wish to find a solution $T(x,\theta)$ of

$$\frac{\partial^2 T}{\partial x^2} = \frac{1}{\alpha} \frac{\partial T}{\partial \theta},$$

which satisfies

$$T = T_i \quad \text{at } \theta = 0, x \geq 0,$$
$$\frac{\partial T}{\partial x} = \frac{h}{k} T \quad \text{at } x = 0, \theta > 0.$$

If we let

$$\xi = T - \frac{k}{h} \frac{\partial T}{\partial x},$$

then

$$\frac{\partial^2 T}{\partial x^2} = \frac{\partial^2 \xi}{\partial x^2} + \frac{k}{h} \frac{\partial}{\partial x} \left(\frac{\partial^2 T}{\partial x^2} \right) = \frac{\partial^2 \xi}{\partial x^2} + \frac{k}{h\alpha} \frac{\partial}{\partial x} \left(\frac{\partial T}{\partial \theta} \right),$$

and

$$\frac{1}{\alpha} \frac{\partial T}{\partial \theta} = \frac{1}{\alpha} \frac{\partial \xi}{\partial \theta} + \frac{k}{h\alpha} \frac{\partial}{\partial \theta} \left(\frac{\partial T}{\partial x} \right) = \frac{1}{\alpha} \frac{\partial \xi}{\partial \theta} + \frac{k}{h\alpha} \frac{\partial}{\partial x} \left(\frac{\partial T}{\partial \theta} \right),$$

or

$$\frac{\partial^2 \xi}{\partial x^2} = \frac{1}{\alpha} \frac{\partial \xi}{\partial \theta}.$$

Then, since $\partial T_i / \partial x = 0$, the initial and boundary conditions to be satisfied by ξ are simply

$$\xi = T_i \quad \text{at } \theta = 0,\ x \geq 0,$$

$$\xi = 0 \quad \text{at } x = 0,\ \theta > 0.$$

With a solution obtained in this way, the original solution in T is determined by an integration of ξ.

REFERENCES

1. F. C. W. Olson and O. T. Schultz, "Temperatures in Solids during Heating or Cooling," *Industrial and Engineering Chemistry*, Vol. 34, July, 1942, pp. 874–877.

2. M. P. Heisler, "Temperature Charts for Induction and Constant-Temperature Heating," *Trans. ASME*, Vol. 69, April, 1947, pp. 227–236.

3. H. S. Carslaw and J. C. Jaeger, *Conduction of Heat in Solids*. London: Oxford University Press, 1947.

4. L. R. Ingersoll, O. J. Zobel, and A. C. Ingersoll, *Heat Conduction (With Engineering and Geological Applications)*. New York: McGraw-Hill, 1948.

PROBLEMS

10–1. A large nickel plate, $1''$ thick, (Table 1–2) is heated to a uniform temperature of 2000°F prior to cold-working the metal in ambient air at 80°F. Neglecting the internal thermal resistance of the plate, and assuming a uniform unit surface conductance of 6 Btu/hr-ft²-°F, show that the working process must be completed within approximately $4\frac{1}{2}$ minutes if the minimum cold-working temperature for this metal is 1680°F.

10–2. A gas-fired preheater for a wind tunnel facility is to absorb 200,000 Btu during a three-minute heating period. The preheater contains 10,000 solid copper spheres $1''$ in diameter and at a uniform initial temperature of 100°F. Neglecting the internal thermal resistance of the spheres, and assuming a uniform unit surface conductance of 25 Btu/hr-ft²-°F, show that the gas temperature must be at least 1655°F.

10–3. A large wall, 3″ thick, of uniform thermal conductivity 10 Btu/hr-ft-°F, thermal capacity 0.8 Btu/lb-°F, and specific weight 80 lb/ft³ has its surface temperature suddenly raised to and maintained at 800°F. If the wall is initially at 80°F throughout, compute the temperature and instantaneous heat rate half-way through the wall after 2 minutes of heating, and check with graphical results in the text.

10–4. A long cylinder, 24″ in diameter, of thermal conductivity 1 Btu/hr-ft-°F and thermal diffusivity 0.1 ft²/hr is initially at a uniform temperature of 1000°F. If its surface temperature is suddenly reduced to and maintained at 32°F, compute its central temperature and cumulative surface heat rate after 2 hours, and check with tabulated and graphical results in the text.

10–5. A rod with insulated surfaces and insulated ends $x = O, L$ has an initial temperature distribution $T(x,0) = T_i(x)$. Derive the solution for the temperature history ($\theta > 0$) as

$$T = \frac{2}{L} \sum_{n=0}^{\infty} e^{-n^2\pi^2\theta} \cos \frac{n\pi}{L} x \int_0^L T_i(x) \cos \frac{n\pi}{L} x dx.$$

10–6. Derive the solutions (10–22), (10–23), (10–24), and (10–25) for the general and central temperature history and instantaneous and cumulative heat rates in a solid sphere initially at t_i and with its surface $r = r_1$ maintained at t_1 for $\theta > 0$.

10–7. A cold wave suddenly reduces and maintains the surface temperature of the earth at $-10°F$. Using the data of Example 10–8, show that (a) after three hours the freezing temperature will have penetrated to a depth of 5.4″ below the earth's surface, (b) at this time and depth the rate of cooling is approximately $5\frac{1}{2}°F/hr$.

10–8. Using (10–31), show that the maximum time rate of cooling, $\dfrac{\partial}{\partial\theta}\left(\partial T/\partial x\right)$, in a semi-infinite solid occurs at a depth equal to $\sqrt{6\alpha\theta}$. Based on Kelvin's estimate of the earth's age (footnote, p. 243), show that this maximum time rate-of-change in cooling is occurring at a depth of 5170 ft, or approximately 1 mile below the earth's surface.

10–9. A long iron rod of rectangular cross section 4″ × 8″ is initially at a uniform temperature of 80°F. If the temperature of its surfaces is suddenly raised to and maintained at 212°F, show that after an elapse of 1 minute the temperature of a point on its axis 3″ from one end is approximately 169°F.

10–10. A food-processing plant is interested in canning a perishable food of thermal diffusivity 0.08 ft²/hr in 30 in.³ containers. The food is to be chilled in the containers from 110°F by placing them in a liquid bath which suddenly lowers the container surface temperature to 40°F. The maximum temperature at any point in the food must not be above 50°F at the end of 5 minutes in the bath. Of the three container shapes, cubical, cylindrical (diameter equal to length), and spherical, show that the spherical container is the only shape which will not satisfy this requirement.

10–11. With reference to problem 10–10: (a) show that the average temperature in the cylindrical container is given by

$$\frac{\bar{t} - t_1}{t_i - t_1} = \frac{32}{\pi^2 r_1^2} \sum_{m=1}^{\infty} \sum_{n=1}^{\infty} \frac{1}{m^2 M_n^2} e^{-[(\pi m/L)^2 + M_n^2]\alpha\theta},$$

so that $\bar{t} = 42.2°F$.

(b) Show that the average temperature in the spherical container is given by

$$\frac{\bar{t} - t_1}{t_i - t_1} = \frac{6}{\pi^2} \sum_{n=1}^{\infty} \frac{1}{n^2} e^{-n^2 \pi^2 \theta},$$

so that $\bar{t} = 43.4°F$.

(c) If $k = 1$ Btu/hr-ft-°F, show that the instantaneous and cumulative surface heat rates for the spherical container are 22.3 Btu/hr and 8.5 Btu.

10–12. Derive the solution (10–39) for the temperature history in a solid sphere with surface resistance.

10–13. Following Article 10–9, derive and plot solutions for the instantaneous and cumulative surface heat rates in the plate, cylinder, and sphere of Articles 10–11, 10–12, and 10–13.

10–14. With reference to the nozzle in Example 10–5, (a) show that the mean nozzle temperature is 835°F at the end of the allowable combustion time, (b) show that at this time the instantaneous heat rate (problem 10–13) at the flameside is 890 Btu/sec per square foot of surface, (c) show that at this time the cumulative heat rate (problem 10–13) at the flameside is 4750 Btu per square foot of surface.

10–15. An 18-gage (0.04″ diameter) iron wire is used in a thermocouple to measure the temperature of still air. If the unit surface conductance for the wire is estimated to be 6 Btu/hr-ft²-°F, show that its capacity lag is approximately 26 seconds.

10–16. A large plate 5″ thick has a thermal conductivity of 100 Btu/hr-ft-°F, a thermal capacity of 0.4 Btu/lb-°F, and a specific weight of 80 lb/ft³. The wall is well insulated on one side, and exposed to a sudden flash fire at 1000°F on the other side. If the initial wall temperature is 80°F throughout, and the unit surface conductance at the exposed face is 15 Btu/hr-ft²-°F, show (using the Heisler charts) that the temperature of this exposed face is 707°F after 1 hour.

10–17. A 6″ length of solid cylinder 6″ in diameter has a thermal conductivity of 1 Btu/hr-ft-°F and a thermal diffusivity of 0.01 ft²/hr. The cylinder is initially at a uniform temperature of 500°F, and cools in ambient air at 80°F with a unit surface conductance of 10 Btu/hr-ft²-°F. Using the Heisler short-time charts, show that after 1 hour of cooling, (a) the temperature at the geometric center of the cylinder is 413°F, (b) the temperature at the center of the end faces is 232°F, (c) the temperature at the surface midway between the two end faces is 220°F, (d) the temperature at the end-face edges is 144°F.

10–18. A large semi-infinite mass of iron is heated to a uniform temperature of 1000°F, and then left to cool by free convection in 100°F ambient air. If the unit surface conductance is given by

$$h = 0.22(t - t_f)^{1/3},$$

show that the surface temperature of the iron is approximately 795°F after one day of cooling.

CHAPTER 11

TRANSIENT SYSTEMS. UNSTEADY BOUNDARY CONDITIONS, STATIONARY AND MOVING SOURCES

In this chapter we examine the important class of transient systems in which boundary conditions are a function of time. A few special cases considered are those of linearly increasing surface temperature, and the periodic flow system for which the surface temperature undergoes a regular periodic change with time. Also considered in this chapter are the practical cases of transient heat flow in systems with internal heat sources, and systems in which transient flow is caused by a moving source of heat within the solid.

TRANSIENT BOUNDARY CONDITIONS

11–1 Duhamel's method. In the classification of transient systems we make a distinction between steady and unsteady (transient) boundary conditions. In the systems of Chapter 10, for example, the boundary conditions were all steady; this meant that either the surface or ambient temperature did not vary with time, even though in the case of steady ambient temperatures the surface temperatures were distinctly transient. In the latter classification, the variation with time of surface or ambient temperatures are specified by the required transient boundary conditions themselves.

While systems with transient boundary conditions can also be treated by the conventional approach, such problems are generally easier to handle by the Laplace transform method or by Duhamel's theorem. The Duhamel method can be applied to systems with arbitrary distributions of initial temperature, and for cases in which the surface temperature or the temperature of the ambient fluid varies not only with time but with position as well.

Consider the application of Duhamel's theorem to a semi-infinite solid which is initially at a uniform temperature t_i throughout, and for which, at time $\theta = 0$, its surface $x = 0$ begins to undergo a general temperature change with time, $t_1(\theta)$. In this case the general temperature history $t(x,\theta)$ within the solid must satisfy the usual partial-differential equation

$$\frac{\partial^2 t}{\partial x^2} = \frac{1}{\alpha} \frac{\partial t}{\partial \theta},\tag{11-1}$$

and the initial and boundary conditions

$$t = t_i \quad \text{at } \theta = 0, \ x \geq 0,$$
$$t = t_1(\theta) \quad \text{at } x = 0, \ \theta > 0. \tag{11–2}$$

If we let

$$t = u + v,$$

then it can be shown that u and v must satisfy a partial-differential equation of the same form as (11–1), but the simplified set of initial and boundary conditions

$$u = t_i \quad \text{at } \theta = 0, \ x \geq 0,$$
$$u = 0 \quad \text{at } x = 0, \ \theta > 0, \tag{11–3}$$

and

$$v = 0 \quad \text{at } \theta = 0, \ x \geq 0,$$
$$v = t_1(\theta) \quad \text{at } x = 0, \ \theta > 0. \tag{11–4}$$

The solution to the problem suggested in (11–3) is already known from Chapter 10, and the solution to the problem in (11–4) can be determined by Duhamel's theorem from the solution for the case where the initial temperature is zero and the surface temperature equal to one. According to *Duhamel's theorem*:

If $f(x,\theta)$ is the solution for the temperature history in a solid whose initial temperature is zero, and whose surface is maintained at a temperature of unity, then the solution $v(x,\theta)$ for the case where its surface is maintained at a transient temperature of $t_1(\theta)$ is given by

$$v(x,\theta) = \int_0^\theta t_1(\lambda) \frac{\partial}{\partial \theta} f(x, \theta - \lambda) d\lambda. \tag{11–5}$$

This theorem can also be applied to cases of surface convection where the solid is initially at a uniform temperature of zero throughout and then suddenly is exposed to an ambient fluid whose temperature varies with time as $t_f(\theta)$.*

11–2 Semi-infinite solid. We now develop the complete solution $t = u + v$ for the general problem with initial and boundary conditions (11–2). The solution $u(x,\theta)$ which satisfies (11–3) is contained in (10–28) with $t_1 = 0$:

$$u(x,\theta) = \frac{2t_i}{\sqrt{\pi}} \int_0^X e^{-\lambda^2} d\lambda = t_i \operatorname{erf} (X). \tag{11–6}$$

To apply Duhamel's theorem, (11–5), for the solution v which satisfies (11–4), we must first determine the solution $f(x,\theta)$ which satisfies the initial and boundary conditions

---

*For a proof of Duhamel's theorem and its extension to cases of nonuniform transient boundary conditions, see Carslaw and Jaeger (1).

$$f = 0 \quad \text{at } \theta = 0, \, x \geq 0,$$

$$f = 1 \quad \text{at } x = 0, \, \theta > 0.$$

This solution is also contained in (10–28), with $t_i = 0$ and $t_1 = 1$,

$$f(x,\theta) = 1 - \text{erf } (X) = \text{erfc } (X) = \frac{2}{\sqrt{\pi}} \int_X^\infty e^{-\lambda^2} d\lambda.$$

Then by substituting $\theta - \lambda$ for θ and using the differentiation procedure in Article 10–8, (10–31), we have

$$f(x,\theta - \lambda) = -\frac{2}{\sqrt{\pi}} \int_\infty^{x/2\sqrt{\alpha(\theta-\lambda)}} e^{-\lambda^2} d\lambda, \qquad \textit{should use another dummy variable here. The λ's are correlated}$$

and the partial derivative of $f(x,\theta - \lambda)$ with respect to θ as

$$\frac{\partial}{\partial \theta} f(x,\theta - \lambda) = -\frac{2}{\sqrt{\pi}} [e^{-x^2/4\alpha(\theta-\lambda)}] \left\{ \frac{-x\alpha}{4[\alpha(\theta-\lambda)]^{3/2}} \right\} = \frac{x}{2\sqrt{\pi\alpha}} \frac{e^{-x^2/4\alpha(\theta-\lambda)}}{(\theta-\lambda)^{3/2}}.$$

Thus, according to Duhamel's theorem (11–5),

$$v(x,\theta) = \frac{x}{2\sqrt{\pi\alpha}} \int_0^\theta t_1(\lambda) \frac{e^{-x^2/4\alpha(\theta-\lambda)}}{(\theta-\lambda)^{3/2}} d\lambda. \qquad (11\text{–}7)$$

The complete solution which satisfies (11–2) is then represented as the sum of u and v in (11–6) and (11–7).

A more convenient form for (11–7) is derived by defining

$$\zeta^2 = x^2/4\alpha(\theta - \lambda),$$

so that $(\theta - \lambda) = x^2/4\alpha\zeta^2$ and $d\lambda/(\theta - \lambda)^{3/2} = (4\sqrt{\alpha}/x)d\zeta$. By substituting in (11–7) and changing integration limits to $\zeta = x/2\sqrt{\alpha\theta}$ for $\lambda = 0$ and $\zeta = \infty$ for $\lambda = \theta$, we have

$$v(x,\theta) = \frac{2}{\sqrt{\pi}} \int_{x/2\sqrt{\alpha\theta}}^\infty t_1\left(\theta - \frac{x^2}{4\alpha\zeta^2}\right) e^{-\zeta^2} d\zeta. \qquad (11\text{–}8)$$

Linear surface temperature. For the special case of a linear rise in surface temperature, we take $t_1(\theta) = t_i + C\theta$, where C is a constant time gradient in °F/hr. In this case, with $X = x/2\sqrt{\alpha\theta}$ (Article 10–8), we must integrate (11–8) in the form

$$v(x,\theta) = \frac{2}{\sqrt{\pi}} \int_X^\infty [t_i + C(\theta - x^2/4\alpha\zeta^2)]e^{-\zeta^2} d\zeta = \frac{2t_i}{\sqrt{\pi}} \int_X^\infty e^{-\zeta^2} d\zeta$$

$$+ \frac{2C\theta}{\sqrt{\pi}} \int_X^\infty e^{-\zeta^2} d\zeta - \frac{Cx^2}{2\sqrt{\pi\alpha}} \int_X^\infty \frac{e^{-\zeta^2}}{\zeta^2} d\zeta.$$

But according to (10–48) the first two integrals are simply $(\sqrt{\pi}/2)$ erfc (X). The third integral must be integrated by parts. If we set $p = e^{-\zeta^2}$ and $dq = d\zeta/\zeta^2$, then $dp = -2\zeta e^{-\zeta^2}d\zeta$, and $q = -1/\zeta$, and the integral $\int p\,dq$ becomes

$$\int_X^\infty \frac{e^{-\zeta^2}}{\zeta^2}\,d\zeta = pq\Big]_X^\infty - \int_X^\infty q\,dp = -\frac{e^{-\zeta^2}}{\zeta}\Big]_X^\infty - 2\int_X^\infty e^{-\zeta^2}d\zeta$$

$$= \frac{e^{-X^2}}{X} - \sqrt{\pi}\ \text{erfc}\ (X).$$

By combining these results, we have

$$v(x,\theta) = C\theta\left[(1 + t_i/C\theta + 2X^2)\ \text{erfc}\ (X) - \frac{2}{\sqrt{\pi}}Xe^{-X^2}\right],$$

and adding to this the expression for $u(x,\theta)$ given in (11–6) puts the complete solution in the final form

$$t = t_i + C\theta\left[(1 + 2X^2)\ \text{erfc}\ (X) - \frac{2}{\sqrt{\pi}}Xe^{-X^2}\right]. \qquad (11\text{–}9)$$

This solution clearly satisfies the initial and boundary conditions in (11–2).

There are many more practical cases for which this method has application, and in Example 11–1 we consider the simple case where the surface temperature is a step-function of time.

EXAMPLE 11–1. A large aluminum casting initially at 80°F throughout is suddenly immersed in a 500°F bath. After being left to heat for a period of $\frac{1}{2}$ hour, the casting is quickly removed and placed in an ice-water bath. What will be the temperature at a point 1 foot below the surface of the casting after it has been in the second bath for a period of 1 hour?

Solution. If the surface resistance is negligible, then we can assume that the surface temperature is a step function of time as given by

$$t_1(\theta) = t_{11} \quad \text{at}\ x = 0,\ 0 < \theta < \theta',$$

$$t_1(\theta) = t_{12} \quad \text{at}\ x = 0,\ \theta > \theta'.$$

Breaking up the integral in (11–7) between 0–θ' and θ'–θ, we have

$$v(x,\theta) = \frac{x}{2\sqrt{\pi\alpha}}\left[\int_0^{\theta'} t_{11}\frac{e^{-x^2/4\alpha(\theta-\lambda)}}{(\theta-\lambda)^{3/2}}\,d\lambda + \int_{\theta'}^{\theta} t_{12}\frac{e^{-x^2/4\alpha(\theta-\lambda)}}{(\theta-\lambda)^{3/2}}\,d\lambda\right],$$

or with $\zeta = x/2\sqrt{\alpha(\theta-\lambda)}$,

$$v(x,\theta) = \frac{2}{\sqrt{\pi}} t_{11} \int_{x/2\sqrt{\alpha\theta}}^{x/2\sqrt{\alpha(\theta-\theta')}} e^{-\zeta^2} d\zeta + \frac{2}{\sqrt{\pi}} t_{12} \int_{x/2\sqrt{\alpha(\theta-\theta')}}^{\infty} e^{-\zeta^2} d\zeta$$

$$= \frac{2}{\sqrt{\pi}} t_{11} \int_{x/2\sqrt{\alpha\theta}}^{\infty} e^{-\zeta^2} d\zeta - \frac{2}{\sqrt{\pi}} t_{11} \int_{x/2\sqrt{\alpha(\theta-\theta')}}^{\infty} e^{-\zeta^2} d\zeta + \frac{2}{\sqrt{\pi}} t_{12} \int_{x/2\sqrt{\alpha(\theta-\theta')}}^{\infty} e^{-\zeta^2} d\zeta.$$

Adding to this the solution $u(x,\theta)$ for finite t_i in (11–6), we have for $\theta > \theta'$

$$t = t_i \operatorname{erf}\left(\frac{x}{2\sqrt{\alpha\theta}}\right) + t_{11} \operatorname{erfc}\left(\frac{x}{2\sqrt{\alpha\theta}}\right) + (t_{12} - t_{11}) \operatorname{erfc}\left[\frac{x}{2\sqrt{\alpha(\theta-\theta')}}\right].$$

Then from the given data and Table 1–2,

$$\frac{x}{2\sqrt{\alpha\theta}} = \frac{1}{2\sqrt{1.5/0.262}} = 0.21,$$

$$\frac{x}{2\sqrt{\alpha(\theta-\theta')}} = \frac{1}{2\sqrt{1/0.262}} = 0.26,$$

wherewith from Table A–10,

$$t = 80 \times 0.234 + 500(1 - 0.234) + (32 - 500)(1 - 0.287) = 18.7 + 383.3$$

$$- 334, \text{ or } t = 68°F.$$

11–3 Periodic flow. The special case in transient boundry conditions which is of most general interest is the regular harmonic boundary condition which leads to a periodic type of heat flow. This type of flow occurs in reciprocating internal-combustion engines, in cyclic regenerators, and in the earth as the result of daily and annual temperature changes which repeat themselves. Although the solution for a semi-infinite solid is also contained in (11–6) and (11–8), we shall use here the conventional separation-of-variables method, which is somewhat easier in this case than a direct application of Duhamel's method.

Consider a semi-infinite solid with a steady periodic surface temperature which has been maintained long enough so that the original transient state due to starting the cyclic surface temperature has built up into a steady type of periodic flow. In particular, we consider a simple *harmonic* surface temperature given by

$$T_1 = t_1 - \bar{t}_1 = t_{01} \cos \omega\theta \quad \text{at } x = 0, \ \theta > 0, \tag{11–10}$$

where $\bar{t}_1$ is the *mean* value of the surface temperature, t_{01} is half the complete surface-temperature range (the temperature *amplitude* at the surface), and $\omega/2\pi$ is the harmonic *frequency* f cycles/hr of the surface temperature fluctuation. The temperature oscillation about $\bar{t}_1$ at the surface

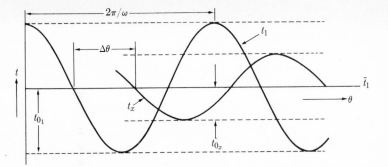

Fig. 11–1.   Amplitude t_{0_x} of the temperature wave t_x in a solid with harmonic surface temperature t_1 of mean value $\bar{t}_1$, amplitude t_{0_1}, and period $2\pi/\omega$.

and at a depth x are sketched in Fig. 11–1 to show the amplitudes t_{01} and t_{0x}, and the *period* of oscillation $P = 1/f = 2\pi/\omega$.

In applying the separation-of-variables method to this problem,* we assume a separation constant for (11–1) in the form $\pm i\lambda$, where $i^2 = -1$. This puts us in possession of the particular integrals

$$T_\lambda = C e^{\pm i\lambda\theta \pm \sqrt{i\lambda/\alpha}\,x},$$

or, since $i = \frac{1}{2}(1 + i)^2$,

$$T = C e^{\pm i\lambda\theta \pm (i+1)\sqrt{\lambda/2\alpha}\,x} = C e^{\pm\sqrt{\lambda/2\alpha}\,x \pm i(\lambda\theta \pm \sqrt{\lambda/2\alpha}\,x)}.$$

We can reduce this further by using the identity $e^{\pm i\varphi} = \cos\varphi \pm i\sin\varphi$:

$$T = C e^{\pm\sqrt{\lambda/2\alpha}\,x}[\cos(\lambda\theta \pm \sqrt{\lambda/2\alpha}\,x) \pm i\sin(\lambda\theta \pm \sqrt{\lambda/2\alpha}\,x)].$$

In view of the boundary condition (11–10), no sine term can be present in the final solution, and since T cannot increase indefinitely as x increases positively, we are forced to drop the positive exponential sign, so that

$$T = C e^{-\sqrt{\lambda/2\alpha}\,x}\cos(\lambda\theta - \sqrt{\lambda/2\alpha}\,x).$$

Finally, we note that this result fits (11–10) only if $C = t_{0_1}$ and $\lambda = \omega$, and therefore the complete *steady periodic* solution must read

$$\frac{t - \bar{t}_1}{t_{01}} = e^{-\sqrt{\omega/2\alpha}\,x}\cos(\omega\theta - \sqrt{\omega/2\alpha}\,x). \qquad (11\text{–}11)$$

---

*The steady periodic state would be represented in Duhamel's method by taking θ large enough to consider that $X = 0$ in the lower integration limit of (11–8).

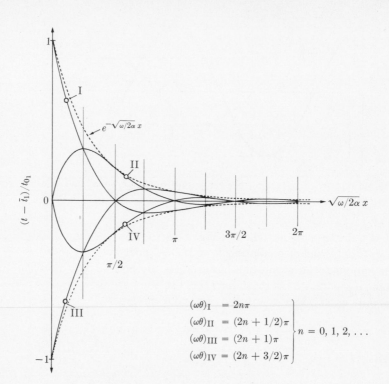

Fig. 11–2. Instantaneous temperature distributions in a semi-infinite solid with harmonic surface temperature.

Several instantaneous temperature distributions according to (11–11) are shown in Fig. 11–2. These curves represent, for a given surface frequency and thermal diffusivity, and for a given instant, the temperature distribution as a function of the depth in a semi-infinite solid with harmonic surface temperature. With increasing time the amplitudes of the temperature wave diminish, and all curves are seen to lie within the envelope determined by $\pm e^{-\sqrt{\omega/2\alpha}\,x}$. Notice that the enveloping curves do not determine the maxima and minima of the internal temperature oscillations. But since the maximum temperature range at any depth is related to $2e^{-\sqrt{\omega/2\alpha}\,x} = 2e^{-\sqrt{\pi/\alpha P}\,x}$, we see that the slower the surface oscillation, ω, or the longer its period, P, the greater is the range of temperature at any depth. The reduction in amplitude with increasing depth is shown in another way by plotting the temperature history at various depths in the semi-infinite solid as in Fig. 11–3. Here we see more clearly how the maxima and minima not only diminish with increasing depth, but occur later and later the farther in from the surface.

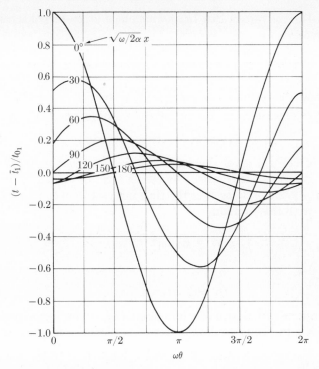

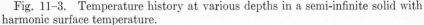

Fig. 11–3. Temperature history at various depths in a semi-infinite solid with harmonic surface temperature.

Time lag, velocity, wavelength, and heat rates. From (11–11) we see that the time at which the surface temperature first reaches the mean $\bar{t}_1$ is when $\cos \omega\theta = 0$, or at a time $(\theta_{\bar{t}_1})_{x=0} = \pi/2\omega$. Likewise, at a depth x in the solid, $\bar{t}_1$ is first reached when $\cos (\omega\theta - \sqrt{\omega/2\alpha}\, x) = 0$, or at a time $(\theta_{\bar{t}_1})_x = \pi/2\omega + \sqrt{1/2\alpha\omega}\, x$. This is later than at the surface by an amount (Fig. 11–1)

$$\Delta\theta = \sqrt{1/2\alpha\omega}\, x = \tfrac{1}{2}\sqrt{P/\pi\alpha}\, x, \qquad (11\text{--}12)$$

which is called the *time lag* of the temperature wave. For a given depth, the lag is seen to be proportional to the square root of the surface period.

Equation (11–12) also expresses the *velocity* with which the temperature wave propagates into the solid as $v = x/\Delta\theta$, or

$$v = \sqrt{2\alpha\omega} = 2\sqrt{\pi\alpha/P}. \qquad (11\text{--}13)$$

The wavelength of the periodic temperature is the distance traveled in one complete oscillation of the wave. Since the time involved is the period, $P = 2\pi/\omega$, we find that the *wavelength* $\nu = vP = \sqrt{2\alpha\omega}\,(2\pi/\omega)$ is

$$\nu = \pi\sqrt{8\alpha/\omega} = 2\sqrt{\pi\alpha P}. \qquad (11\text{--}14)$$

From (11–11), the rate in Btu/hr at which heat is conducted across each A ft^2 of surface is

$$q_1 = -kA_1 \left(\frac{\partial t}{\partial x}\right)_1 = -kA_1 t_{01} \sqrt{\omega/2\alpha} \,(\sin \omega\theta - \cos \omega\theta).$$

Then by using the identity $\cos(\omega\theta + \pi/4) = (\cos \omega\theta - \sin \omega\theta)/\sqrt{2}$, we can reduce this expression for the *instantaneous surface heat rate* to

$$q_1 = A_1 t_{01} \sqrt{kCw\omega} \cos(\omega\theta + \pi/4). \tag{11–15}$$

Integration of (11–15) gives the *cumulative surface heat rate* Q_1 Btu. In this case Q_1 is positive only when the cosine term in (11–15) is positive, that is, from $-\pi/2$ to $\pi/2$, or over the time interval from $\theta_1 = -3\pi/4\omega$ to $\theta_2 = \pi/4\omega$. With this in mind,

$$\int_{\theta_1}^{\theta_2} q_1 d\theta = (A_1 t_{01} \sqrt{kCw\omega}) \frac{2}{\omega},$$

or

$$Q_1 = 2A_1 t_{01} \sqrt{kCw/\omega}. \tag{11–16}$$

This is the positive cumulative rate for one-half cycle; during the remaining half of the cycle this same total quantity of heat flows out of the surface.

EXAMPLE 11–2. Earth surface temperatures at a particular location were recorded over a 24-hour interval and found to range from 29 to 41°F. Investigate the periodic heat flow in the earth under these observed conditions, assuming that the surface temperature of the earth varies harmonically, and that the thermal conductivity, thermal capacity, and specific weight of soil are 0.325 Btu/hr-ft-°F, 0.5 Btu/lb-°F, and 100 lb/ft^3 respectively.

Solution. Since the surface of the earth undergoes daily temperature fluctuations which repeat themselves in a periodic manner, we can assume, as suggested, that the daily or *diurnal* temperature wave is a simple harmonic sinusoidal or cosinusoidal function with a 24-hour period.

With the given data, $\alpha = k/Cw = 0.325/0.5 \times 100 = 0.0065$ ft^2/hr, $\omega = 2\pi/P = 2 \times 3.14/24 = 0.262$/hr, and $\sqrt{\omega/2\alpha} = 4.49$/ft. The temperature range at the surface is $41 - 29 = 12$°F, and this determines the temperature amplitude at the surface as $t_{01} = 6$°F and the mean surface temperature as $\bar{t}_1 = 35$°F. If we choose the time scale θ to begin at t_{01}, then by (11–10) the surface temperature becomes

$$t_1 = 35 + 6 \cos[(0.262\theta)57.3],$$

and, for example, the temperature $t(x,\theta)$ at a depth of 0.2 ft in the earth and after 2 hours is computed to be

$$t = 35 + 6e^{-4.49 \times 0.2} \cos[(0.262 \times 2 - 4.49 \times 0.2)57.3],$$

or $t = 37.3$°F.

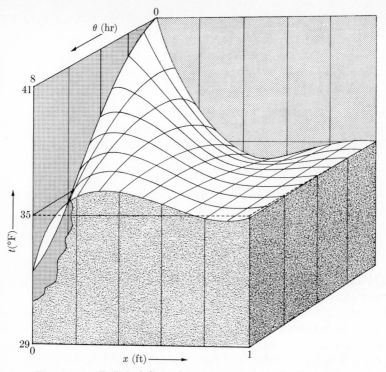

Fig. 11–4. Relief of diurnal temperature wave in the earth.

The complete computation is shown in three-dimensional relief in Fig. 11–4 for an 8-hour interval. Here we see that the diurnal temperature wave is damped out at a relatively shallow depth.

For the conditions of this example, we compute by (11–12) the time lag of the diurnal temperature wave as $\Delta\theta = 0.5\sqrt{24/3.14 \times 0.0065}\, x$, or 3.43 hours at 0.2 ft, 6.86 hours at 0.4 ft, and so on. According to (11–13), the propagation velocity of the diurnal wave is $v = 2\sqrt{3.14 \times 0.0065/24}\ (12) = 0.7$ in./hr, or 16.8 in./day at all depths, and by (11–14) its wavelength at all depths is $\nu = 2\sqrt{3.14 \times 0.0065 \times 24}$, or 1.4 ft (Fig. 11–4). Also, for the conditions of this example, the half-cycle instantaneous and cumulative surface heat rates are calculated by (11–15) and (11–16) to be $q_1 = 8.75$ Btu/hr and $Q_1 = 94.5$ Btu, both values computed on the basis of one square foot of earth surface.

The equations of this article can also be applied to an infinite plate of finite thickness if the thermal properties of the plate are such that the temperature wave is damped out at a relatively shallow depth below the surfaces. As an example, we consider the important case of periodic flow in the cylinder wall of an internal-combustion engine. The depth at which the temperature wave in a semi-infinite solid is damped to within, say, 1% of the surface amplitude is derived from (11–11) according to

$$\ln \frac{T}{t_{01}} = -\sqrt{\omega/2\alpha}\, x,$$

as

$$x_{1\%} = \sqrt{\frac{2\alpha}{\omega}} \ln 100 = 2\sqrt{\frac{\alpha}{\pi f}}.$$

If we consider a steel semi-infinite solid for which $\alpha = 0.5\ \text{ft}^2/\text{hr}$, and choose a frequency of $f = 1000 \times 60$ cycles/hr, then the depth at which the amplitude is just 1% of the surface amplitude becomes

$$x_{1\%} = 2\sqrt{0.5/3.14 \times 60{,}000}\ (12) = 0.04''.$$

Since this depth is very shallow, it would appear reasonable that the equations for the semi-infinite solid would also give a close approximation to the cylinder-wall behavior in a reciprocating engine.

Stationary and Moving Sources

11–4 Infinite plate with stationary distributed sources. In this article we examine the temperature history $t(x,\theta)$ in an infinite plate of thickness L, and generating heat in uniform amount. The plate is initially at a uniform temperature t_i throughout, and at time $\theta = 0$ both free surfaces $x = 0$ and L are suddenly changed to, and maintained at, a uniform temperature t_1 for all $\theta > 0$. Also at time $\theta = 0$, the plate begins to generate distributed and uniform heat independent of time as q_0''' Btu/hr-ft^3.

If the plate is of uniform thermal conductivity k, then its internal temperature history must satisfy the partial-differential equation

$$\frac{\partial^2 T}{\partial x^2} + a = \frac{1}{\alpha}\frac{\partial T}{\partial \theta}, \tag{11–17}$$

and the initial and boundary conditions

$$\begin{aligned}
T &= T_i &&\text{at } \theta = 0,\ 0 \le x \le L, \\
T &= 0 &&\text{at } x = 0,\ \theta > 0, \\
T &= 0 &&\text{at } x = L,\ \theta > 0,
\end{aligned} \tag{11–18}$$

where now $T = t - t_1$ and $a = q_0'''/k$. To reduce (11–17) to a separable partial-differential equation we introduce an auxiliary variable T' by setting $T = T' + X$, where $T' = T'(x,\theta)$ and $X = X(x)$. Then $\partial^2 T/\partial x^2 = \partial^2 T'/\partial x^2 + d^2X/dx^2$ and $\partial T/\partial\theta = \partial T'/\partial\theta$, and this transforms (11–17) into

$$\frac{\partial^2 T'}{\partial x^2} + \frac{d^2 X}{dx^2} + a = \frac{1}{\alpha}\frac{\partial T'}{\partial \theta}.$$

Now if

$$\frac{d^2 X}{dx^2} + a = 0, \tag{11–19}$$

then we have only to integrate the Fourier partial-differential equation

$$\frac{\partial^2 T'}{\partial x^2} = \frac{1}{\alpha} \frac{\partial T'}{\partial \theta}, \tag{11-20}$$

subject to initial and boundary conditions reinterpreted in T'.

To find the conditions under which (11–19) is true, we determine the integration constants of its general solution,

$$X = -\frac{a}{2} x^2 + C_1 x + C_2,$$

as $C_1 = aL/2$ and $C_2 = 0$ so that X satisfies the spatial boundary conditions $X = 0$ at $x = 0, L$. Thus $X = (a/2)(Lx - x^2)$, whereby

$$T' = T - \frac{a}{2} (Lx - x^2).$$

The general solution $T'(x, \theta)$ of (11–20) must evidently satisfy the initial and boundary conditions

$$T' = T_i - \frac{a}{2} (Lx - x^2) = F(x) \quad \text{at } \theta = 0, \; 0 \le x \le L,$$

$$T' = 0 \quad \text{at } x = 0, \; \theta > 0,$$

$$T' = 0 \quad \text{at } x = L, \; \theta > 0.$$

If we take this general solution from Article 10–5 as

$$T'_\lambda = e^{-\lambda^2 \alpha \theta} (C_3 \cos \lambda x + C_4 \sin \lambda x),$$

then we see immediately that $C_3 = 0$ and $\lambda = n\pi/L$, $n = 1, 2, 3, \cdots$, so that

$$T' = \sum_{n=1}^{\infty} C_n e^{-(n\pi/L)^2 \alpha \theta} \sin \frac{n\pi}{L} x.$$

To finally satisfy the initial condition, the C_n must be evaluated such that

$$F(x) = T_i - \frac{a}{2} (Lx - x^2) = \sum_{n=1}^{\infty} C_n \sin \frac{n\pi}{L} x,$$

or as

$$C_n = \frac{2}{L} \int_0^L F(x) \sin \frac{n\pi}{L} x \, dx = \frac{4T_i}{n\pi} - \frac{4aL^2}{n^3 \pi^3}; \quad n = 1, 3, 5, \cdots.$$

The complete solution in t then reads

$$\frac{t - t_1}{(q_0''' L^2 / k)} = \frac{1}{2} \left[\left(\frac{x}{L} \right) - \left(\frac{x}{L} \right)^2 \right] + \left(\frac{4k}{\pi q_0''' L^2} \right) \sum_{n=1}^{\infty} \frac{1}{n} \left(t_i - t_1 - \frac{q_0''' L^2}{n^2 \pi^2 k} \right)$$

$$\times e^{-(n\pi/L)^2 \alpha \theta} \sin n\pi \left(\frac{x}{L} \right); \quad n = 1, 3, 5, \cdots. \tag{11-21}$$

Here we see that for large θ the series portion of the solution becomes negligibly small, leaving the steady-state solution represented mathematically by $\theta \to \infty$. A numerical solution for this problem is obtained in Chapter 12 and compared with (11–21).

11–5 Induction heating. Another important type of transient heat-source system is represented by low-frequency *induction heating*, where heat is generated within the solid as a function of the electrical frequency and depth below the surface. In the case of high-frequency induction heating the generation of heat is concentrated in such a thin layer near the surface that the process can be regarded as one of simple surface heating. Heisler (Ref. 2, Chapter 10) has shown that the analytical solutions for the special case of induction heating with very high frequencies are identical in form to those for transient heating from an ambient fluid with finite internal and surface resistance as treated in Articles 10–11, 12, and 13. For these cases the Heisler temperature-time charts can be used as long as one reinterprets the ordinates of the long-time charts in Fig. 10–11(a) as $[1 - (h/q_1'')(t_0 - t_i)]$, where q_1'' is the rate of heat in Btu/hr-ft^2 supplied to the surface by the high-frequency induction-heating process, and the ordinates of the position-correction charts in Fig. 10–11(b) as $[1 - (h/q_1'')(t_x' - t_i)]/[1 - (h/q_1'')(t_0 - t_i)]$. For the short-time charts of Fig. 10–11(c), the ordinates are to be reinterpreted for high-frequency induction heating as $(h/q_1'')(t - t_i)$ for the left-hand scales, and $(h/q_1'')(t - t_i)/N_u$ for the right-hand scales.

11–6 Moving source systems. The subject of transient heat flow originating from a *moving source of heat* has extensive application in sliding friction, internal ballistics, machining, and numerous metal-treating operations such as welding, casting, quenching, and flame-hardening.

The early approximate theory of moving heat sources has been reviewed by Spraragen and Claussen (2), and the exact analytical theory is due to Rosenthal (3). By Rosenthal's theory, a constant heat source s (Fig. 11–5) is on the ξ-axis of a rectangular coordinate system which is moving with a uniform velocity v with respect to a stationary, rectangular coordinate system (x,y,z). Here v is directed parallel to x. With this scheme a stationary observer on the x-axis would notice a change in tem-

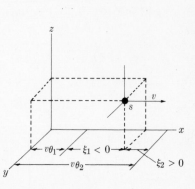

Fig. 11–5. Dual coordinate system for moving heat sources ($\xi = x - v\theta$).

perature of his surroundings as the source moved along, while if the observer were stationed at a point on the moving ξ-axis he would notice no such change in temperature. This condition of "apparent" steady-state temperature has been verified experimentally, and has come to be known as the *quasi-steady state*. This state is represented mathematically by $\partial t/\partial\theta = 0$ in the moving coordinate system.

Now consider the suggested transformation from stationary to moving coordinates. In the stationary system the temperature history must satisfy

$$\frac{\partial^2 T}{\partial x^2} + \frac{\partial^2 T}{\partial y^2} + \frac{\partial^2 T}{\partial z^2} = \frac{1}{\alpha}\frac{\partial T}{\partial\theta}, \tag{11-22}$$

where, for convenience, we take $T = t - t_i$. If we define two new variables (only one being chosen arbitrarily) as (Fig. 11-5)

$$\xi = x - v\theta, \quad \theta' = \theta,$$

then $\partial\xi/\partial x = 1$, $\partial\xi/\partial\theta = -v$, $\partial\theta'/\partial x = 0$, and $\partial\theta'/\partial\theta = 1$, so that

$$\frac{\partial T}{\partial x} = \frac{\partial T}{\partial\xi}\frac{\partial\xi}{\partial x} + \frac{\partial T}{\partial\theta'}\frac{\partial\theta'}{\partial x} = \frac{\partial T}{\partial\xi}\,; \quad \frac{\partial^2 T}{\partial x^2} = \frac{\partial^2 T}{\partial\xi^2},$$

and

$$\frac{\partial T}{\partial\theta} = \frac{\partial T}{\partial\xi}\frac{\partial\xi}{\partial\theta} + \frac{\partial T}{\partial\theta'}\frac{\partial\theta'}{\partial\theta} = -v\frac{\partial T}{\partial\xi} + \frac{\partial T}{\partial\theta'}.$$

Substituting these partial derivatives in (11-22), we have

$$\frac{\partial^2 T}{\partial\xi^2} + \frac{\partial^2 T}{\partial y^2} + \frac{\partial^2 T}{\partial z^2} = \frac{-v}{\alpha}\frac{\partial T}{\partial\xi} + \frac{1}{\alpha}\frac{\partial T}{\partial\theta'},$$

and since this puts us in the moving coordinate system, $\partial T/\partial\theta' = 0$, and

$$\frac{\partial^2 T}{\partial\xi^2} + \frac{\partial^2 T}{\partial y^2} + \frac{\partial^2 T}{\partial z^2} = -\frac{v}{\alpha}\frac{\partial T}{\partial\xi}. \tag{11-23}$$

This result is identified as the characteristic partial-differential equation of the quasi-steady state.

11-7 Moving heat source in an infinite solid. As an example in the application of (11-23), consider an infinite solid initially at t_i through which passes a uniform *plane* source q_0'' Btu/hr-ft^2 at a constant velocity of v ft/hr.

For an infinite solid, $\partial T/\partial y = 0 = \partial T/\partial z$, and (11-23) reduces to the total-differential equation

$$\frac{d^2T}{d\xi^2} + \frac{v}{\alpha}\frac{dT}{d\xi} = 0,$$

whose familiar general solution

$$T = C_1 e^{-(v/\alpha)\xi} + C_2$$

must, in this case, satisfy the following boundary conditions stated in terms of the transformation variable ξ;

$$\frac{dT}{d\xi} = 0 \quad \text{as } \xi \to \pm\infty,$$

$$-k\frac{dT}{d\xi} = q_0'' \quad \text{as } \xi \to 0.$$

The first condition suggests that t is not affected at large distances from the source, and the second condition simply equates the heat added by the source to that gained by the solid at the source $\xi = 0$ ($x = v\theta$).

For convenience, we symbolize T in the two ranges $\xi \gtrless 0$ as

$$T \text{ for } \xi < 0 \quad \text{and} \quad \dot{T} \text{ for } \xi > 0.$$

Then

$$\frac{dT}{d\xi} = -C_1\frac{v}{\alpha}e^{-(v/\alpha)\xi} \quad \text{and} \quad \frac{d\dot{T}}{d\xi} = -\dot{C}_1\frac{v}{\alpha}e^{-(v/\alpha)\xi},$$

from which we see that in order to satisfy the first of the dual boundary conditions,

$$T = C_2, \quad \dot{T} = \dot{C}_1 e^{-(v/\alpha)\xi} + \dot{C}_2.$$

But as $\xi \to \infty$, $\dot{T} = 0$, so that $\dot{C}_2 = 0$, and at $\xi = 0$, $T = \dot{T}$, as

$$C_2 = [\dot{C}_1 e^{-(v/\alpha)\xi}]_{\xi=0},$$

which means that $\dot{C}_1 = C_2$. By the second boundary condition,

$$-k\left[-\dot{C}_1\frac{v}{\alpha}e^{-(v/\alpha)\xi}\right]_{\xi=0} = q_0'',$$

whereby $\dot{C}_1 = q_0''\alpha/kv$. The two-part final solution is therefore

$$t = t_i + q_0''\alpha/kv,$$

$$\dot{t} = t_i + \frac{q_0''\alpha}{kv}e^{-(v/\alpha)\xi}. \tag{11-24}$$

From t of the solution (11–24), we see that the temperature remains constant in the region behind the source ($\xi < 0$), and that this is the maximum temperature excess attained, that is, $q_0''\alpha/kv$ as given by $\dot{t}$ at $\xi = 0$.

11–8 Moving heat source in an adiabatic plate. As an extension of Article 11–7, we examine the more practical case of a line source q_0' Btu/hr-ft moving with constant velocity v (again directed parallel to x) in a large plate with adiabatic faces.

In this case of two-dimensional conduction, the temperature field must satisfy the partial-differential equation given by (11–23) as

$$\frac{\partial^2 T}{\partial \xi^2} + \frac{\partial^2 T}{\partial y^2} = -\frac{v}{\alpha}\frac{\partial T}{\partial \xi}.$$

To integrate this equation, let

$$T = e^{-(v/2\alpha)\xi} f(\xi, y),$$

in which f is an undetermined function. The differential equation in terms of f is then

$$\frac{\partial^2 f}{\partial \xi^2} + \frac{\partial^2 f}{\partial y^2} - \left(\frac{v}{2\alpha}\right)^2 f = 0.$$

We will also find it convenient to work in cylindrical coordinates with $f(r, \varphi)$, where $x^2 + y^2 = r^2$ and $\varphi = \tan^{-1}(y/x)$. This transformation is immediately written down as

$$\frac{\partial^2 f}{\partial r^2} + \frac{1}{r}\frac{\partial f}{\partial r} + \frac{1}{r^2}\frac{\partial^2 f}{\partial \varphi^2} - \left(\frac{v}{2\alpha}\right)^2 f = 0,$$

but since in this case the temperature field is symmetrical about $r = 0$, the function f must satisfy the simpler total-differential equation

$$\frac{d^2 f}{dr^2} + \frac{1}{r}\frac{df}{dr} - \left(\frac{v}{2\alpha}\right)^2 f = 0.$$

The differential equation above is recognized as a Bessel form having the general solution

$$f = C_1 J_0\left(\frac{v}{2\alpha}ir\right) + C_2 Y_0\left(\frac{v}{2\alpha}ir\right),$$

or, in terms of the modified Bessel functions (Article 3–5), and re-expressed in T,

$$T = e^{-(v/2\alpha)\xi}\left[C_1 I_0\left(\frac{v}{2\alpha}r\right) + C_2 K_0\left(\frac{v}{2\alpha}r\right)\right].$$

Again, this general solution must satisfy the boundary conditions

$$\frac{dT}{dr} = 0 \quad \text{as } r \to \infty,$$

$$-k(2\pi r)\frac{dT}{dr} = q_0' \quad \text{as } r \to 0.$$

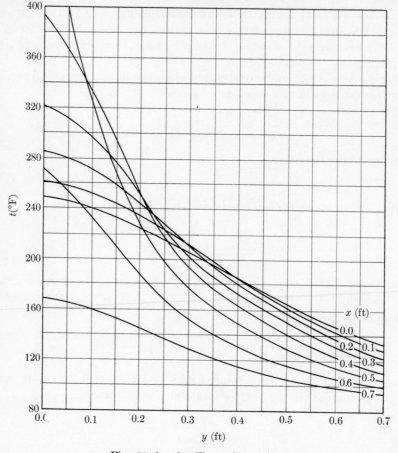

Fig. 11–6. Auxiliary plot of (11–26).

But from Fig. 3–3 we observe that of the two functions I_0 and K_0, only K_0 will satisfy the first condition that T must vanish for large r. Accordingly, $C_1 = 0$ and

$$T = Ce^{-(v/2\alpha)\xi}K_0\left(\frac{v}{2\alpha}r\right).$$

With reference to the second boundary condition,

$$-k(2\pi r)\left.\frac{dT}{dr}\right\}_{r=0} = -k(2\pi r)\left[-\frac{v}{2\alpha}Ce^{-(v/2\alpha)\xi}K_1\left(\frac{v}{2\alpha}r\right)\right]\Big\}_{r=0} = q_0'.$$

The evaluation at $r = 0$ hinges on recalling that the asymptotic approximation to $K_1(x)$ for small x is $1/x$ (Article 8–2), so that with $\xi = 0$ at $r = 0$ we have $2\pi kC = q_0'$. This value of the arbitrary constant C serves to complete the solution as

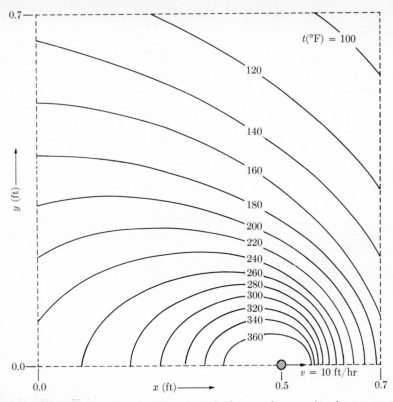

Fig. 11–7.   Instantaneous temperature field around a moving heat source in an infinite adiabatic plate initially at 80°F.

$$t = t_i + \frac{q_0'}{2\pi k} e^{-(v/2\alpha)\xi} K_0\left(\frac{v}{2\alpha} r\right). \qquad (11\text{–}25)$$

Note that this solution gives the fictitious result at the origin that $t \to \infty$ as $r \to 0$. This is a consequence of assuming the source q_0' as a line, whereas the source must actually occupy a finite volume.

EXAMPLE 11–3.   An infinite plate with insulated faces has a thermal conductivity of 1 Btu/hr-ft-°F, thermal diffusivity of 2 ft²/hr, and is initially at a uniform temperature of 80°F. At time $\theta \geq 0$ a uniform line source of strength 10^3 Btu/hr-ft moves along the plate at a constant velocity of 10 ft/hr. Develop a picture of the temperature field in the plate after a time lapse of 3 min.

Solution.   This is an example of welding thin plates with negligible surface heat loss. Since the temperature field is two-dimensional, the solution (11–25) applies. Re-expressed in rectangular coordinates, the solution becomes

$$t = t_i + \frac{q_0'}{2\pi k} e^{-(v/2\alpha)(x-v\theta)} K_0\left(\frac{v}{2\alpha}\sqrt{(x - v\theta)^2 + y^2}\right), \qquad (11\text{–}26)$$

in which $q_0'/2\pi k = 10^3/6.28 \times 1 = 159$, $v/2\alpha = 10/2 \times 2 = 2.5$,   and $v\theta$ $= 10 \times 3/60 = 0.5$.

Since the solution (11–26) cannot be solved for either x or y, we choose x as a parameter and then compute t as a function of y alone. The results of this computation are plotted in Fig. 11–6 for a suitable range of both x and y.

Figure 11–7, obtained from Fig. 11–6 by taking isothermals in 20°F increments above the initial plate temperature $t_i = 80°F$, is a picture of the temperature surrounding the source at the instant $\theta = 0.05$ hr. From the pattern of isothermals we see that the plate temperature rises much more steeply in front of the source than it falls behind the source. It can also be seen that points of maximum temperature rise in the plate are located farther back from the source as one gets farther away from the source in the y-direction.

REFERENCES

1. H. S. Carslaw and J. C. Jaeger, *Conduction of Heat in Solids.* London: Oxford University Press, 1947.

2. W. Spraragen and G. E. Claussen, "Temperature Distribution During Welding — A Review of the Literature to January, 1937," *The Welding Journal*, Vol. 16, Sept. 1937.

3. D. Rosenthal, "The Theory of Moving Sources of Heat and Its Application to Metal Treatments," *Trans. ASME*, Vol. 68, 1946, pp. 849–866.

PROBLEMS

11–1. The surface temperature of a large mass of iron increases linearly 5°F/min. If the iron is initially at a uniform temperature of 80°F, show that after 3 hours of heating the temperature at a depth of 2 ft below the surface is approximately 240°F.

11–2. If a constant rate of heat is supplied to the surface of a semi-infinite solid, then the surface temperature will be found to increase with the square root of time as $t_1(\theta) = t_i + C\sqrt{\theta}$. Show that under these conditions the transient temperature within the solid is given by

$$t = t_i + C\sqrt{\theta}\,[e^{-X^2} - \sqrt{\pi}\,X\,\text{erfc}\,(X)].$$

11–3. The temperature of the earth's surface is measured over a 24-hour period and found to range from 62°F to 93°F. If the thermal conductivity of the soil is 0.5 Btu/hr-ft-°F, its thermal capacity 0.6 Btu/lb-°F, and its specific weight 125 lb/ft³, then, (a) show that for a cosinusoidal surface temperature, the temperature of the earth at 1:00 p.m. and at a depth of $\frac{1}{2}$ ft is 76.9°F; (b) plot a graph of the temperature history in the earth down to a depth of 1 ft, and at time intervals of 2 hr from noon to midnight.

11–4. With reference to problem 11–3, (a) show that the time lag of the temperature wave is 8.46 hr, (b) show that the velocity of the temperature wave is 17 in. per day, (c) show that the wavelength is 1 ft, 5 in., (d) show that the instantaneous surface heat rate is 24.3 Btu/hr per square foot of surface, (e) show that the cumulative surface heat rate is 371 Btu per square foot of surface.

11–5. We wish to compute the thermal diffusivity of the earth's soil at a particular location, and find that the mean surface temperature at 6:00 p.m. is first reached at a depth of 0.2 ft at 8:00 p.m., (a) show that the thermal diffusivity of the soil in this location is 0.0122 ft^2/hr, (b) discuss several other possible methods for computing thermal diffusivities from observed data.

11–6. A single-cylinder two-stroke cycle IC engine has a bore of 3″ and a stroke of 4″, and its cylinder material has a thermal conductivity and diffusivity of 25 Btu/hr-ft-°F and 0.5 ft^2/hr respectively. If the range of cylinder surface temperatures recorded during operation at 800 r.p.m. is 8°F, then, (a) plot a graph of the temperature range as a function of the depth in the cylinder wall, (b) show that 0.135 Btu is absorbed by the cylinder wall during each power stroke.

11–7. Plot a dimensionless graph of the temperature in an infinite solid, heated by a plane moving heat source.

11–8. Replot the temperature field in Fig. 11–7 for the earlier instant $\theta = 1.5$ min.

11–9. If the plate in Example 11–3 loses heat from its plane face surfaces 1 and 2 to an ambient medium at t_i, then the temperature history within the plate must satisfy the partial-differential equation

$$\frac{\partial^2 T}{\partial x^2} + \frac{\partial^2 T}{\partial y^2} - \left(\frac{h_1 + h_2}{k\delta} \right) T = \frac{1}{\alpha} \frac{\partial T}{\partial \theta} \,,$$

where h_1 and h_2 are uniform unit surface conductances, and δ is the plate thickness. Show that the solution for t is given in this case by

$$t = t_i + \frac{q_o}{2\pi k} e^{-\frac{v}{2\alpha}\xi} K_o \left[\sqrt{(h_1 + h_2)/k\delta + (v/2\alpha)^2} \, r \right],$$

where q_0 is the total heat liberated by the source.

11–10. The plate in Example 11–3 is 1″ thick and nonadiabatic. If the unit surface conductance at both faces is 20 Btu/hr-ft^2-°F, and surroundings are at 80°F, compute and plot the temperature field in the plate at $\theta = 3$ min, and compare with the adiabatic case in Fig. 11–7.

CHAPTER 12

TRANSIENT NUMERICAL METHOD

In this chapter we calculate temperature histories by an approximate numerical iteration procedure which represents a modification of the steady-state numerical method of Chapter 7.

12–1 Introduction. The numerical method for transient conduction is similar to the numerical treatment of the steady state only in that for both states the physical region in question is lumped, and the characteristic differential equation is replaced by an equivalent expression in finite differences. In contrast to the "residual equations" of the steady state, which express simple relations between temperatures at adjacent nodal points, the "difference equations" of the transient state express the "future" temperature of a given nodal point as a function of time, its present temperature, and the present temperature of adjacent nodal points. Although the relaxation method can still be applied in the transient state,* it is more convenient to adopt a time-iteration procedure, whereby instantaneous temperatures are calculated for successive time intervals. In this respect, we follow the general methods outlined by Dusinberre (2), (3).

In addition to these essential differences in detail, the transient numerical method introduces several questions on accuracy which must be considered. In this connection we consider the magnitude of truncation errors due to finite-difference substitutions for the second derivative in space and first derivative in time, and the behavior of round-off errors in the numerical solution, which may proceed to grow with time. These are important matters of convergence and stability which arise in numerical integrations of nonelliptic partial-differential equations of the parabolic type, and which impose certain restrictions on the selection of allowable time increments and subdivision size.

12–2 One-dimensional difference equations. We begin, as in the steady-state numerical method, by subdividing the given system into a number of regular physical or geometrical subvolumes. The thermal properties of each subvolume are considered to be concentrated at the central nodal point of each subvolume, and heat is imagined to be conducted between nodal points through a network of fictitious heat-conducting rods of appropriate thermal conductance. In the transient state, however, heat

---

*Cf. Allen (1), p. 225.

is not only conducted to and from
each nodal point in the lumped network, but additionally each nodal
point experiences a change in internal
energy in amount which depends upon
its temperature change during a given
time increment, its thermal capacity,
the total volume of material which it
represents, and the specific weight of
this material.

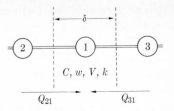

Fig. 12–1. Subdivision and numerical network for a transient one-dimensional system.

Consider the one-dimensional network of Fig. 12–1, and assume that the
thermal capacity and conductivity of the conducting material are uniform
as C and k. The heat q conducted by each rod is $-Kdt$ and, as before, if
δ is chosen sufficiently small, then we can express the q's as the finite difference $-K\Delta t$, where Δt is the temperature difference between the adjacent
nodal points in question. The total heat conducted in the finite time
increment $\Delta\theta$ is $Q = q\Delta\theta = -K\Delta t\Delta\theta$. Now the change in internal energy
of a given nodal point is given by (1–4) as $CwVdt'$, or as a finite difference
$CwV\Delta t'$, where w and V represent subregion specific weight and volume
respectively. In this expression we consider t' to belong to $\theta + \Delta\theta$, so that
in reality we are assuming $\Delta\theta$ small enough to allow basing the internal
energy change on the temperature of the nodal point at the end of the
finite time interval $\Delta\theta$. Then in terms of finite differences we have the
heat balance

$$-\sum K\Delta t\Delta\theta = CwV\Delta t',$$

or, specifically, for a typical internal nodal point such as ① in Fig. 12–1,
the *difference equation*

$$K_{21}(t_2 - t_1) + K_{31}(t_3 - t_1) = \frac{CwV}{\Delta\theta}(t_1' - t_1). \qquad (12\text{–}1)$$

Now for a one-dimensional network based on $A = \delta \times 1 \text{ ft}^2$ of conducting area (see also Fig. 7–1), $K = k(\delta \times 1/\delta) = k$, and on introducing this
along with the diffusivity $\alpha = k/Cw$ into the difference equation (12–1),
we have for t_1',

$$t_1' = \theta\left[t_2 + t_3 + \left(\frac{1}{\theta} - 2\right)t_1\right]. \qquad (12\text{–}2)$$

In this expression the *Fourier modulus* for the "internal" subdivision is
given by (10–2) as

$$\theta = \frac{k\Delta\theta}{CwV} = \frac{\alpha\Delta\theta}{\delta^2}. \qquad (12\text{–}3)$$

From this we see that the future temperature of ① depends on its present temperature and the present temperature of adjacent nodal points ② and ③.

Equation (12–2) is the basis of the transient-state numerical method; it replaces the residual equations of the steady-state method, which were always to be reduced to zero with a correct selection of temperatures, by a reduced difference equation which predicts the change in nodal-point temperature over a small finite time interval. Since the system is lumped with respect to both time and space, we have to select both a Δx and a $\Delta \theta$, in contrast to selecting only a Δx in the steady-state method. But Δx and $\Delta \theta$ cannot be selected independently, since restrictions must be placed on Θ and hence, by (12–3), on the allowable ratio $\Delta\theta/\delta^2$. Looking at (12–2), we find that to avoid violating the first law of thermodynamics, the term $(1/\Theta - 2)$ must be greater than or at least equal to zero. The value of the Fourier modulus is therefore restricted to

$$\Theta \leq \tfrac{1}{2}, \tag{12–4}$$

and for a given choice of spacing δ, this limits our choice of time increment such that, by (12–3),

$$\Delta\theta \leq \frac{\delta^2}{2\alpha}.$$

If we select the highest permissible value of the Fourier modulus as $\Theta = \tfrac{1}{2}$, then by (12–2)

$$\Theta = \tfrac{1}{2}; \quad t_1' = \tfrac{1}{2}(t_2 + t_3), \qquad (\Delta\theta = \delta^2/2\alpha). \tag{12–5}$$

This is to say that after a time interval $\Delta\theta$, the temperature of point ① is the simple arithmetic mean of the temperatures at the two adjacent nodal points ② and ③ at the beginning of this time increment. We also see, for this limiting case, that the future temperature of a given nodal point is independent of its present temperature. On selecting $\Theta = \tfrac{1}{3}$ or $\tfrac{1}{4}$, we arrive at the slightly more involved results for internal nodal points

$$\Theta = \tfrac{1}{3}; \quad t_1' = \tfrac{1}{3}(t_2 + t_1 + t_3), \qquad (\Delta\theta = \delta^2/3\alpha), \tag{12–6}$$

and

$$\Theta = \tfrac{1}{4}; \quad t_1' = \tfrac{1}{4}(t_2 + 2t_1 + t_3), \qquad (\Delta\theta = \delta^2/4\alpha). \tag{12–7}$$

The selection of successively smaller values of Θ is seen by (12–5), (12–6), and (12–7) to increase not only the labor of computation but, by (12–3), to increase (for a given network spacing) the number of such computations. While the use of larger moduli approaching $\tfrac{1}{2}$ is to render the calculations easier and less in number, we shall find that such results are nevertheless obtained at a sacrifice in accuracy.

12–3 Negligible surface resistance. As a first example in the application of transient-state numerical methods, consider an infinite plate of uniform thermal diffusivity $\alpha = 0.25$ ft^2/hr. The plate is imagined to be perfectly insulated against heat loss from its face $x = L = 2.4''$. Its initial temperature is taken to be $t_i = 100°$F throughout, and at time $\theta = 0$ the temperature of its face $x = 0$ is suddenly raised to $t_1 = 500°$F and maintained at this value for all $\theta > 0$. We want to find the temperature history at the insulated face for a total heating time of 4 minutes.

Let the plate be subdivided into four equal slices of thickness $\delta = 2.4/4 \times 12 = 0.05$ ft, with half slices at the two surfaces. Then, on selecting $\theta = \frac{1}{2}$, we have for the time increment in each calculation $\Delta\theta = \delta^2\theta/\alpha = (0.05)^2(\frac{1}{2})/0.25 = 0.005$ hr, or 0.3 min. In this case the reduced difference equation (12–2) can be used for each of the four internal nodal points ②, ③, ④, and ⑤.

The averaging calculation governed by (12–5) for $\theta = \frac{1}{2}$ is carried out in Table 12–1 for a total elapsed time of 3.9 min. For $\theta < 0$, $t_{i_1} = 100$, and for $\theta > 0$, $t_{i_1} = 500$. To start the calculation, we must first decide which of these initial surface temperatures to use. Many authors suggest getting by this difficulty at the first time interval by starting the calculation with results from an exact analytical solution. But it would seem that the availability of an exact analytical solution eliminates, in itself, the need for a numerical solution, which is always approximate. A better answer to our question is that we will have to use either 100°F, or 500°F, and accept

TABLE 12–1

NUMERICAL TEMPERATURES IN AN INFINITE PLATE $(\theta = \frac{1}{2})$

θ(min)	①	②	③	④	⑤
0.0	300	100.0	100.0	100.0	100.0
0.3	500	200.0	100.0	100.0	100.0
0.6	500	300.0	150.0	100.0	100.0
0.9	500	325.0	200.0	125.0	100.0
1.2	500	350.0	225.0	150.0	125.0
1.5	500	362.5	250.0	175.0	150.0
1.8	500	375.0	268.8	200.0	175.0
2.1	500	384.4	287.5	221.9	200.0
2.4	500	393.8	303.2	243.8	221.9
2.7	500	401.6	318.8	262.6	243.8
3.0	500	409.4	332.1	281.3	262.6
3.3	500	416.0	345.4	297.4	281.3
3.6	500	422.7	356.7	313.4	297.4
3.9	500	428.4	368.0	327.0	313.4

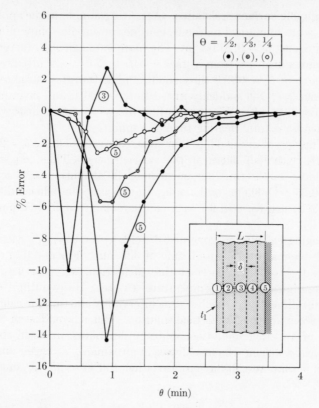

Fig. 12–2. Percent error in the transient numerical solution for various subdivision moduli Θ.

the inaccuracy that will appear in the early time intervals. The error, however, is generally least pronounced if we choose the mean of these two values rather than one of the extremes.

For initial values we take, as suggested above, the mean surface temperature of 300°F, and 100°F at internal nodal points, as in the first line of Table 12–1. From here on the surface temperature remains, as required, at $t_1 = 500°F$. After the first 0.3 min interval the temperature of point ② will be the arithmetic mean of points ① and ③ at the beginning of the interval, or $t_2' = (300 + 100)/2 = 200$. At the same time, the temperature of point ③ will be $t_3' = (100 + 100)/2 = 100$, and so on along the second line of Table 12–1. Since the exposed face at ⑤ is insulated, we know the temperature gradient there is zero, and hence we give double weight to point ④ as $t_5' = \frac{1}{2}(2t_4) = t_4$.

It is of interest to recompute the temperature history based on a modulus of $\Theta = \frac{1}{3}$, according to (12–6). This means that for the same subdivision the time increment is shortened to $\Delta\theta = \frac{2}{3}(0.3) = 0.2$ min, and that $\frac{1}{3}$

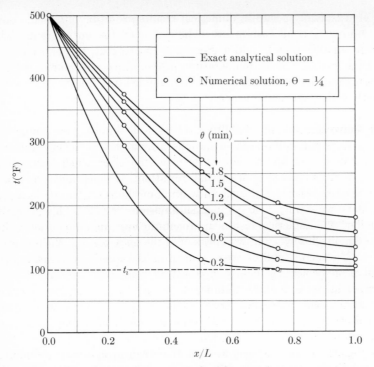

Fig. 12–3.　Numerical results compared with exact instantaneous temperature distributions.

again as many intervals are required to cover the same total elapsed time of 4 min.　In this case the nodal point ⑤ enters the computation as $t'_5 = (2t_4 + t_5)/3$, and again the initial surface temperature is to be taken as $t_{i_1} = 300°F$.

A further calculation by (12–7) for $\Theta = \frac{1}{4}$ shortens the time increment to $\Delta\theta = \frac{2}{4}(0.3) = 0.15$ min, and point ⑤ goes by $t'_5 = (t_4 + t_5)/2$.　Preparation of these last two tables is left here as an exercise for the reader.

The numerical solutions for $\Theta = \frac{1}{2}, \frac{1}{3}$, and $\frac{1}{4}$ are compared with the exact solution (10–8) in Fig. 12–2.　Here we see that for all three moduli, an appreciable error is introduced by the use of a mean initial surface temperature.　While this error cannot be avoided, we nevertheless see that it averages out as time goes on, and that the general error becomes less and less as we go to smaller values of the modulus.　In this case (Fig. 12–2) the percent error is always negative for points on the insulated face, although we see that for points midway in the plate numerical temperatures are alternately greater and less than exact values.　The first represents a type of one-sided convergence, and the second an oscillating type of convergence.

It is apparent from these results that for a short-time heating or cooling process, as in quenching, it is necessary to use a modulus even smaller than

$\Theta = \frac{1}{4}$ if reasonably accurate numerical results are to be obtained. Generally, however, good results are achieved over the entire range with moduli no smaller than $\frac{1}{4}$, and in Fig. 12–3 we see that, to the usual scale of plotting instantaneous temperature distributions, the numerical and exact temperatures in the early portion of the heating process of this case are nearly indistinguishable when $\Theta = \frac{1}{4}$.

12–4 Convergence and stability. It is well known that numerical solutions of partial-differential equations are subject to several different types of errors. The first of these is the *truncation error*, which is due to the use of a finite subdivision or spatial iteration. Truncation errors have already been experienced in the steady-state methods of Chapter 7, and to reduce them we simply choose a finer subdivision. As Δx is chosen smaller and smaller, the numerical results approach the corresponding exact values more and more closely. This we speak of as the *convergence* of the numerical solution. A second kind of error, known as the *numerical error*, is often thought of as consisting mainly of so-called "round-off" errors. Thus, if we carried along an infinite number of decimal places in the numerical computations, the numerical error would vanish. The way in which numerical errors grow or decay with time is a problem having to do with the *stability* of the difference equation.

With regard to convergence, we note that truncation errors are inherent in the substitution of a finite-difference equation for a partial-differential equation. Consider, for example, the approximations contained in the difference equation (12–1) expressed as

$$\frac{t_2 + t_3 - 2t_1}{\delta^2} = \frac{t_1' - t_1}{\alpha \Delta \theta} \left\} \frac{\partial^2 t}{\partial x^2} = \frac{1}{\alpha} \frac{\partial t}{\partial \theta} . \right. \tag{12–8}$$

Expanding t_2, t_3, and t_1' in a Taylor's series about t_1 (Article 7–3), we have

$$t_2 = t_1 - \delta \left(\frac{\partial t}{\partial x}\right)_1 + \frac{\delta^2}{2} \left(\frac{\partial^2 t}{\partial x^2}\right)_1 - \frac{\delta^3}{6} \left(\frac{\partial^3 t}{\partial x^3}\right)_1 + \frac{\delta^4}{24} \left(\frac{\partial^4 t}{\partial x^4}\right)_1 - \cdots ,$$

$$t_3 = t_1 + \delta \left(\frac{\partial t}{\partial x}\right)_1 + \frac{\delta^2}{2} \left(\frac{\partial^2 t}{\partial x^2}\right)_1 + \frac{\delta^3}{6} \left(\frac{\partial^3 t}{\partial x^3}\right)_1 + \frac{\delta^4}{24} \left(\frac{\partial^4 t}{\partial x^4}\right)_1 + \cdots ,$$

$$t_1' = t_1 + \Delta \theta \left(\frac{\partial t}{\partial \theta}\right)_1 + \frac{\Delta \theta^2}{2} \left(\frac{\partial^2 t}{\partial \theta^2}\right)_1 + \cdots ,$$

and therewith

$$\frac{t_2 + t_3 - 2t_1}{\delta^2} = \left(\frac{\partial^2 t}{\partial x^2}\right)_1 + \frac{\delta^2}{12} \left[\left(\frac{\partial^4 t}{\partial x^4}\right)_1 + \cdots\right],$$

$$\frac{t_1' - t_1}{\alpha \Delta \theta} = \frac{1}{\alpha} \left(\frac{\partial t}{\partial \theta}\right)_1 + \frac{\Delta \theta}{2\alpha} \left[\left(\frac{\partial^2 t}{\partial \theta^2}\right)_1 + \cdots\right].$$

The spatial truncation error is therefore, according to (12–8), of the order δ^2, while the time error is of the order $\Delta\theta$.

In the consideration of round-off errors, we investigate the conditions under which the errors either damp out or increase in amplitude with time. The first of these conditions is said to reflect stability of the numerical calculations, and the second instability. Stability criteria may be developed for simple systems, and without regard to the degree of stability or instability, either by considering the effect of a unit error at a given nodal point (4), or by assuming a series distribution of errors at a given moment and then studying the conditions under which a general term of this series is damped out. We examine briefly the second of these methods, which is due to von Neumann and which has been described in detail by O'Brien (5).

Let $E(x,\theta)$ be the error at a point x and time θ due to the accumulation of round-off errors in the numerical calculations. If we again focus attention on the general internal difference equation (12–8), then it can be shown that $E(x,\theta)$ must satisfy a "variational" equation of the same form as

$$\frac{E_2 + E_3 - 2E_1}{\delta^2} = \frac{t_1' - t_1}{\alpha\Delta\theta} . \tag{12–9}$$

By von Neumann's method, we assume that the distribution of a line of errors at time $\theta = 0$ can be expanded in a harmonic series

$$E(x) = \sum_n A_n e^{i\mu_n x}, \tag{12–10}$$

where the possible values of μ are infinite or finite depending on whether x is limited to an infinite or to a finite value. In the former case μ can run from 0 to π/δ, and in the latter case $\mu = n\pi/m\delta$, $n = 1, 2, 3, \cdots, m - 1$, where m is the finite number of spatial subdivisions. A solution of (12–9) which reduces to (12–10) is

$$E(x,\theta) = e^{i\mu x} e^{\eta\theta}, \tag{12–11}$$

and hence the initial error, $e^{i\mu x}$, will not grow with time (i.e., the solution will be stable) if

$$| e^{\eta\theta} | \leq 1. \tag{12–12}$$

To see how this leads to a stability criterion, we substitute (12–11), with $E_2 = E(x - \Delta x, 0) = E(-\delta)$, $E_3 = E(x + \Delta x, 0) = E(\delta)$, $E_1 = E(0,0)$, $t_1' = E(0,\Delta\theta)$, and $t_1 = E(0,0)$, into (12–9) as

$$\frac{e^{-i\mu\delta} + e^{i\mu\delta} - 2}{\delta^2} = \frac{e^{\eta\Delta\theta} - 1}{\alpha\Delta\theta} .$$

On reducing this result to

$$e^{\eta\Delta\theta} = 1 + \Theta(e^{i\mu\delta} + e^{-i\mu\delta} - 2) = 1 - 4\Theta \sin^2\left(\frac{\mu\delta}{2}\right),$$

and imposing the condition (12–12), we have (for a nontrivial criterion)

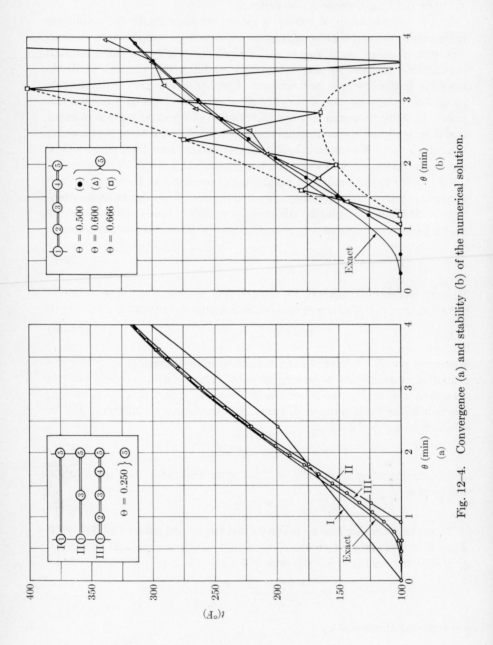

Fig. 12-4. Convergence (a) and stability (b) of the numerical solution.

$$\mid e^{\eta \Delta \theta} \mid = -1 + 4\Theta \sin^2 \left(\frac{\mu \delta}{2}\right) \leq 1. \qquad (12\text{–}13)$$

For the case of infinite solids, the maximum value of $\sin^2 (\mu\delta/2) = \sin^2 (\pi/2)$ is 1, and therefore the stability criterion (12–13) becomes $\Theta \leq 1/2 \sin^2 (\mu\delta/2)$, or

$$\Theta \leq \tfrac{1}{2}. \qquad (12\text{–}14)$$

This is the largest value of the internal modulus for which stability of the difference equation (12–2) is guaranteed. Note that it imposes the same limitations on Θ as suggested by (12–4).*

The concepts of convergence and stability are illustrated graphically in Fig. 12–4, using the example problem of Article 12–3. We have computed in (a) the temperature history at the insulated face of the plate using a stable value of the modulus $\Theta = 0.250$ and three different subdivisions shown as I, II, and III. The way in which these three solutions more nearly approach the exact solution over the entire range of time as successively finer subdivisions are used is clear evidence of the convergence of the numerical method.

In part (b) of the figure we have computed temperature histories at the insulated face of the plate using the finest subdivision in (a), and unstable as well as stable values of the modulus Θ. The numerical solution for the stable value of $\Theta = 0.500$ is seen to agree quite well with the exact solution after the initial surface-temperature error has averaged out (Article 12–3, Fig. 12–2). Now according to $\Theta \leq 1/2 \sin^2 \left(\dfrac{m-1}{m} \dfrac{\pi}{2}\right)$, the limiting stable value for the $m = 4$ of this system is $1/2 \sin^2 67.5°$, or $\Theta \leq 0.586$. The solution for $\Theta = 0.500$ is therefore stable as illustrated. But if we choose a value somewhat higher than this, such as $\Theta = 0.600$, then the corresponding numerical solution should be expected to be unstable. The onset of instability for this case is clearly seen in (b) of Fig. 12–4. Choosing even a slightly higher value of the modulus, such as $\Theta = 0.666$, results in the strong instability shown here as an extremely rapid and severe oscillating divergence of the numerical results.

---

*It is clear that this stability criterion is more restrictive than it need be for a finite solid with m subdivisions, since in this case $\Theta \leq 1/2 \sin^2 \left(\dfrac{m-1}{m} \dfrac{\pi}{2}\right)$. For example, if a plate were subdivided in half, then $m = 2$ and the maximum stable limit is $\Theta \leq 1$. In the more practical situation with $m = 5$ or 10, the stability limits on the modulus are $\Theta \leq 0.552$ and 0.513.

12–5 Finite surface resistance. As an extension of the transient numerical method to cases where the surface resistance cannot be ignored, let the simple system of Article 12–3 be subdivided as in Fig. 12–2, and denote by h and t_f the uniform values of a unit surface conductance and the temperature of an ambient fluid at $x = 0$. Then for the surface nodal point ①, we have for heating

$$K_{f1}(t_f - t_1) + K_{21}(t_2 - t_1) = \frac{CwV}{\Delta\theta}(t_1' - t_1).$$

In this case $K_{f1} = h(\delta \times 1) = h\delta$ and $K_{21} = k$ as before. By noting that the surface subvolume is only one-half of an internal subvolume, $V = \delta^2/2$, and by introducing the *Nusselt number* given by (10–2) as $N_u = h\delta/k$, we have

$$N_u(t_f - t_1) + (t_2 - t_1) = \frac{1}{2\Theta}(t_1' - t_1),$$

so that

$$t_1' = 2\Theta\left[t_2 + N_u t_f + \left(\frac{1}{2\Theta} - N_u - 1\right)t_1\right]. \tag{12–15}$$

Since the coefficient of the local temperature t_1 must exceed or equal zero, the criterion for the choice of Θ becomes $1/2\Theta - N_u - 1 \geq 0$, or*

$$\Theta \leq \frac{1}{2N_u + 2}. \tag{12–16}$$

Let the thermal conductivity of the wall be 20 Btu/hr-ft-°F, the unit surface conductance at $x = 0$ be 100 Btu/hr-ft²-°F, the initial wall temperature at $\theta = 0$ be a uniform 100°F, and the ambient temperature 1000°F for $\theta > 0$. The characteristic Nusselt number is computed as $N_u = h\delta/k = 100 \times 0.05/20 = 0.25$, and hence the upper limit on the choice of modulus is $\Theta \leq 0.4$. Selecting $\Theta = \frac{1}{3}$, we have $t_1' = (t_f + t_1 + 4t_2)/6$ at the surface and (12–6) at internal points, and for $\Theta = \frac{1}{4}$, we have $t_1' = (t_f + 3t_1 + 4t_2)/8$ at the surface and (12–7) at the internal nodal points.

---

*Fowler (6), in developing formal convergence criteria for parabolic numerical solutions, finds that for this case

$$\Theta \leq \frac{1}{\sqrt{N_u^2 + 1} + 1},$$

which is a much less restrictive criterion than (12–16). Notice that the two criteria are equal only if $N_u = 0$ as in (12–14). For example, if $N_u = \frac{1}{2}$, then Fowler's criterion limits the modulus to $\Theta \leq 0.472$ as compared with the smaller limit of 0.333 given by (12–16).

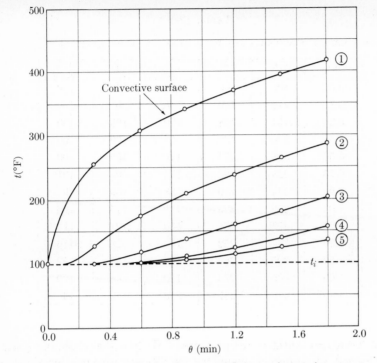

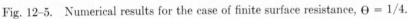

Fig. 12–5. Numerical results for the case of finite surface resistance, $\Theta = 1/4$.

TABLE 12–2

NUMERICAL TEMPERATURES WITH SURFACE RESISTANCE $(\Theta = \frac{1}{3})$

$\theta(\text{min})$	①	②	③	④	⑤
0.0	100	100	100	100	100
0.2	250	100	100	100	100
0.4	275	150	100	100	100
0.6	312	175	117	100	100
0.8	335	201	131	106	100
1.0	356	222	146	112	104
1.2	374	241	160	121	109
1.4	390	258	174	127	117
1.6	404	274	186	139	124
1.8	417	288	200	150	134

The numerical calculations with $\Theta = \frac{1}{3}$ and $\frac{1}{4}$ are carried out in Tables 12–2 and 12–3, the results of the latter being shown in Fig. 12–5. These solutions can be checked against the Heisler charts in Chapter 10.

TABLE 12-3

NUMERICAL TEMPERATURES WITH SURFACE RESISTANCE $(\Theta = \frac{1}{4})$

θ(min)	①	②	③	④	⑤
0.00	100	100	100	100	100
0.15	212	100	100	100	100
0.30	254	128	100	100	100
0.45	284	152	107	100	100
0.60	308	174	116	102	100
0.75	328	193	126	105	101
0.90	344	210	138	109	103
1.05	359	226	149	115	106
1.20	373	238	160	121	111
1.35	384	252	170	128	116
1.50	395	264	180	136	122
1.65	405	276	190	144	129
1.80	415	287	200	152	136

12-6 Transient surface temperature. Within the class of systems characterized by transient boundary conditions, we consider the case, treated by Duhamel's method in Article 11-2, of a semi-infinite solid with surface temperature linearly dependent on time. Assume that the thermal diffusivity of the solid is $\alpha = 0.1041 \text{ ft}^2/\text{hr}$, and that the initial temperature state is $t_i = 0°F$ throughout. It is required to determine the temperature history of points located at $\frac{1}{2}''$ intervals from the surface, if at time $\theta = 0$ the surface temperature begins to rise linearly as $t_1 = 3600\theta°F$.

Subdividing in $\delta = \frac{1}{2}''$ intervals with a half subvolume at the surface, and selecting a modulus of $\Theta = \frac{1}{2}$, we have for the time increment $\Delta\theta = (\frac{1}{2})(1/2 \times 12)^2 \times 60/0.1041 = 0.5$ min. The linear surface temperatures are then computed for a heating period of 4 minutes and entered in the first column of Table 12-4. Again, we can do no better than to choose a mean value for the initial surface temperature, in this case $t_{i_1} = \frac{1}{2}(0 + 30) = 15$. The number of nodal points required for an infinitely extended solid depends on the total heating time. In some cases we might reduce this number by assuming an adiabatic condition near the end of the heating period where the temperature gradient is nearly zero, although there is no set rule.

The temperature histories computed in Table 12-4 are compared at points ②, ③, and ④ with the exact solution (11-9) shown in Fig. 12-6. In this case the numerical results with a high modulus of $\Theta = \frac{1}{2}$ are stable but far from convergent as compared with the results shown for $\Theta = \frac{1}{4}$.

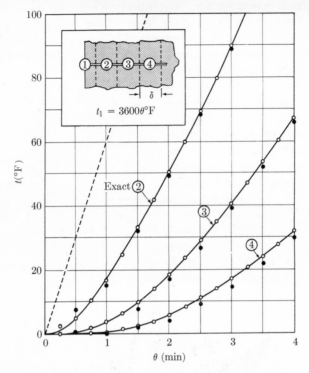

Fig. 12–6. Numerical results compared with exact temperature histories in a semi-infinite solid with surface temperature linearly increasing with time, $\Theta = 1/2,\ 1/4$.

TABLE 12–4

NUMERICAL TEMPERATURES WITH LINEAR SURFACE TEMPERATURE $(\Theta = \frac{1}{2})$

θ (min)	①	②	③	④	⑤	⑥	⑦	⑧	⑨
0.0	15	0.0	0.0	0.0	0.0	0.0	0.0	0.0	0.0
0.5	30	7.5	0.0	0.0	0.0	0.0	0.0	0.0	0.0
1.0	60	15.0	3.8	0.0	0.0	0.0	0.0	0.0	0.0
1.5	90	31.9	7.5	1.9	0.0	0.0	0.0	0.0	0.0
2.0	120	48.8	16.9	3.8	1.0	0.0	0.0	0.0	0.0
2.5	150	68.5	26.3	9.0	1.9	0.5	0.0	0.0	0.0
3.0	180	88.2	38.8	14.1	4.8	0.8	0.3	0.0	0.0
3.5	210	109.4	51.2	21.8	7.5	2.6	0.4	0.1	0.0
4.0	240	130.6	65.6	29.4	12.2	3.4	1.4	0.2	0.1

12-7 Graphical interpretation. The difference equations of Article 12–2 can also be solved graphically, and the *Binder-Schmidt* graphical procedure is based on the simplest of these, namely, (12–5) for a modulus of $\Theta = \frac{1}{2}$. In this case the future temperature of a given point in a subdivided structure does not depend on its present temperature, but is simply the arithmetic mean of present temperatures at adjacent nodal points. Then instead of performing the calculations by mental averaging, as in the numerical method, we carry them out graphically as suggested in Fig. 12–7.

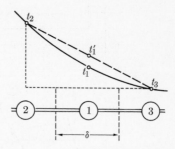

As an example in the application of the graphical method based on a modulus of $\frac{1}{2}$, we consider the problem in Article 12–3 for which numerical results are tabulated in Table 12–1. In this example an insulated

Fig. 12–7. Binder-Schmidt graphical method for $\Theta = 1/2$.

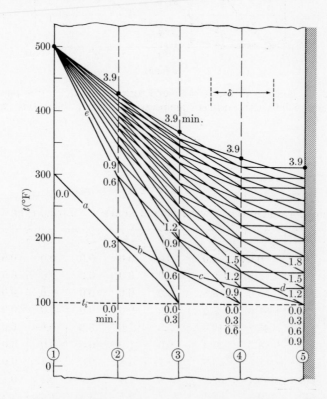

Fig. 12–8. Graphical solution of the plate system in Fig. 12–2 (Table 12–1).

plate, initially at 100°F throughout, is being heated with a face temperature
of 500°F. The graphical construction for determining the arithmetic mean
temperature at points ②, ③, ④, and ⑤ (Fig. 12–2) is shown in Fig. 12–8.

We begin the construction by assuming, as in the numerical method
(Table 12–1), that the initial surface temperature is 300°F. The line a is
then drawn in, connecting points ① and ③ at their respective initial temperatures of 300 and 100°F. This determines the temperature at point ②
for the end of the first time increment $\Delta\theta = 0.3$ min as 200°F (Table 12–1).
Now at this time, $\theta = 0.3$ min, the temperature of point ④ is still 100°F.
The line b is thus drawn in, connecting this value with 200°F at ② for the

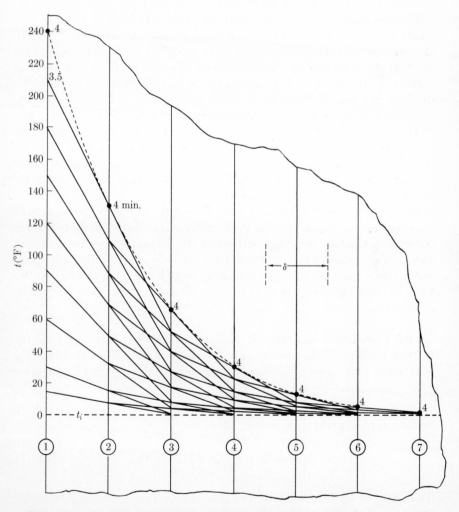

Fig. 12–9. Graphical solution of the semi-infinite system in Fig. 12–6
(Table 12–4).

same instant. This gives the temperature of point ③ at the end of the next time interval as 150°F at $\theta = 0.3 + 0.3 = 0.6$ min. Line c follows by the same reasoning, and line d is drawn in horizontally because at the adiabatic face ⑤ the temperature gradient is zero. Now at time $\theta = 0.3$ min, the left face is at 500°F, and at the same instant point ③ is at 100°F. Line e then gives the temperature of point ② as 300°F at $\theta = 0.6$ min.

The graphical averaging is carried on in this fashion, always keeping in mind that only temperatures at the *same* instant are used to determine the temperature at the end of the *next* time interval. The construction in Fig. 12–8 is completed up to $\theta = 3.9$ min, at which time the temperatures are those in the last line of Table 12–1.

The problem of transient surface temperatures is handled in much the same way. In Fig. 12–9 we consider graphically the problem in Article 12–6 of a semi-infinite solid with surface temperature linearly dependent on time. In this example the solid was initially at 0°F throughout, and the variable surface temperature was given by $t_1 = 3600\theta°F$, as recorded in the first column of Table 12–4. The construction is again started by assuming a mean value for the initial surface temperature of 15°F. At the end of the first time increment, $\Delta\theta = 0.5$ min, the surface temperature has risen to 30°F. This starts the second series of constructions, and the third series begins with a surface temperature of 60°F. The final graphical temperatures in Fig. 12–9 correspond to the numerical temperatures at $\theta = 4$ min in the last line of Table 12–4.

The graphical method can also be extended to cylindrical and spherical systems, and can be used for composite solids, structures with finite surface resistances, and for cases where either or both the unit surface conductance and ambient temperature vary with time. We do not consider such applications here, since in all cases and from nearly every point of view the graphical method has little to offer as an alternate to the tabular type of numerical approach.

12–8 Distributed sources. If a plate generates steady and uniform distributed heat q_0''' Btu/hr-ft^3 as in Article 11–4, then the transient-state heat balance for a general internal nodal point of volume $V = \delta^2$ is given by

$$-\sum K\Delta t\Delta\theta + q_0'''V\Delta\theta = Cw V\Delta t',$$

or for a typical point ① as in Fig. 12–1,

$$t_1' = \Theta\left[t_2 + t_3 + \left(\frac{1}{\Theta} - 2\right)t_1\right] + \Theta q_0'''\frac{\delta^2}{k}. \qquad (12\text{–}17)$$

The criterion for Θ is therefore the same as for a nongenerating transient system, and the method is unchanged except for the addition of a constant temperature term $\Theta q_0'''\delta^2/k$ during each time interval.

TABLE 12–5

NUMERICAL TEMPERATURES WITH DISTRIBUTED SOURCES $\left(\Theta = \frac{1}{4}\right)$

θ(min)	①	②	③
0	46	60	60
3	32	76	80
6	32	86	99
9	32	96	116
12	32	105	131
15	32	113	144
18	32	120	156
21	32	127	167
24	32	133	177
27	32	139	186
30	32	144	194

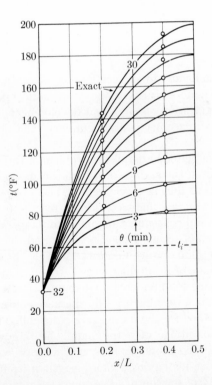

Fig. 12–10.   Numerical results for the case of distributed heat sources, $\Theta = 1/4$.

To compare results with the exact solution (11–21), we subdivide a plate of thickness $L = 1$ ft into five slices $\delta = \frac{1}{5}$ ft with half subvolumes at each surface, and select $\alpha = 0.2$ ft^2/hr, $k = 20$ Btu/hr-ft-°F, $q_0''' = 4 \times 10^4$ Btu/hr-ft^3, $t_i = 60$°F, and $t_1 = 32$°F on each face. Then with $\Theta = \frac{1}{4}$, the time increment becomes $\Delta\theta = (\frac{1}{4})(\frac{1}{5})^2 \times 60/0.2 = 3$ min, and by (12–17) for an internal nodal point such as ②, $t_2' = (t_1 + 2t_2 + t_3)/4 + 20$.

The work is carried out in Table 12–5 for half the plate and a total elapsed time of $\frac{1}{2}$ hour, the results being compared with (11–21) in Fig. 12–10. As is frequently the case, the time required for the numerical calculations is but a small fraction of the time consumed in computing the exact curves for comparison.

The problem of nonuniform heat generation is easily included. If the heat development is linearly dependent on local temperature as $q_t''' = q_0'''(1 + a_0 t)$, then the expression for t_1' corresponding to (12–17) is

$$t_1' = \Theta\left[t_2 + t_3 + \left(\frac{1}{\Theta} - 2 + \frac{\Delta\theta}{\Theta} \frac{\alpha q_0''' a_0}{k} \right) t_1 \right] + \Theta q_0''' \frac{\delta^2}{k}, \quad (12\text{–}18)$$

and the criterion for Θ becomes

$$\Theta \leq \tfrac{1}{2}[1 + (\alpha q_0''' a_0/k)\Delta\theta]. \quad (12\text{–}19)$$

This determines the maximum permissible subdivision size δ for a given time increment $\Delta\theta$.

12–9 Temperature history in an accelerating supersonic wing.

This is a modern system which more nearly typifies the practical problems which are likely to arise in engineering research and development. Here the system is somewhat complex in geometry, and boundary conditions are dependent on time.

Kaye (7) has investigated in detail the problem of transient temperature increases within and on the surface of a high-speed wing uniformly accelerated at a given rate during level flight. The process of *aerodynamic heating* under these variable flight conditions results in large increases in surface temperature and consequent nonuniform temperature distributions within the wing, both of which depend on time and the particular rate of acceleration. These temperature histories must be computed in order to estimate the magnitude of resultant thermal stresses and structural deflections, necessary cooling requirements, and so on.

In this study, temperature histories during acceleration were computed by the numerical method for the special case of level flight at an altitude of 50,000 ft, special conditions of aerodynamic heating without radiation exchange, and the special geometry of a solid wing of symmetrical double wedge-shaped cross section having a chord length of 5.5 ft and a maximum thickness equal to 8% of the chord. The wing was assumed to have a large span, a constant planform, and a uniform cross-sectional profile at all spanwise stations so that wing-tip effects could be ignored and only the two-dimensional field in the profile need be considered. The solid wing was imagined to be constructed of steel having a uniform thermal conductivity of 22 Btu/hr-ft-°F, a uniform thermal capacity of 0.118 Btu/lb-°F, and a specific weight of 486 lb/ft³. Flight history begins with the wing at a uniform temperature corresponding to steady flight at a Mach number of 1.4. Then at time $\theta = 0$ the wing is suddenly accelerated at a rate of 1 Mach number every 30 sec up to a maximum Mach number of 6.0. The problem is to examine the transient heating of the wing during this entire period of acceleration from Mach number 1.4. We have space here to look only at the general methods used and a small portion of the results.

The first problem is to compute the ambient conditions and the properties of two-dimensional supersonic flow in the four different airflow regions around the wedge for the specific angle of attack and wing loading corresponding to each Mach number. These calculations are fully described in (7). Heat transfer from the high-speed air flow to the wing surface s is described as

$$q = hA\,(t_{as} - t_s),$$

where h is an "effective" unit surface conductance, A is the surface area in question, t_s is the actual surface temperature for given free-stream conditions, and t_{as} is the *adiabatic surface temperature*. The adiabatic surface temperature is defined in terms of the mean temperature $\bar{t}_f$ of the ambient fluid and the mean stream velocity $\bar{v}_f$ as

$$t_{as} = \bar{t}_f + r\left(\frac{\bar{v}_f^2}{2gC_f}\right).$$

The term $(\bar{v}_f^2/2gC_f)$ is the difference between the stagnation temperature and t_f, and r is a "recovery factor" determined by experiment. The adiabatic surface temperature is the temperature which the surface would attain if, for the same free-stream conditions, it were insulated against heat exchange. For subsonic and transonic speeds, t_{as} does not greatly exceed the free-stream air temperature, while at supersonic speeds t_{as} rises very rapidly with increasing Mach number. Hence at very high speeds large temperature differences become available for heat transfer to the wing surface.

A second important nonuniformity which enters the problem is the variation in the effective unit surface conductance. Values of h are not only nonuniformly distributed along the wing surface, but at any local point the surface conductance varies with time as well. These instantaneous distributions during the acceleration period must be evaluated from boundary-layer considerations and available data for high-speed flow over flat plates. Figure 12–11 shows the estimated distributions of h as actually used in the numerical calculations. Distributions along the upper and

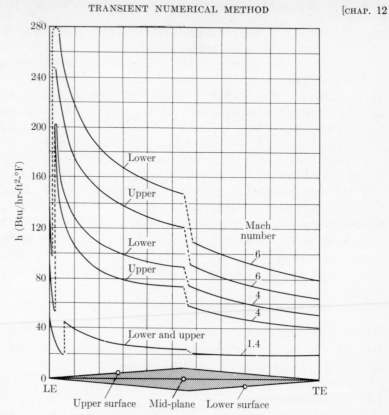

Fig. 12–11.   Calculated distributions of the unit surface conductance for flight of a wedge wing at constant Mach numbers (courtesy of Professor Kaye).

lower wing surfaces are shown for the initial state of Mach number 1.4, and for additional Mach numbers of 4.0 and 6.0 only. The discontinuities in these curves represent the transition from laminar to turbulent flow in the vicinity of the leading edge, and the effect of expansion waves at mid-chord. A further examination of these data shows that at any chordwise station the value of h increases with the Mach number in a very nearly linear manner. An assumption that h increases linearly with time was therefore used in the study to reduce the labor of the numerical computations.

The numerical solution was carried out with a rectangular network having a total of 113 nodal points, as shown in the unscaled quarter-symmetrical section of (a) in Fig. 12–12. Then for a typical internal nodal point such as ① in (b) of Fig. 12–12,

$$k\frac{\delta_2}{\delta_1}(t_2 - t_1) + k\frac{\delta_1}{\delta_2}(t_3 - t_1) + k\frac{\delta_2}{\delta_1}(t_4 - t_1) + k\frac{\delta_1}{\delta_2}(t_5 - t_1)$$

$$= \frac{Cw\delta_1\delta_2}{\Delta\theta}(t_1' - t_1).$$

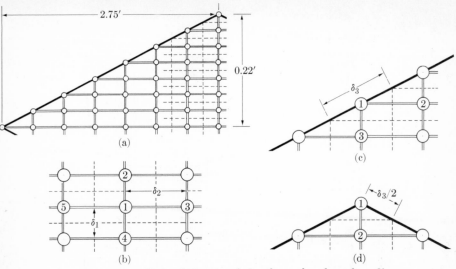

Fig. 12–12.   Numerical network for the wedge-shaped profile.

By choosing a time increment

$$\Delta\theta = \frac{Cw\delta_1^2}{2k(1 + A^2)}, \tag{12–20}$$

the temperature t_1 was eliminated, whereby

$$t_1' = \frac{B}{2}[(t_2 + t_4) + A^2(t_3 + t_5)], \tag{12–21}$$

in which $A = \delta_1/\delta_2$ and $B = 1/(1 + A^2)$. Also, for a typical surface nodal point such as ① in (c) of Fig. 12–12,

$$k\frac{\delta_1}{\delta_2}(t_2 - t_1) + k\frac{\delta_2}{\delta_1}(t_3 - t_1) + h\delta_3(t_{as} - t_1) = \frac{Cw\delta_1\delta_2/2}{\Delta\theta}(t_1' - t_1),$$

or by substituting $\Delta\theta$ from (12–20),

$$t_1' = B\left[A\delta_3\frac{h}{k}(t_{as} - t_1) + t_3 + A^2t_2\right] + (1 - B - A^2)t_1. \tag{12–22}$$

Finally, for a typical mid-chord surface nodal point such as ① in (d) of Fig. 12–12,

$$k\frac{\delta_2}{\delta_1}(t_2 - t_1) + h\delta_3(t_{as} - t_1) = \frac{Cw\delta_1\delta_2/4}{\Delta\theta}(t_1' - t_1),$$

or by (12–20),

$$t_1' = 2B\left[A\delta_3\frac{h}{k}(t_{as} - t_1) + t_2\right] + (1 - 2B)t_1. \tag{12–23}$$

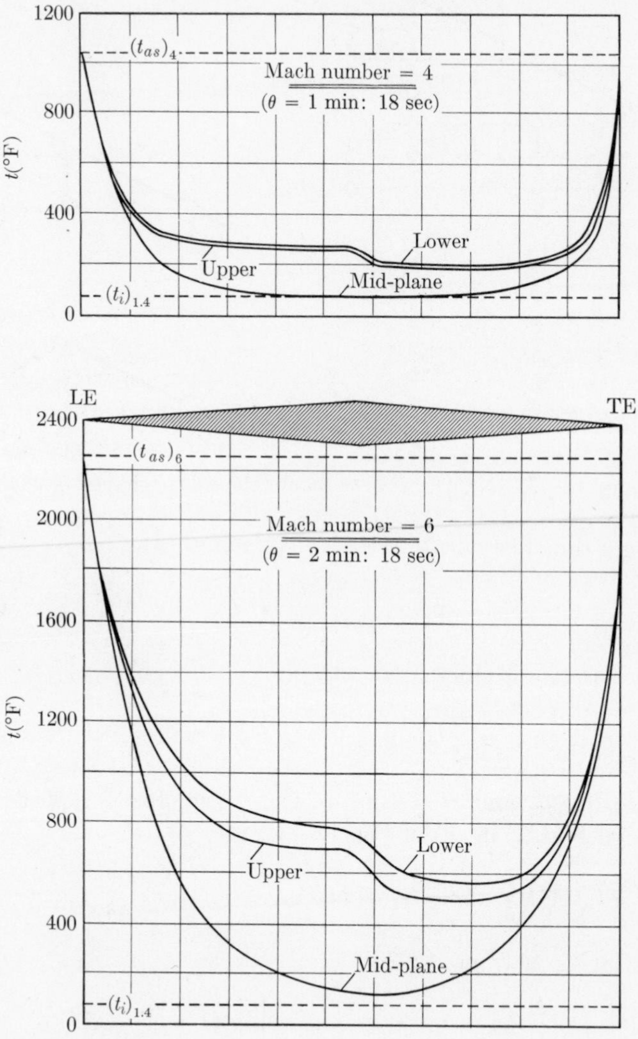

Fig. 12–13. Instantaneous chordwise temperature distributions in the wedge wing for a uniform acceleration of 1 Mach number/30 sec from initial Mach number 1.4 to Mach numbers 4 and 6 (courtesy of Professor Kaye).

The numerical constants were $\delta_1 = 0.0314$ ft, $\delta_2 = 0.3928$ ft, $\delta_3 = 0.3941$ ft, $A = 0.0800$, and $B = 0.9935$ so that (12–21), (12–22), and (12–23) reduced to the computational forms

(b) $t_1' = 0.4968(t_2 + t_4) + 0.0032(t_3 + t_5),$

(c) $t_1' = 0.0313\dfrac{h}{k}(t_{as} - t_1) + 0.9935t_3 + 0.0064t_2 + 0.0001t_1,$

(d) $t_1' = 0.0626\dfrac{h}{k}(t_{as} - t_1) + 1.9871t_2 - 0.9871t_1.$

According to these data and (12–20) the time increment was $\Delta\theta = 0.118 \times 486 \times (0.0314)^2 \times 3600/2 \times 22[1 + (0.08)^2] = 4.60$ sec.* The entire computation was therefore a long one of 30 steps at each of 113 points to cover the field of acceleration from Mach number 1.4 to 6.0. For each of the 30 steps the difference equations were altered to account for the change in unit surface conductance and adiabatic surface temperature over the previous time increment. The recovery factor was taken as $r = 0.9$.

A few quantitative results are reproduced in Fig. 12–13. The substantial difference in local unit surface conductance on the upper and lower surfaces of the wing results in a higher temperature of the lower surface, and both upper and lower surfaces appear to operate at a temperature considerably higher than the mid-plane temperature. It is also clear from these results that the severest temperature gradients occur in the chordwise direction near the leading and trailing edges where the thermal lag is smallest, and in the vertical direction normal to the mid-plane in the mid-chord region of the wing. The maximum temperature occurs, as expected, at the leading and trailing edges, and is equal to the adiabatic surface temperature (70°F at the initial Mach number of 1.4, 1060°F at a Mach number of 4.0, and 2250°F at the highest Mach number of 6.0). This would suggest either using high-temperature materials for these leading and trailing edges, or providing some means of artificially cooling these local portions of the structure.

12–10 Closure. A number of other important systems for which the numerical methods of this chapter are well suited are composite structures with and without contact resistances, structures subdivided on a physical

---

*For a rectangular network with $\Theta_1 = \alpha\Delta\theta/\delta_1^2$ and $\Theta_2 = \alpha\Delta\theta/\delta_2^2$, we have

$$t_1' = \Theta_1(t_2 + t_4) + \Theta_2(t_3 + t_5) + (1 - 2\Theta_1 - 2\Theta_2)t_1,$$

from which, as in this example with $\Theta_1 = 0.4968$ and $\Theta_2 = 0.0032$,

$$\Theta_1 + \Theta_2 \leq \tfrac{1}{2}.$$

The limiting stability criterion was automatically satisfied by (12–20).

basis, structures receiving a uniform rate of heat to the surface as in radiation or induction heating, and structures involving cylindrical or spherical geometry. The numerical method is also capable of handling periodic flow systems, and moving sources of heat within the solid material. If the periodic flow is steady, then both of these systems can be handled by relaxation, provided certain convergence criteria are observed. All of these problems, along with general methods for including effects of variable properties, have been treated by Dusinberre (3).

The graphical method of Article 12–7 was presented here only because of its wide popularity. Since the method is based on a limiting modulus, it can give only the crudest estimate of temperature distributions even when the construction is perfect. It is claimed that in all cases the graphical method has the advantage of giving a running picture of the changing temperature distribution. But this is even better visualized in a column of figures, and since the results must eventually be expressed in figures there is little advantage to interpreting the problem in terms of a scaled drawing.

The power of numerical methods is particularly evident in the problem of Article 12–9. In view of the uncertainties in the original data, the results obtained by numerical means were clearly as accurate as could be obtained by any other method. For this reason, and in all such cases as this, an exact solution is meaningless.

REFERENCES

1. D. N. de G. Allen, *Relaxation Methods*. New York; McGraw-Hill, 1954.

2. G. M. Dusinberre, "Numerical Methods for Transient Heat Flow," *Trans., ASME*, Vol. 67, No. 8, 1945, pp. 703–712.

3. G. M. Dusinberre, *Numerical Analysis of Heat Flow*. New York; McGraw-Hill, 1949.

4. R. P. Eddy, "Stability in the Numerical Solution of Initial-Value Problems in Partial-Differential Equations," *U.S. Naval Ordnance Laboratory Memorandum* 10232, Oct., 1949.

5. G. G. O'Brien, M. A. Hyman, and S. Kaplan, "A Study of the Numerical Solution of Partial-Differential Equations," *U.S. Naval Ordnance Laboratory Memorandum* 10433, Jan., 1949.

6. C. M. Fowler, "Analysis of Numerical Solutions of Transient Heat-Flow Problems," *Quarterly of Applied Mathematics*, Vol. 3, No. 4, 1945, pp. 361–376.

7. J. Kaye, "The Transient Temperature Distribution in a Wing Flying at Supersonic Speeds," *Journal of the Aeronautical Sciences*, Vol. 17, No. 12, Dec., 1950, pp. 787–807, 816.

PROBLEMS

12–1. An infinite plate $12''$ thick and of thermal diffusivity $\frac{5}{9}$ ft^2/hr is initially at a uniform temperature of $0°$F. At time $\theta = 0$ its surface temperatures at $x = 0$ and L are suddenly raised to and maintained at $400°$F for all $\theta > 0$. Show by the numerical method with a modulus of $\frac{1}{2}$ that the instantaneous temperature distribution after 15 min is 400, 337, 290, and 274°F corresponding to points $x/L = 0, \frac{1}{6}, \frac{2}{6},$ and $\frac{3}{6}$.

12-2. With reference to problem 12-1, (a) repeat the numerical calculations for moduli $\frac{1}{3}$ and $\frac{1}{4}$, (b) plot the exact temperature history t vs. θ according to (10-8) at $x/L = \frac{1}{6}, \frac{2}{6},$ and $\frac{3}{6}$, and the numerical results for moduli $\frac{1}{2}, \frac{1}{3},$ and $\frac{1}{4}$.

12-3. The plate in problem 12-1 is of thermal conductivity 20 Btu/hr-ft-°F. If the unit surface conductance and ambient temperature on both sides is 60 Btu/hr-ft²-°F and 1000°F respectively, compute the instantaneous temperature distribution within the plate after 15 minutes using the numerical method with a modulus of $\frac{1}{3}$. Compare numerical results with the Heisler charts in Figs. 10-11(a) and 10-11(b).

12-4. Repeat problem 10-16 using the numerical method of solution.

12-5. Consider two large plates each 8″ thick and each of the same material whose thermal diffusivity is 0.695 ft²/hr. One of the plates is at a uniform temperature of 700°F, and the other is at a uniform temperature of 100°F, and each plate has one insulated face. If, at time $\theta = 0$, the free faces of the plates are placed together in perfect contact, (a) determine the temperature distribution in the plates for a 12-min contact period, using the numerical method with a 2″ network spacing and full elements at the contact faces, (b) plot the temperature history at a point halfway through the high-temperature plate for moduli $\frac{1}{2}, \frac{1}{3},$ and $\frac{1}{4}$.

12-6. Repeat problem 11-1 using the numerical method of solution.

12-7. Repeat problem 12-1 using the Binder-Schmidt graphical method.

12-8. Repeat problem 11-1 using the Binder-Schmidt graphical method.

12-9. Compute the corresponding temperature distribution in the plate of problem 12-1 if it is of thermal conductivity 1 Btu/hr-ft-°F and if it begins, at time $\theta = 0$, to generate steady and uniformly distributed heat in amount 1800 Btu/hr-ft³. Use the numerical method and compare results with an exact solution.

12-10. Develop the difference equation and convergence criterion for an internal point of a two-dimensional network. For the application of this difference equation consider the cooling of a long piece of bar stock of 4″ square cross-section and of thermal diffusivity 0.278 ft²/hr. The initial temperature of the stock is 500°F throughout, and surface temperatures are suddenly reduced to and maintained at 100°F. Using a 1″ network spacing and choosing a modulus of $\frac{1}{6}$, compute and plot temperature histories for a total cooling time of 3 min. Compare results with an exact solution.

CHAPTER 13

EXPERIMENTAL ANALOGIC METHOD

In this final chapter we outline a number of experimental techniques for handling conduction problems which would otherwise resist solution by exact analytical means or for which an approximate numerical solution would become too tedious. The basis for this approximate experimental approach lies in the mathematical similarities between temperature distributions and analogous potential fields.

13–1 Experimental solutions by analogy. Let each of n distinct physical phenomena P_I, P_{II}, $\cdots$, P_n be exhibited in terms of its characteristic analytical relations p_{μ_1}, p_{μ_2}, $\cdots$ which are functions of the independent variables ψ_1, ψ_2, $\cdots$ as

$$P_I = P_I\,[p_{i_1}(\psi_1),\, p_{i_2}(\psi_2),\, \cdots\,],$$

$$P_{II} = P_{II}\,[p_{j_1}(\psi_1),\, p_{j_2}(\psi_2),\, \cdots\,],$$

$$\cdot$$
$$\cdot$$
$$\cdot$$

$$P_n = P_n\,[p_{\mu_1}(\psi_1),\, p_{\mu_2}(\psi_2),\, \cdots\,].$$

Now if it should happen that these n phenomena are all identical in the formal mathematical sense of $i = j = \cdots = \mu$, then it follows that the n phenomena themselves are identical in their physical behavior. When this occurs for any two or more of the P's, the phenomena involved are said to be *mathematically analogous*, and corresponding dependent variables expressed by the p's are said to be *analogues*.

In ordinary potential-field problems the p's are characteristic differential equations which stem from the P's and which must be satisfied by the particular potential function in question. Therefore, all fields whose potential functions satisfy the same total- or partial-differential equation must be analogous and thereby susceptible to *analogous interpretations*. Offhand, we can think of many phenomena with analogues, such as ideal gravitational, electrical, electromagnetic, and fluid velocity potentials; all of these are analogous, one to the other, in that each satisfies the Laplace equation. It is therefore possible to predict the behavior of a given phenomenon from the behavior of a second, perhaps better-known phenomenon, provided the second is analogous to the first.

318

In conduction heat-transfer we are concerned with solutions of the general heat-conduction equation (1–6), and its simpler forms, the Fourier equation (1–8), Poisson equation (1–9), and Laplace equation (1–10). Therefore, a typical heat-conduction problem which resists solution by ordinary means might advantageously be reinterpreted as an analogous problem in an entirely different but analogous field whose solution satisfies one of these four equations. The solution sought in the analogous field will obviously not be an analytical one, since the same mathematical difficulties are present in the analogous field as exist in the original problem. The chief advantage comes in finding an analogous problem which has an easily obtained experimental solution. Once the solution is obtained in the analogous field, it can be reinterpreted in terms of the original problem. This is the foundation of the *experimental-analogic method.*

13–2 Fluid-flow analogy. The field of fluid mechanics offers a number of possibilities for the solution of complex problems in steady heat conduction. One of the most familiar applications of this sort is the so-called *fluid-flow analogy* with which certain types of steady two-dimensional potential fields can be approximately simulated by the irrotational flow of an ideal fluid in a model of the region in question. By this analogy it is possible to actually make visible the distribution of adiabatic points in an analogous thermal system.

From the elementary theory of hydrodynamics, we recall that the velocity components $u = V_x$ and $v = V_y$ of an ideal incompressible fluid must satisfy the demand of continuity that $\partial u/\partial x + \partial v/\partial y = 0$. This continuity relation implies that some function $\Psi(x,y)$ exists for which $vdx - udy$ is its exact differential. Thus

$$d\Psi = \frac{\partial \Psi}{\partial x}\,dx + \frac{\partial \Psi}{\partial y}\,dy = vdx - udy,$$

and therefore

$$v = \frac{\partial \Psi}{\partial x}\,; \qquad \frac{\partial v}{\partial x} = \frac{\partial^2 \Psi}{\partial x^2}\,,$$

$$u = -\frac{\partial \Psi}{\partial y}\,; \qquad \frac{\partial u}{\partial y} = -\frac{\partial^2 \Psi}{\partial y^2}\,.$$

But if the flow is irrotational, then evidently $\partial u/\partial y = \partial v/\partial x$, and this means that

$$\frac{\partial^2 \Psi}{\partial x^2} + \frac{\partial^2 \Psi}{\partial y^2} = 0. \qquad (13\text{–}1)$$

The function Ψ is called the *stream function,* and curves for which Ψ = const. are the *streamlines* of the flow. The conjugate function of Ψ (Article 6–2) is called the *velocity potential* of the flow; it must also satisfy the Laplace equation, and hence the curves for which the stream function and velocity potential are constant intersect orthogonally.

The fluid-flow analogy for conduction heat-transfer is based on the observation that both the stream function and velocity potential of an ideal fluid in steady irrotational flow satisfy the Laplace equation, as do the heat-flow function and temperature potential in a nongenerating region of uniform thermal conductivity. The streamlines of such an ideal flow are therefore analogous to lines of heat flow in this region, and the velocity potential is analogous to temperature potential where lines of constant velocity potential correspond to isothermals. But the streamlines can be made visible by well-known methods of flow visualization, and hence, by analogy, corresponding lines of heat flow can be exhibited experimentally. All one has to do is set up an approximately ideal irrotational flow across the conducting region in question, photograph the stream lines of this flow, and finally reinterpret these as similarly oriented adiabatic lines.

The hydrodynamic analogy, while originally due to the English physicist

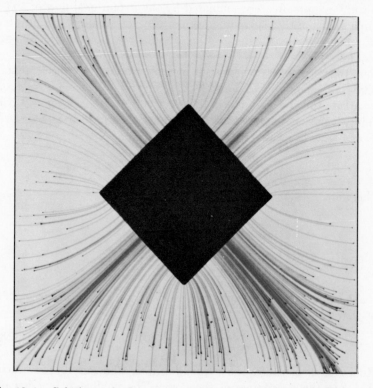

Fig. 13–1. Solution of the furnace-wall problem by fluid-flow analogy. (Courtesy of Professor Moore.)

Lord Kelvin (1824–1907) and others of this period, was first used successfully by Hele-Shaw, *et al.* (1) nearly fifty years ago for solutions in electromagnetic field theory, and has since been elaborately developed for other applications by Moore (2). The essential feature of Moore's *"fluid-mapper"* apparatus (2), (3) is the use of water or glycerol as an approximation to an ideal liquid, the flow being set up in the narrow "two-dimensional" space between a lower slab cast from dental stone and an upper plate of glass placed $\frac{1}{16}''$ above the slab. Visualization of the field of streamlines is accomplished by introducing crystals of potassium permanganate into the

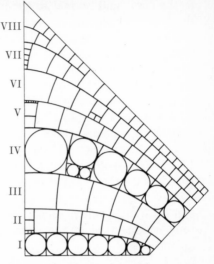

Fig. 13–2.   Evaluation of the streamline pattern in Fig. 13–1.

flow. These crystals are carried along with the flow, each one, in dissolving, forming the head of a clearly visible streamline of color. This streamline pattern is then photographed to give a permanent record of the flow conformation.

Figure 13–1 shows a partial fluid-mapper solution contributed by Moore for the furnace-wall problem of Article 6–8, Fig. 6–11. Note that the visible flow lines (here interpreted as the locus of adiabatic points) clearly obey the theoretical orthogonality property for such a field. In this case the analogy is completed by noting that Ψ = const. along the boundaries is the same boundary condition as t = const. along the boundaries as required in the analogous thermal system of Fig. 6–11.

Evaluation of the flow pattern. The fluid-mapper pattern in Fig. 13–1 does not represent a complete solution in itself, but rather an accurate beginning for a graphical analysis of the potential field. Here the random flow lines are not uniformly spaced, as was arbitrarily chosen in Article 6–8, and accordingly a somewhat different graphical technique is required.

Moore (4) has developed a convenient *"circling-in"* technique for the freehand construction of curvilinear squares (Fig. 6–10) and a method for evaluating curvilinear-square remainders. By way of illustration consider the lower one-eighth section of the second quadrant in Fig. 13–1, and from the pattern of flow lines select seven flow channels, as in Fig. 13–2.

Beginning on the inside of channel I, we fit a circle tangent to the two adiabatic lines and inner boundary, and then draw an isothermal tangent to the circle and normal to the flow lines.* Continuing this throughout the length of channel I, we find that the channel contains, by chance, seven curvilinear squares. This is also true of channel III. Channel IV is mapped from both sides with a remainder somewhere in the middle. This remainder is $1/(1 + \frac{1}{2}) = 0.666$ in the fifth curvilinear square, and therefore channel IV contains $S = 5.666$ curvilinear squares. Channel V is mapped from inside out, and with a remainder at the outer edge of $1/(2 + \frac{1}{6}) = 0.462$, so that for this channel $S = 12.462$. The seventh channel is a combination of channels VII and VIII. The divided remainder in channel VII is $1/(3 + \frac{1}{5}) = 0.312$ and in channel VIII is $1/[4 + 1/(\frac{1}{3} + \frac{1}{2})] = 0.192$. This gives a combined remainder of $1/(0.312 + 0.192) = 1.983$, so that for the seventh channel $S = 17.983$.

Now the thermal conductance of each channel is $K_c = k(\Delta l_a/\Delta l_i)/S$, and since k for this problem is 1 Btu/hr-ft-°F, we have $K_c = 1/S$. The total conductance of the section is then the sum of the channel conductances:

$$K = \frac{1}{7.000} + \frac{1}{7.429} + \frac{1}{6.000} + \frac{1}{5.666} + \frac{1}{12.462} + \frac{1}{14.666} + \frac{1}{17.983} = 0.825,$$

and from this we compute the heat loss per foot length of the kiln as

$$q = 8 \times 0.825(300 - 100) = 1{,}320 \text{ Btu/hr.}$$

This result is approximately 3.7% below the crude result obtained in Article 6–8 by complete freehand sketching.

The fluid-flow analogy described here is most useful for cases of steady conduction in regions of uniform thermal conductivity and having a known distribution of boundary temperature. The analogy can also be used, however, for systems containing local heat sources or sinks, and by incorporating Moore's additional feature of a *sandbed* (5) the analogy can handle systems containing distributed heat sources or sinks as well.

It is worth while mentioning here, additionally, that another type of hydrodynamic analogy exists between the temperature in a region of this sort and the stream function of a vortex type of fluid flow. We again consider an ideal incompressible fluid, this time with a constant vorticity ω. This vorticity is related to the velocity components $u = V_x$ and $v = V_y$ of the flow by the well-known partial-differential equation

$$\frac{\partial v}{\partial x} - \frac{\partial u}{\partial y} = -2\omega.$$

---

*This method of forming curvilinear squares from a circle is found by Moore (4) to be quite accurate for flow lines which are not severely divergent and for curvilinear squares which have close diagonal symmetry. The method is often superior to freehand sketching with even a trained eye, and for the essentially untrained it eliminates the need for tedious and repeated diagonal measurements.

Then, by recognizing that $v = \partial\Psi/\partial x$ and $u = -\partial\Psi/\partial y$, we have in terms of the stream function Ψ the Poisson equation

$$\frac{\partial^2\Psi}{\partial x^2} + \frac{\partial^2\Psi}{\partial y^2} + 2\omega = 0, \tag{13–2}$$

which is identical to that for $t(x,y)$ in a region of uniform thermal conductivity k and generating uniform distributed heat q''' as

$$\frac{\partial^2 t}{\partial x^2} + \frac{\partial^2 t}{\partial y^2} + \frac{q'''}{k} = 0. \tag{13–3}$$

Thus $\Psi(x,y)$ and $t(x,y)$ are completely analogous, and values of $t(x,y)$ can be computed from the vortex flow according to

$$t(x,y) = \frac{q'''}{2k\omega}\,\Psi(x,y).$$

This analogy is not at all easy to carry out experimentally because of the difficulty both in obtaining a flow with constant vorticity and in photographing the streamline pattern. Den Hartog (6) explains in some detail the experimental procedures involved.

13–3 Membrane analogy. Membrane analogy is an offspring of the elasticity phenomenon. We consider a true membrane, i.e., a film of infinitesimal weight and flexural rigidity, suspended with uniform edge tension on any closed boundary, as in Fig. 13–3. The membrane is dilated by a uniform overpressure p on one side of its surface (see Frontispiece), and as such it is in equilibrium under the balance of this external dilation pressure and the tensile forces within the membrane at the boundary s. Under these conditions we can derive the characteristic differential equation of the membrane surface $z(x,y)$ by simply writing down the equations for static equilibrium of a differential element of membrane surface.

Consider the isolated element of surface shown in Fig. 13–3. The tensile forces along the edges of this element are due to the surface tension, which we assume to be the same at all points in the membrane. If the membrane deflections $z(x,y)$ are "small," then these edge forces are simply τdx and τdy, where τ is a constant coefficient of surface tension for the membrane. The downward vertical component of τdy on the left-hand edge is $F_1 = \tau dy\sin\theta$, and the upward vertical component of τdy on the right-hand edge is $F_2 = \tau dy\sin\gamma$. Now θ and γ differ by the change in slope between x and $x + dx$. This change is evidently the product of the rate of change in slope and dx, $-(\partial^2 z/\partial x^2)dx$, so that $\gamma = \theta + (-\partial^2 z/\partial x^2)dx$. But we are assuming small deflections, and hence these angles are small and their sine can be replaced by the angles themselves:

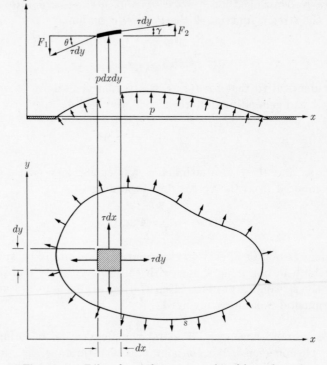

Fig. 13–3.   Dilated membrane on a closed boundary S.

$$F_1 = \tau dy \sin \theta = \tau dy \theta,$$

$$F_2 = \tau dy \sin \gamma = \tau dy \left(\theta - \frac{\partial^2 z}{\partial x^2} dx \right).$$

Vertical components F_3 and F_4 of τdx on the remaining two edges of the element can be shown in like manner to be

$$F_3 = \tau dx \sin \theta' = \tau dx \theta',$$

$$F_4 = \tau dx \sin \gamma' = \tau dx \left(\theta' - \frac{\partial^2 z}{\partial y^2} dy \right).$$

Summing these forces in the vertical direction and imposing the state of static equilibrium, we have

$$\tau dy \theta - \tau dy \left(\theta - \frac{\partial^2 z}{\partial x^2} dx \right) + \tau dx \theta' - \tau dx \left(\theta' - \frac{\partial^2 z}{\partial y^2} dy \right) + p dx dy = 0,$$

or

$$\frac{\partial^2 z}{\partial x^2} + \frac{\partial^2 z}{\partial y^2} + \frac{p}{\tau} = 0. \qquad (13\text{–}4)$$

This is identified as the partial-differential equation satisfied by small deflections $z(x,y)$ of a homogeneous membrane having a constant coefficient of surface tension τ lb/ft and dilated by a uniform overpressure p lb/ft^2.

Prandtl was the first to point out the formal identity between the differential equation for the membrane (13–4) and the differential equation satisfied by the stress function in an elastic bar subject to torsion. In 1903 he suggested in the literature (7) that experimental solutions of the Saint-Venant torsion problem for prismatic bars (1855) be obtained from investigations of analogous membrane deflections, and in 1906 the Prandtl analogy was experimentally confirmed by Anthes (8). Since that time membrane analogy has been repeatedly used for experimental applications of torsional and bending stress analysis.* In 1950, Wilson and Miles (10) applied membrane analogy to problems of steady temperature fields satisfying the Laplace equation, and in 1952 the analogy was extended to include systems generating or absorbing uniform distributed heat (11).

In nearly all applications of the Prandtl analogy, a soap film is used to approximate a true membrane. The value of τ is then interpreted as the uniform coefficient of surface tension for the particular soap material employed.

13–4 Membrane analogy for distributed heat-source systems. In this case the temperature field must satisfy the Poisson equation (13–3) if the conducting region is of uniform conductivity and if it generates or absorbs distributed heat in uniform amount. We then see that the mathematical analogy between the analogs $t(x,y)$ of the temperature field and $z(x,y)$ of the membrane deflection field (13–4) is simply (11)

$$t(x,y) = \left(\frac{q'''}{k}\right)\left(\frac{\tau}{p}\right) z(x,y). \qquad (13\text{–}5)$$

In other words, to convert experimental membrane data $z(x,y)$ to analogous and corresponding temperatures $t(x,y)$, we simply multiply the membrane deflections by the constant ratio of heat generation to thermal conductivity and the constant ratio of membrane surface-tension coefficient to membrane dilation pressure.

The boundary of the dilated membrane is to be geometrically similar to the boundary of the conducting region in question, and known boundary temperatures t_1 are to be duplicated by building up the membrane boundary to some convenient scale such that $z_1 = ct_1$.

---

*The reader who is interested in applications of membrane analogy to mechanical stress fields will want to consult papers encompassed in a complete bibliography compiled by Higgins (9).

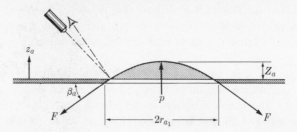

Fig. 13–4.   Dilated soap film on an auxiliary circular boundary.

Evaluation of p/τ. To obtain quantitative results, it is necessary either to measure p and τ separately or their ratio p/τ in each experiment. In all cases this can be accomplished with sufficient accuracy by employing an "auxiliary" soap film, as first suggested in a method developed by Griffith and Taylor (12). Thus for a dilated film on an auxiliary *circular* boundary, as in Fig. 13–4, the vertical component of the tensile forces between the boundary and film is $F \sin \beta_a = \tau \, (2\pi r_{a1}) \sin \beta_a$. At equilibrium this component is in balance with the vertical component of the uniform pressure force $p(\pi r_{a_1}^2)$, whereby

$$\left(\frac{p}{\tau}\right)_a = \frac{2}{r_{a1}} \sin \beta_a. \tag{13–6}$$

The value of $\sin \beta_a$ must be computed from the measured value of β_a. Then if the auxiliary film is of the same soap solution as the main film under investigation, and both films are dilated by the same uniform pressure, $(p/\tau) = (p/\tau)_a$.

The principal objection to evaluating the experimental ratio p/τ in this way is the lack of confidence which can be placed in the measured angle β_a. A number of investigators using "pressure" films for experimental stress analysis (9) have employed optical techniques for determining this maximum film angle. A single light source is focused on the film boundary (Fig. 13–4), and the angle β_a is computed from the measured angle of light reflection. It is found, however, that this light-reflection technique is subject to error because the film does not attach itself precisely to the boundary edge, but instead overlaps slightly onto the boundary model (13). This requires focusing the light source onto the film at a point some distance above the actual boundary edge, and accordingly the measured angle β_a errs on the low side.

An alternate technique for evaluating p/τ is to integrate the differential equation for a symmetrical dilated film on a circular boundary. The film profile equation then gives a simple expression relating $(p/\tau)_a$ to the maximum deflection Z_a at $r_a = 0$ and the known boundary radius r_{a1}. Thus with (13–4) in cylindrical coordinates as

$$\frac{d^2 z_a}{dr_a^2} + \frac{1}{r_a}\frac{dz_a}{dr_a} + \left(\frac{p}{\tau}\right)_a = 0,$$

we find the particular solution

$$z_a = \frac{1}{4}\left(\frac{p}{\tau}\right)_a (r_{a_1}^2 - r_a^2)$$

satisfying the required boundary deflection $z_a = 0$ at $r_a = r_{a_1}$ and the symmetry condition $dz_a/dr_a = 0$ at $r_a = 0$. Therefore, in terms of the easily measured maximum deflection Z_a as in Fig. 13–4 (11),

$$\left(\frac{p}{\tau}\right)_a = \frac{4}{r_{a_1}^2} Z_a. \tag{13-7}$$

Soap-film apparatus. The marginal durability of an ordinary soap film requires isolating the film from incipient vibration and atmospheric contamination. Once a film is spread and maintained on an accurately constructed boundary, the eventual success of the method lies wholly in the accuracy with which the spatial ordinates $z(x,y)$ of the film surface can be measured above a convenient datum plane $z = c$.

One type of successful soap-film apparatus is shown in Fig. 13–5. The structure is in the form of a split cast-aluminum chamber which houses and securely clamps an aluminum-sheet boundary model. A glass plate seals the upper chamber and carries a vertical micrometer head fitted with a needle point for locating vertical ordinates $z(x,y)$. The plate is

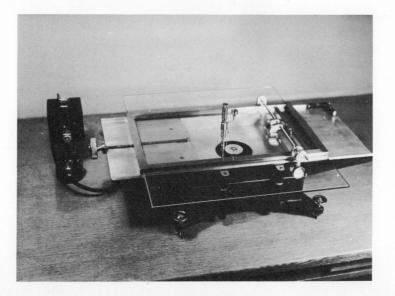

Fig. 13–5.   Soap-film apparatus.

propelled horizontally by machine screws, its position being recorded by vernier scales. Auxiliary equipment shown in Fig. 13–5 includes a support for annular boundaries, a small reservoir fitted to the vertical micrometer for lubricating the probe point with soap solution, and finally an adjustable height reservoir for distilled water used in dilating the film by introducing a controlled quantity of water into the sealed chamber below the boundary model (14).

In operation, a film is formed across the clean boundary model wetted with fresh soap solution by drawing a celluloid spreader along the boundary plate. The film is then dilated and symmetrically probed with the apparatus in a room that is dark except for a single low-powered light focused on the film. This type of lighting is most satisfactory for maintaining isothermal conditions and for watching the reflection of the probe as it approaches the film. When contact with the film is made (Fig. 13–6), this reflection blurs.

Durable soap films are obtained with a suitably proportioned solution of sodium oleate, glycerine, and distilled water.

Fig. 13–6.   View of a dilated soap film on a hollow circular boundary.   Dilated auxiliary film in background.

Fig. 13–7.   Dilated soap film on a hollow rectangular boundary.

13–5 Application to electrical coils. Consider a coil of hollow rectangular profile whose outer dimensions are $4''$ by $3''$ and whose inner dimensions are $2''$ by $1''$. The coil is to generate uniform Joulean heat q''', and is of uniform thermal conductivity k. The data obtained from the soap film appearing in Fig. 13–7 is plotted in Fig. 13–8, and with the maximum deflection of the auxiliary circular film of radius $r_{a1} = 1.75''$ recorded as $Z_a = 0.529$, we have, by (13–7), $p/\tau = 8.2923$. Then by reference to (13–5) and Fig. 13–8 we can compute the temperature at corresponding points in the actual coil for any combination of electrical loading and thermal conductivity, and for any coil of the same relative dimensions and with inner and outer boundaries at the same uniform temperature.

The more practical case of an annular profile with a different uniform temperature on each boundary is handled by first selecting a particular value of Z_a, say Z_a', and then computing by (13–7) the $(p/\tau)_a$ ratio which belongs to this Z_a'. The boundaries of the main film are then elevated according to z_1 and z_2 computed by (13–5), and both films are dilated until the maximum deflection of the auxiliary film is Z_a'.

In all cases, care must be taken to preserve small film slopes, as required in the derivation of (13–4).

To compare membrane data with an exact solution, consider a coil of solid circular profile with $q''' = 10^4$ Btu/hr-ft^3, $k = 1$ Btu/hr-ft-°F, $r_1 = 1/6$ ft, and $t_1 = 0$°F. With $t(r_1) = 0$, then also $z(r_1) = 0$ for the membrane boundary, and the film appears as in the Frontispiece.

Typical experimental membrane data r vs. z for this case are listed in the first two columns of Table 13–1. By (13–7), $p/\tau = 7.200$, and the analogic relation (13–5) reads

$$t_{\text{membrane}} = \left(\frac{q'''}{k}\right)\left(\frac{\tau}{p}\right) z = 115.741 z''.$$

For the exact analytical solution with uniform heat generation, we obtain

$$t_{\text{exact}} = \frac{1}{4}\left(\frac{q'''}{k}\right) (r_1^2 - r^2) = 17.361\,(4 - r''^2),$$

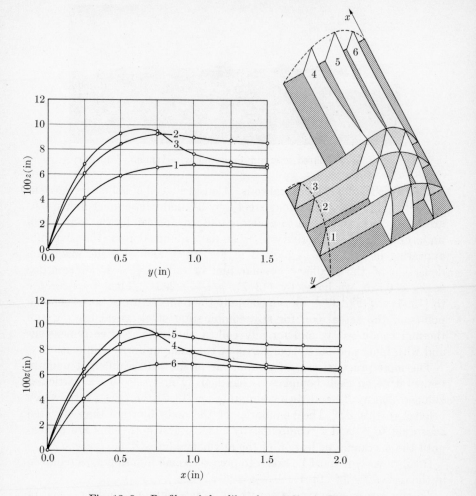

Fig. 13–8. Profiles of the dilated soap film in Fig. 13–7.

and therewith the comparative results between theory and analogic experiment as shown in Table 13–1.* This table gives, in effect, a comparison between the profile shape of the actual soap film and that of a true dilated membrane.

Under carefully controlled conditions the membrane analogue will give results accurate to within $\pm 3\%$ at best. The outstanding feature of the analogy, however, is its ability to handle boundaries of any conceivable shape.

*An approximate method for taking into account a linear variation in the heat development is reported in (15).

TABLE 13–1

TEMPERATURE DISTRIBUTION IN A COIL OF SOLID CIRCULAR PROFILE

z''	r''	Membrane	Exact	% Error
0.600	0.000	69.44	69.45	−0.01
0.575	0.461	65.55	65.76	−0.32
0.525	0.721	60.76	60.43	0.55
0.475	0.921	54.98	54.72	0.48
0.425	1.093	49.19	48.71	0.98
0.375	1.223	43.40	43.48	−0.18
0.325	1.363	37.62	37.29	0.88
0.275	1.485	31.83	31.16	2.15
0.225	1.599	26.04	25.06	3.91
0.175	1.693	20.25	19.69	2.84
0.125	1.793	14.47	13.61	6.31
0.075	1.879	8.68	8.15	6.50
0.025	1.961	2.89	2.68	7.84
0.000	2.000	0.00	0.00	

13–6 Membrane analogy for nongenerating systems. A membrane under zero dilation pressure is a special case where small deflections $z(x,y)$ of the freely suspended membrane surface satisfy the partial-differential equation

$$\frac{\partial^2 z}{\partial x^2} + \frac{\partial^2 z}{\partial y^2} = 0. \tag{13–8}$$

This equation states the geometric fact that at any point in a "zero-pressure" film, the sum of the x- and y-surface curvatures is zero. From this, Wilson and Miles (10) recognized that a zero-pressure soap film could be interpreted as an analogue for Laplacian temperature fields in

Fig. 13–9.   Zero-pressure soap film on a hollow rectangular boundary.

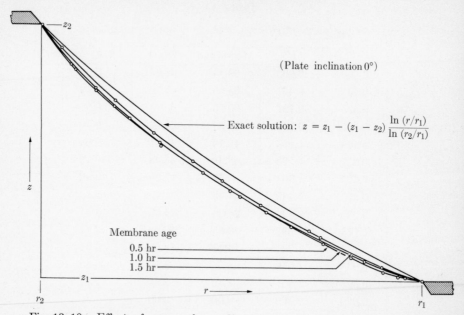

(Plate inclination $0°$)

Exact solution: $z = z_1 - (z_1 - z_2)\dfrac{\ln (r/r_1)}{\ln (r_2/r_1)}$

Membrane age
0.5 hr
1.0 hr
1.5 hr

Fig. 13–10.   Effect of age on the profile contour of a zero-pressure soap film. (Courtesy of Professor Wilson.)

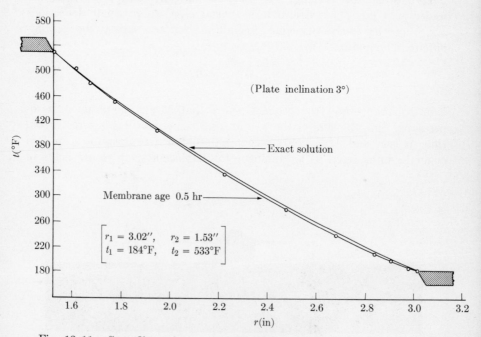

(Plate inclination $3°$)

Exact solution

Membrane age 0.5 hr

$$\begin{bmatrix} r_1 = 3.02'', & r_2 = 1.53'' \\ t_1 = 184°F, & t_2 = 533°F \end{bmatrix}$$

Fig. 13–11.   Soap-film solution for the temperature distribution in a hollow cylinder.   (Courtesy of Professor Wilson.)

regions of uniform thermal conductivity and free of heat sources and sinks, the analogic relation in this case being simply

$$t(x,y) = z(x,y). \tag{13–9}$$

Boundary temperatures are again duplicated by building up the edge of the boundary model z_1 to some convenient scale such that $z_1 = ct_1$. A zero-pressure soap film on a hollow rectangular boundary is shown in Fig. 13–9, the surface $z(x,y)$ representing to scale the steady temperature $t(x,y)$ in a furnace wall with isothermal surfaces.

In experiments performed by Wilson and Miles (10), it was found that the shape of a zero-pressure soap film depends to some extent on the age of the film. Thus with membranes unsupported by dilation pressure, the older the film the more closely its shape will conform to that suggested by (13–8). This is illustrated in Fig. 13–10 by comparing the profiles of an actual soap film on a hollow circular boundary with the exact profile shape given by (13–8) as $z = C_1 \ln r + C_2$. If the plate containing the boundaries is inclined slightly with the horizontal, the film will assume its theoretical shape in a much shorter period of time owing to increased draining off of excess soap solution and consequent thinning of the film itself.

Figures 13–11, 13–12, and 13–13 are solutions to three practical problems by the zero-pressure membrane analogue (10). Figure 13–11 is the solution for $t(r)$ in a long hollow cylinder with uniform boundary temperatures, as compared with the exact solution $t = t_1 - (t_1 - t_2) \ln (r/r_1)/$

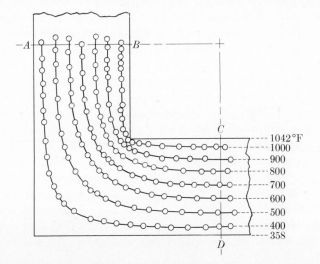

Fig. 13–12.   Trace of isothermals in a furnace wall by membrane analogy. (Courtesy of Professor Wilson.)

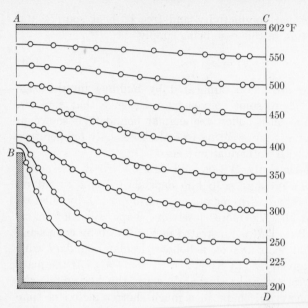

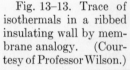

Fig. 13–13. Trace of isothermals in a ribbed insulating wall by membrane analogy. (Courtesy of Professor Wilson.)

ln (r_2/r_1). In this case the boundary plates were inclined 3° for drainage. Figures 13–12 and 13–13 are solutions for the furnace and ribbed-wall structures similar to those whose solutions were considered by graphical means in problems 6–13 and 6–14.*

13–7 Photographic methods in membrane analogy. Numerous attempts have been made to eliminate the experimental difficulties in determining the exact contour of a soap film by direct-contact measurement. All of these techniques are photographic, and therefore they offer the convenience that the film need last only long enough to photograph it. Photographic methods are also attractive in that no actual contact is made with the surface, and this eliminates the common hazard of inadvertently breaking the film before its entire surface is mapped.

In experiments using the membrane analogue for torsional stress analysis, Ikeda (16) improved a successful photographic technique originally developed by Salet (17). In Ikeda's apparatus, shown in Fig. 13–14, s is a light source made up of equally spaced concentric circles formed by passing 500-watt collimated light through transparent concentric circles on a blackened glass plate. A lens L_1 is placed at its focal length f_1 from s with optical axis a-a' passing through the center circle of s. In the plane b-b', with normal o-n, is placed a soap film f boundary chamber with dilated film center on the optical axis a-a' at o. On a second axis c-c'

---

*Symmetrical structures are dealt with by placing vertical plates in planes of geometric symmetry, i.e., adiabatic planes such as AB and CD in both Fig. 13–12 and Fig. 13–13.

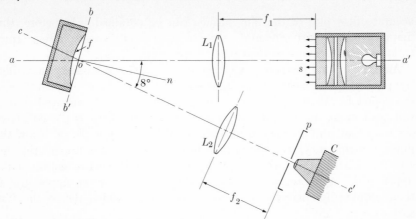

Fig. 13–14. Optical determination of equislope lines on the surface of a dilated soap film.

through o and displaced from a-a' is placed a second lens L_2 and a pinhole p located at the focal distance f_2 of L_2, and behind p is a camera C.

A typical photograph of a dilated soap film on a square boundary obtained from Ikeda's apparatus is shown in Fig. 13–15. While an equi-slope line photograph of this sort is particularly appropriate for torsion analysis, we can also look upon Fig. 13–15 as the solution for the temperature field in a long, square conductor of uniform conductivity, and generating or absorbing uniform distributed heat. Then, since the change in slope between consecutive equi-slope lines on the photograph is constant and proportional to the distance between concentric light circles at s, an

Fig. 13–15. Photograph of contour lines for a dilated soap film on a square boundary. (Courtesy of Professor Ikeda.)

accurate field plot of the film surface can be obtained. As before, this mapping leads to experimental values of $z(x,y)$ and thence to a reinterpretation of these values as analogous temperatures $t(x,y)$.

Another unique method of indirect measurement of a soap-film surface by photographic means is a light-reflection technique originated and developed by Moore (5). In Moore's apparatus an illuminated spider-web grid made up of concentric circles and radial lines is placed above the soap film, and a second grid with radial lines only is placed below the film. Looking down through a hole in the center of the upper grid, one sees the dilated film and, in the film surface, a distorted reflection of the upper grid. A photograph of this distorted image of the upper grid is then graphically analyzed to find contour lines which define the film surface.

13–8 Separation surfaces as membranes. Some of the previously mentioned difficulties encountered in probing nondurable soap films can also be avoided through use of a so-called *separation surface*. With this method a membrane surface is replaced by the interface between two nondiffusing liquids of equal density, as first proposed by Piccard and Baes (18).

For direct-contact measurement, a closed-end cylinder c of cross-sectional shape similar to that of the conducting region in question is partially filled with a liquid of density d_1, and then placed within a container filled with another liquid of the same density $d_2 = d_1$ as in Fig. 13–16. The liquids 1 and 2 are so chosen that little or no diffusion between them occurs. When liquid 1, introduced through the connecting reservoir r, just fills the inner cylinder c, the interface between the nonmixing liquids is the same surface $z(x,y)$ as a true membrane under zero dilation pressure. Under these conditions the interface deflections above or

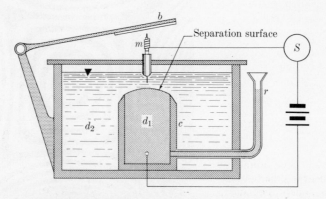

Fig. 13–16.   Use of a separation surface in membrane analogy.

below the outermost edge of c satisfy the Laplace equation, and are therefore analogous to steady temperatures at corresponding points in a region
of uniform thermal conductivity and free of heat sources and sinks. The
liquid interface will conform to any irregular boundary built up to simulate
any set of boundary temperatures on either a simply-connected or multiply-
connected region.

To facilitate mapping of the hidden interface contour, the liquids 1 and
2 are selected as electrically conducting and nonconducting respectively.
Such a scheme provides a conducting circuit between probe and liquid
1 which, when closed by contact with the interface, energizes either an
audio or visual signal S in the circuit.

Again, a suitable system of recording $z(x,y)$ is used, such as the arrangement shown in Fig. 13–5. A more common method of recording is
illustrated in Fig. 13–16, where recording paper fixed to a recording board
b is swung down and punched by contact with the sharp upper end of
the micrometer probe m.

For solutions of the Poisson equation, additional fluid 1 is introduced
through r so that the separation surface of the two liquids is slightly
expanded upwards. This operation is analogous to dilating a soap film,
where now the deflections of the separation surface are analogous of steady
temperatures at points similarly situated in a region of uniform thermal
conductivity and generating or absorbing uniform distributed heat.
Here p/τ is identified as the ratio of overpressure between liquids 1 and
2 to the surface-tension coefficient for the separation surface of liquid 1.
Evaluation of p/τ is accomplished exactly as with a dilated soap film;
in this case a second cylinder c_a of circular cross section provides an auxiliary
separation surface.

Several optical methods utilizing the difference in refractive coefficients of each liquid have been devised to measure $z(x,y)$ of a separation
surface, and these are fully described in a paper by Sunatani *et al.* (19).
Figure 13–17 shows a number of contours in a plane triangle obtained
from a separation surface by such optical methods.

The chief advantage in using a
separation surface in place of a soap
film is that a liquid surface is inher-
ently more stable. Not only will it
retain its life and shape almost indefinitely, but no deformation takes
place due to the weight of its surface,
as occurs with the soap film. Therefore, in an effort to increase the accuracy of measurement by employing
larger surfaces, the liquid separation
surface has advantages over a soap

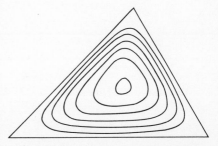

Fig. 13–17. Contour lines for a separation surface on a triangular boundary.

film, which suffers the weight deformation shown in Figs. 13–10 and 13–11.

13–9 Electrical analogy. The direct mathematical similarity between heat and electrical conduction is by far the best known and most widely used analogy for the study of complex problems in both steady and transient heat conduction. The analogy is immediately recognized on comparing the characteristic partial-differential equation governing the transient distribution of electric potential (electromotive force) e in an electrically-conducting two-dimensional region of uniform electrical resistance per unit length $\Re_L = \Re/L$ and uniform electrical capacity per unit length $\mathfrak{C}_L = \mathfrak{C}/L$,

$$\frac{\partial^2 e}{\partial x^2} + \frac{\partial^2 e}{\partial y^2} = \Re_L \mathfrak{C}_L \frac{\partial e}{\partial \theta}, \tag{13–10}$$

with the familiar characteristic partial-differential equation governing the transient distribution of thermal potential (temperature) t in a thermally-conducting two-dimensional region of uniform diffusivity α,

$$\frac{\partial^2 t}{\partial x^2} + \frac{\partial^2 t}{\partial y^2} = \frac{1}{\alpha} \frac{\partial t}{\partial \theta}. \tag{13–11}$$

According to previous notation, θ represents time. The transient-state analogy between the analogues of electric and temperature potential is therefore complete if, on the same time scale, the electrical diffusivity $1/\Re_L \mathfrak{C}_L$ and thermal diffusivity α are equal. In this state, there is a direct analogy between two laws: the conservation of charge in the electrical system corresponds to the conservation of heat in the thermal system; and the obedience of current flow in the electrical system to Ohm's law corresponds to the obedience of heat flow in the thermal system to Fourier's law. The complete electrical-thermal analogy is summarized in Table 13–2.

TABLE 13–2

ANALOGOUS ELECTRICAL-THERMAL QUANTITIES

Electrical	Thermal
Charge $= Q_e$(coulomb)	Heat $= Q$(Btu)
Voltage $= e$(volt)	Temperature $= t$(°F)
Resistance $= \Re$(ohm)	Resistance $= R$(hr-°F/Btu) $= \dfrac{L}{kA} = \dfrac{1}{hA}$
Current $= i$(ampere) $= \dfrac{\Delta e}{\Re}$	Flow $= q$(Btu/hr) $= \dfrac{\Delta t}{R}$
Capacitance $= \mathfrak{C}$(farad) $= \dfrac{i}{de/d\theta}$	Unit capacity $= CwV$(Btu/°F) $= \dfrac{q}{dt/d\theta}$

The steady-state analogy is completed by the simple recognition that under the condition of steady electrical conduction ($\partial e/\partial \theta = 0$) and steady thermal conduction ($\partial t/\partial \theta = 0$) both of the potentials e and t satisfy the simple Laplace equation. Thus a steady electric potential field $e(x,y)$ can be regarded as the analogue of a steady temperature field $t(x,y)$, where equipotential lines in the voltage field correspond to isothermals in the temperature field, and where orthogonal lines of electric current flow correspond to orthogonal lines of heat flow. These are both conjugate functions like the stream function and velocity potential in the fluid-flow analogy of Article 13–2.

The outstanding feature of electrical analogy is its ability to simulate the transient state of heat flow. In addition to this, the analogy is exceptionally flexible; it can handle systems with either nonuniform or unknown boundary temperatures, systems with either local or distributed heat sources or sinks, and, within certain limitations, systems in which the variation of thermal properties must be taken into account.

13–10 Electrical models. A large variety of experimental methods are available for taking advantage of the electrical analogy discussed in Article 13–9. In all of these methods the thermal system is imitated by the flow of electric current in models which are made up either of a continuous conducting material, or of an equivalent "lumped" electrical circuit. The former are referred to as *geometrical analogues*, since they preserve not only the geometry of the analogous system but its continuous nature as well, and the latter as *network analogues*. The class of geometrical analogues includes both liquid and solid conductors.

Liquid models. A fairly convenient model for determining the potential distribution in an electrical conductor is provided by a so-called *electrolytic bath*, in which an electrolyte of constant resistivity is contained in a shallow basin similar in shape to the two-dimensional region under study. The boundaries of the basin, which are to be at a specific potential e_1 (corresponding to a boundary temperature of t_1 in the thermal system) are constructed of an electrically conducting material through which an alternating current is fed into the electrolyte. Adiabatic portions of the boundary are simply constructed from a suitable dielectric.

The electrolytic method is illustrated in Fig. 13–18 for the solution of the furnace-wall problem of Articles 6–8 and 13–2. The electrolytic basin in this case has two insulated boundaries for the adiabatic planes in the one-eighth symmetrical section of the kiln, and two conducting boundaries at a uniform potential difference corresponding to the temperature difference between the inner and outer isothermal surfaces of the wall. Equipotential lines are recorded by a vertical stylus in the electrolyte in conjunction with a null potentiometer and a pantograph connecting the stylus with the recording paper shown in Fig. 13–18. Similar evaluation

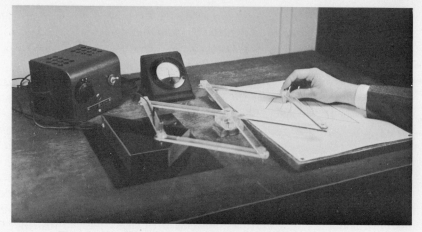

Fig. 13–18.   Electrical analogy by electrolytic-bath model.

of the orthogonal system of flow lines is accomplished by reversing the insulating and conducting portions of the boundary.

Solid models.   A more recent method which retains the principal advantages of the electrolytic method and at the same time avoids some of its difficulties and extends its possibilities makes use of a thin *conductive sheet* to represent the continuous heat-flow path.   The conducting sheet is cut out in the same shape as the region in question, and boundary potentials are applied by low-resistance metallic electrodes, or by painting the boundary portions with low-resistance conducting paint.   Recording of equipotential and flow lines is accomplished by indenting the current sheet with a probing stylus connected to a null potentiometer, as indicated in Fig. 13–19 for the furnace-wall problem.

Network models.   The network type of electrical model is primarily reserved for the more complex problems of transient heat conduction. The model is derived by lumping the region into a number of regular subvolumes, as in the numerical method.   This effectively replaces the governing partial-differential equation by an equation in finite differences, so that potential values are obtained for a finite number of individual points rather than at all points covering the field.   An electrical network is then built up to simulate the subdivided region with series electrical resistances and parallel electrical capacitances concentrated at the nodal points of the network.   For steady-state applications only resistors are required in the network, while for simulation of transient conduction condensers are added and charged or discharged to imitate changes in internal energy in the thermal system.   Either uniform or nonuniform heat sources are duplicated by introducing a power supply at any one or more points in the electrical network for local sources, or at all nodal points in the network for distributed sources.

Fig. 13-19.   Electrical analogy by conductive-sheet model.

It is important to note that there is no geometric similarity between a thermal system and its electrical network analogue made up of one-dimensional current-carrying cables.   Also note that since the conductor is subdivided (iterated) with its properties concentrated at individual points along the cable, it is subject to errors much like those which occur from sectioning or lumping a thermal system for a numerical solution.

13-11 Steady-state liquid geometrical-analogue method.   While the principle of the electrolytic bath type of liquid geometrical analogue goes back to Kirchhoff, it was first used in a practical way by Langmuir (20) in 1913 for the study of steady heat conduction in thick rectangular structures.   A portion of Langmuir's results were presented in Article 2-9 as empirical formulas for the effective conducting area in parallelepiped shells.

The Langmuir model was constructed of glass with copper-plate conducting boundaries.   If the mean ratio of normal conducting area to path length between these boundaries is $(\overline{A/L})$, then the current i conducted between the boundaries maintained at a voltage difference Δe and through the electrolyte of electrical conductivity k_e is $i = k_e(\overline{A/L})\Delta e$, according to Ohm's law.   But a *standard* resistance in the form of a unit-volume cube filled with the same electrolyte and having just two opposite conducting sides of copper was placed in series with the model so that the total current flow through the model could be measured as $i = k_e(\Delta e)_s$.   This meant that $(\overline{A/L}) = (\Delta e)_s/\Delta e$, so that if the heat flow in the analogous thermal system obeyed the Fourier law according to $q = k(\overline{A/L})\Delta t$, then

$$q = k\,\frac{(\Delta e)_s}{\Delta e}\,\Delta t. \qquad (13\text{-}12)$$

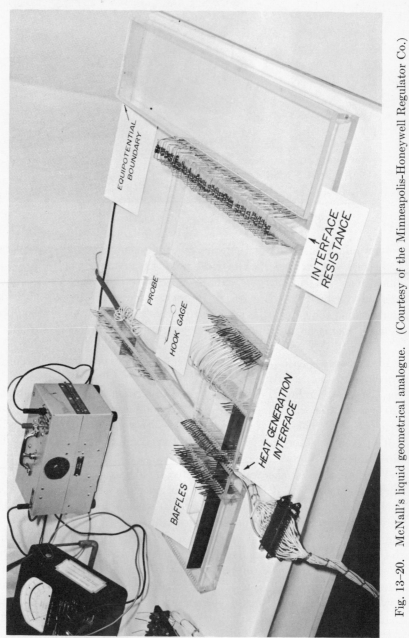

Fig. 13–20. McNall's liquid geometrical analogue. (Courtesy of the Minneapolis-Honeywell Regulator Co.)

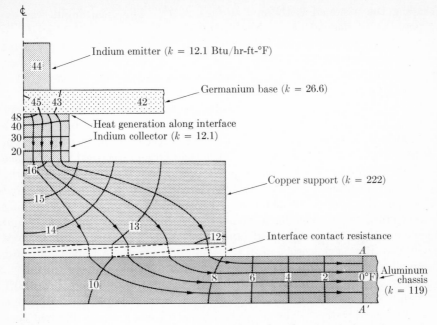

Fig. 13–21. Temperature field in a transistor by the electrical analogue of Fig. 13–20. (Courtesy of the Minneapolis-Honeywell Regulator Co.)

Therefore, the only experimental measurements required were the voltage differences across the standard cube and across the model. If the model was, say, one-tenth size, then evidently the heat rate q computed in this way would have to be increased tenfold.

Following the pioneer work of Langmuir, the electrolytic bath was used frequently in other fields as well. Malavard (21) describes its use for studies in aerodynamics, Relf (22), Cheers (23), and Hubbard (24) have used it for hydrodynamic studies of two-dimensional potential flow, and Farr (25) for studies in electrodynamics. Malvard (26) discusses its application in problems of heat transfer, and Einstein (27) its limits of accuracy.

Recently, McNall and Janssen (28) have used the electrolytic method of geometrical analogue to determine the operating temperatures within the complicated structure of a *transistor*. A symmetrical portion of the transistor along with the solution obtained with the electrolytic-bath apparatus in Fig. 13–20 is shown in Fig. 13–21. The heat-flow path through the five-piece transistor composed of four different materials could be assumed as two-dimensional, and the transistor itself was encased in a way that allowed the simplification of assuming all noncontact surfaces as adiabatic. Heat was generated along the base-collector interface, conducted through the collector-support-chassis series path, and removed along the assumed isothermal surface A-A'. This heat input was exponentially dependent on local temperature as $q_t''' = q_0''' \times 2^{(t-t_0)/18}$. An interface contact resistance had to be considered between the support and chassis, since these two members were merely clamped together, while all other contact joints were soldered and therefore considered as resistance-free.

The possibility of direct temperature measurements was ruled out because of the difficulties in instrumenting such a small structure as a transistor. Even if such were possible, the presence of instrumentation in this case would have changed both the thermal and electrical performance of the transistor itself. An analytical solution was possible only if the system was oversimplified, and a numerical approach was not attempted because it was of particular interest to study the effect on peak operating temperatures of changing a number of the transistor dimensions, and assuming several possible heat-input distributions. The authors therefore decided that for this problem an analogue approach would provide the most practical method of solution.

The electrolytic model for this study (Fig. 13–20) was scaled 100:1 with lucite basins containing an electolytic solution of potassium chloride and distilled water.* The electrolyte in each basin was at a different concentration in order to obtain a resistance level in each basin which would result in a minimum power dissipation and yet provide potential differences of measurable magnitude. Insulated baffles provided for changes in component dimensions, and thin copper strips provided the conducting paths at regular intervals along all interfaces. The support-chassis resistance was simulated by inserting carbon resistors of appropriate value between these interface strips. A separate current-input circuit was provided for each strip joining the base and collector to imitate the distribution of heat generated along this interface. The scale factor in each experiment was determined by Langmuir's method of passing the total analogue current through a standard basin.

A description of instrumentation, test procedure, and analysis of data is contained in the original paper (28), along with a detailed discussion of errors, the order of which was estimated to be 6–8%. These total errors represent the sum of individual errors in both the electrolyte and instrumentation. There is some difficulty in maintaining the electrolyte at a uniform resistance due to the presence of impurities and because of temperature changes which accompany the resistance heating of the current-carrying electrolyte. It is therefore necessary for the bath to be kept as pure and uniform in concentration as possible, and to use low currents in an effort to decrease the resistance-heating effect. Low ac currents are

---

*See Einstein (27) or chemical handbooks for additional information on suitable electrolytes.

used to prevent polarization of the electrodes, and this in turn adds some error in voltage regulation and measurement. It can also be expected that additional errors will be introduced by the effects of vibration, pickup of stray ac voltage, and so on.

It is worth while to mention here that certain extensions of the common electrolytic-analogue techniques are possible. Malavard (26), Hartill (29), and Mickelson (30) describe how a conducting region having areas of different thermal conductivity can be simulated by either stepped-bottom basins or by subdividing the basin into compartments and filling each with the same electrolyte at a different level. The partitions are of a thin insulating material and fitted with a large number of conducting strips to ensure equal potential values on each side of the partition line. Malavard (26) also describes how to simulate normal temperature gradients at the boundary in order to include either evaporation from a free surface or convection at a solid boundary. Beuken (31) reports that continuous boundary electrodes can be replaced by strips connecting graded resistors which are adjusted by trial and error to imitate a temperature dependency in the unit surface conductance.

13-12 Steady-state solid geometrical-analogue method. The first use of a solid geometrical analogue in conduction studies goes back to the early work of Awberry and Schofield (32) in which the heat flow through a thick insulated wall was investigated by means of current flow through a solid model cut from a thin metal sheet of uniform resistance. Bruckmayer (33) used a low-resistance metallic foil for studies of heat conduction in composite walls with isothermal surfaces, and some time later Kayan (34) reported on a "conductive-sheet" method in which the model for a complex composite structure was cut out from a sheet of continuously metallized paper. Areas of different thermal conductivity were accounted for by perforating the sheet with a mesh of cut-out squares so as to reduce the electrical conductivity in areas of lower thermal conductivity. Boundary conductances were simulated by introducing a surface resistance, this being accomplished by simply extending the conducting sheet beyond the boundaries. The conductive-sheet analogue was also used in a second study (35) which dealt with the thermal "short-circuit" effect for an I-beam of high thermal conductivity embedded in an otherwise plane homogeneous wall.

A third paper, by Kayan (36), treats by the same method the problem of heat transfer through a thick corner composed of two unlike materials of different thermal conductivity and of different thicknesses. No contact resistance between the two materials was considered, and inner and outer unit surface conductances and ambient temperatures were assumed uniform. The analogue solution for the temperature field within the corner obtained by Kayan's conductive-sheet apparatus, sketched in Fig. 13-22, is shown in Fig. 13–23. The resistance of the conducting sheet for the inner portion of the corner of lower thermal conductivity was increased by cutting out a square mesh of such a grade that the resistance of wall 1 was four times that of wall 2, i.e., in inverse ratio as the thermal conductivities k_1 and k_2. This resistance ratio was obtained by trial-and-error cutting and direct resistance measurements. The thermal boundary resistivities $1/h_1$ and $1/h_2$ were accounted for by adding an equivalent resistance at each surface. From Article 2–3 we know that the thickness of these fictitious layers is k_1/h_1 for surface 1 and k_2/h_2 for surface 2, and this means that in Kayan's model $0.2''$ had to be added along the inner boundary and $2''$ added long the outer boundary. Direct current for the metallized sheet was supplied by batteries, and a null contact probe was used for locating equipotential lines as in Fig. 13–23.

Kayan (34) suggests that areas of different thermal conductivity can also be represented by using conductive sheets of different unit resistance, and that for sheets of uniform resistance the mesh can be adjusted to include the anisotropic property of different thermal conductivities in different directions.

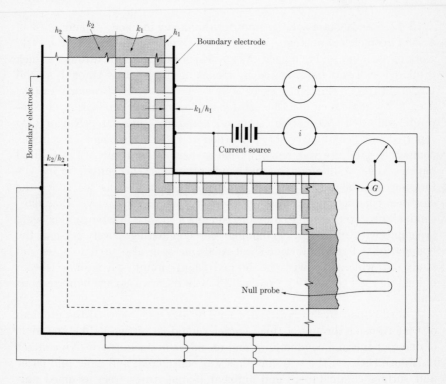

Fig. 13–22. Kayan's conductive-sheet geometrical analogue. (Courtesy of Professor Kayan.)

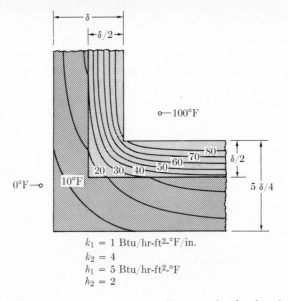

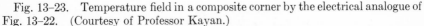

$k_1 = 1$ Btu/hr-ft^2-°F/in.
$k_2 = 4$
$h_1 = 5$ Btu/hr-ft^2-°F
$h_2 = 2$

Fig. 13–23.   Temperature field in a composite corner by the electrical analogue of Fig. 13–22.   (Courtesy of Professor Kayan.)

The accuracy of the conductive-sheet method depends not only on the accuracy of the model but on the resistance uniformity of the sheet as well. The unit resistance of commercially available conductive sheet has been known to vary as much as 10% locally and in different directions, and even a slightly inaccurate mesh may introduce errors of the same magnitude. Conductive-coated glass plates promise high resistance-uniformity, but are not yet available commercially.*

13–13 Steady-state network-analogue method.   As mentioned in Article 13–10, the resistance-type of network analogue represents a replacement of the lumped thermal system by an electrical circuit of resistors and condensers.   For steady-state situations only the resistors are required, these playing the role of fictitious heat-conducting rods in an equivalent numerical network.

Consider the simple application of a network analogue to the turbine-blade problem considered in Article 7–4, choosing the same lumped sub-division (Fig. 7–3) as used in the numerical solution.   An equivalent

---

*The General Electric Company has developed a commercial model "current-sheet" analogue using a sheet of conducting "Teledeltos" paper 0.004″ thick and a low-resistance conducting paint for boundary electrodes.   A description of the apparatus and the techniques to be used is contained in the catalogue of Ref. (37).

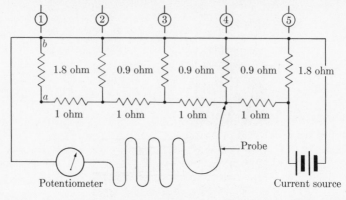

Fig. 13–24. Electrical network analogue for the turbine-blade problem of Article 7–4.

electrical network analogue for this system is shown in Fig. 13–24, with the electrical resistance values of the resistors standing in the same ratio to one another as the thermal resistance values in the analogous thermal system. These thermal resistances are the reciprocals of the thermal conductances computed in Article 7–4 as $R_{12} = 1/1.8 = 0.557 = R_{23} = R_{34} = R_{45}$, $R_{g2} = 1/2.0 = 0.500 = R_{g3} = R_{g4}$, and $R_{g1} = 1/1.0 = 1.000 = R_{g5}$. The ratios of surface-to-internal resistances are therefore $R_{g1}/R_{12} = 1.8$ and $R_{g2}/R_{12} = 0.9$. This means that if we arbitrarily choose 1-ohm electrical resistors to represent the internal thermal resistances, then the electrical resistors representing the thermal surface resistances will have to be $1.8 \times 1 = 1.8$ ohms for nodal points ① and ⑤ and $1 \times 0.9 = 0.9$ ohms for nodal points ②, ③, and ④. According to the electrical analogy, the voltage at any point i in the electrical system corresponds to the temperature at the same point in the thermal system, or $\Delta e_i/\Delta e = \Delta t_i/\Delta t$. If we measure Δe between a and b, then this potential difference corresponds to $\Delta t = t_g - t_r = 1500 - 1000 = 500°F$, and therewith $t_i = 1500 - 500(\Delta e_i/\Delta e)°F$.

Ellerbrock (38) has successfully employed a resistance network made up of calibrated *resistance wires* instead of fixed resistors for the study of temperature patterns within the cross section of cooled turbine blades. A portion of this study was concerned with finding the operating temperature field within a blade cooled internally by heat removal to water in five circular coolant passages. An average outer unit surface conductance of $h_g = 76$ Btu/hr-ft²-°F was computed for a turbine speed of 14,000 rpm, a turbine-inlet total temperature of 1233°F and total pressure of 38.71 in. Hg. abs., and a total gas flow rate of 7 lb/sec. Two average values for the unit surface conductance in coolant passages were computed as $h_w = 146$ and 1460 Btu/hr-ft²-°F, based on coolant flow-rates of 4.5 and 139 lb/hr per blade, and a coolant temperature of $t_w = 133°F$.

The blade form and its resistance network analogue are sketched in Fig. 13–25. The square grid was built up to a scale of 25:1 from No. 24-gage bright-drawn chromel wire. With the grid prepared on a template and overlapped wires spot-welded, the maximum over-all resistance variation in the grid was measured and found to be less than 0.2%. No. 28-gage chromel wire was used to represent the boundary resistance along the outer surface of the blade, and No. 24-gage to represent the boundary resistance along the inner surfaces of the coolant passages. To determine the appropriate lengths of these wires and suitable means of attaching them to the main grid, it was necessary to first examine the wire network analogue method for a system whose exact solution was known. The problems of precalculating the wire lengths and of determining the error in attaching these wires at nodal points in the grid which do not lie on the boundary (Fig. 13–25) were studied for a simple pipe operating under conditions similar to those existing for the turbine blade. After approximate methods were devised (38), the analogue temperatures in the pipe were compared with exact temperatures; the largest errors found were generally 1% or less. Final application of these methods to the actual blade analogue gave the temperature-field solutions shown in Fig. 13–26.

The accuracy of the wire network analogue was checked by using the blade analogue temperatures in a numerical solution. For a large proportion of the field the relaxed analogue temperatures gave residuals small

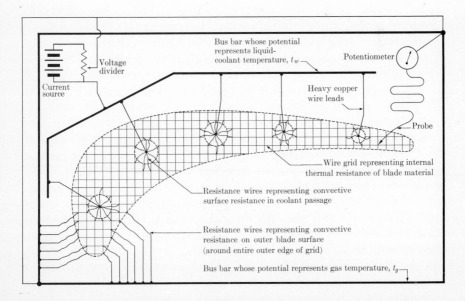

Fig. 13–25.   Ellerbrock's wire network analogue.   (Courtesy of the NACA.)

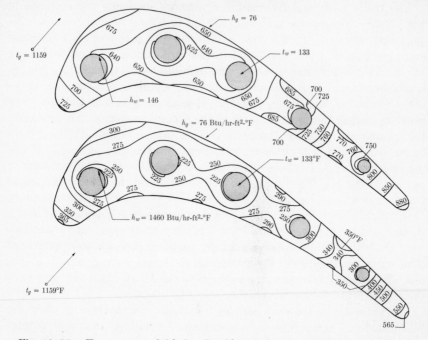

Fig. 13–26.   Temperature fields in a liquid-cooled turbine blade by the electrical analogue of Fig. 13–25.   (Courtesy of the NACA.)

enough to indicate that these data were quite satisfactory compared with numerical temperatures in a network of the same grade.   Since analogue temperatures in the trailing portion of the blade exhibited the largest errors, a separate analogue for this rear portion was constructed having a wire grid four times as fine as the original.   Analogue temperatures relaxed in this case gave residuals which were nearly all close to zero.

13–14 Transient network-analogue method.   In Article 13–9 it was shown that the electrical analogy for transient heat conduction is complete if, in addition to recognizing the correspondence between voltage and temperature and between current and heat flow, we identify the product of electrical resistance and capacity for the electrical system as corresponding to the thermal diffusivity of the thermal system.   In the practical application of this analogue, the thermal system is to be imitated by an equivalent noninductive electrical circuit in the form of an iterated cable of series resistors and parallel condensers.

A one-dimensional thermal system and its network analogue are shown in (a) of Fig. 13–27.   Note that the length of cable between ① and ② has nothing to do with the actual length between these two points; the only condition to be met is that $\Re_{12}$ must stand in some scale to the actual

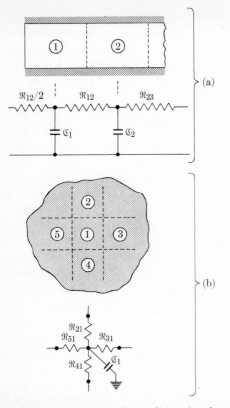

Fig. 13–27. One- and two-dimensional network analogues.

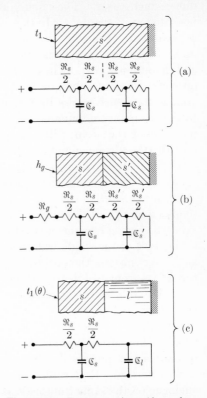

Fig. 13–28. Incorporation of boundary conditions in one-dimensional network analogues.

thermal resistance between ① and ②. This $\mathfrak{R}$-$\mathfrak{C}$ circuit could be taken to represent either a long insulated rod or a semi-infinite plate with adiabatic faces. Here the electric capacity of the condensers represents to some scale the thermal capacity of the volume element associated with each nodal point. The Fourier law for the heat flow $q = \Delta t / R$ is now represented by the Kirchhoff law for the current flow as $i = \Delta e / \mathfrak{R}$, and the change in internal energy of the thermal system $dE/d\theta = CwV dt/d\theta$ is now imitated in the network by the accumulation of electric charge Q_e in the condensers as $dQ_e/d\theta = \mathfrak{C} de/d\theta$. If the plate is rectangular, then the one-dimensional circuit is replaced by a two-dimensional circuit as in (b) of Fig. 13–27, with four resistors and one condenser for each nodal point. Similarly, the analogous circuit for a three-dimensional system would have, concentrated at each nodal point, six resistors and one condenser.

Boundary conditions. Network analogues also have to satisfy required boundary conditions, and in Fig. 13–28 we consider a few elementary one-dimensional cases. The circuit in (a) is for, say, a large wall perfectly insulated at its rear face. In this case only internal resistors and condensers are required. The wall is initially at some uniform temperature t_i, whereupon the temperature of the surface of its front face is suddenly changed to and maintained at t_1. The initial state is simulated in the analogue by an open circuit, and subsequent states $\theta > 0$ are imitated by impressing a voltage difference across its terminals. If this voltage difference is scaled to the temperature difference $t_1 - t_i$, then the rise in voltage with time at points along the circuit will correspond in the same scale to the temperature growth at analogous points in the wall.

The insulated composite wall in (b) is initially at t_i, and then is suddenly exposed to surrounding gas at a uniform and constant temperature t_g. In this case the internal resistors and condensers are scaled to the two different solids s and s', and the surface thermal resistivity $1/h_g$ is simulated by the external electric resistor of resistance $\Re_g$.

One face of the single wall in (c) is exposed to a finite volume of liquid at t_1. We imagine the wall to be at t_1 initially, and for $\theta > 0$ the temperature of its front face is to vary as $t_1(\theta)$. In this case the thermal capacity of the liquid is represented by the condenser $\mathfrak{C}_1$. If the volume of liquid is large, then its temperature will not rise, and this is imitated by completing the circuit at the rear face of the wall just as if the temperature of this face were t_1. The surface temperature of the front face is simulated by manually regulating the impressed voltage to vary in the same manner as $t_1(\theta)$.

Scale factors. It is rarely convenient or possible to base the network analogue on the same time scale as used in its thermal counterpart, and to take $\Re\mathfrak{C}$ equal numerically to $1/\alpha$. In practice, the thermal process may take several hours, weeks, or even years, and moreover the available values of $\Re$ and $\mathfrak{C}$ for electrical circuits are numerically much lower than the usual range of values for α in the thermal system. Thus, an $\Re$-$\mathfrak{C}$ circuit, to represent transient one-dimensional conduction through a unit length of common materials, would require resistors and condensers ranging in approximate values from 10 to 2000 ohms and 0.1 to 1 farad respectively, and these are much higher values than can be obtained in practice.

These practical problems are taken care of by a suitable choice of scale factors a, b, and c for θ, $\Re$ and $\mathfrak{C}$, and e. It is possible to scale all such quantities without altering the characteristic differential equation, for if we replace θ by $a\theta$, $\Re$ by $b\Re$, $\mathfrak{C}$ by $\mathfrak{C}/b$, the product of $\Re\mathfrak{C}$ by $a\Re\mathfrak{C}$, and finally e by ce, then (13–10) becomes

$$\frac{\partial^2 (ce)}{\partial x^2} + \frac{\partial^2 (ce)}{\partial y^2} = a(b\Re)\left(\frac{\mathfrak{C}}{b}\right)\frac{\partial (ce)}{\partial (a\theta_e)},$$

which is still completely analogous to (13–11). Thus, practical magnitudes of resistances and capacitances can be obtained by a proper choice of ab

to increase or decrease the required value of the $\mathfrak{R}$'s and a proper choice of b to increase or decrease the required value of the $\mathfrak{C}$'s. It is equally important to be able to expand or contract the time scale in the network analogue in order to conveniently represent heating processes of any time duration. The analogue time interval should not be too long for convenience, and yet should be long enough to change boundary potentials, record readings, and the like. From the above equation, it is apparent that if we build the $\mathfrak{R}$-$\mathfrak{C}$ circuit so that $\mathfrak{R}\mathfrak{C} = 1/a\alpha$, then its time scale is changed to $\theta_e = \theta/a$. For example, if a heating process takes six hours to reach either some prescribed temperature level or thermal equilibrium, then we would select, say, $a = 180$. This means that if $\mathfrak{R}\mathfrak{C} = 1/180\alpha$, then the analogue experiment can be performed in just two minutes. If the analogue voltages are scaled to ce and $\mathfrak{R}$ is scaled to $ab\mathfrak{R}$, then by Ohm's law $i = \Delta e/\mathfrak{R} = c\Delta e/ab$. This means that one ampere recorded in the analogue will correspond to ab/c Btu/hr in the thermal system.

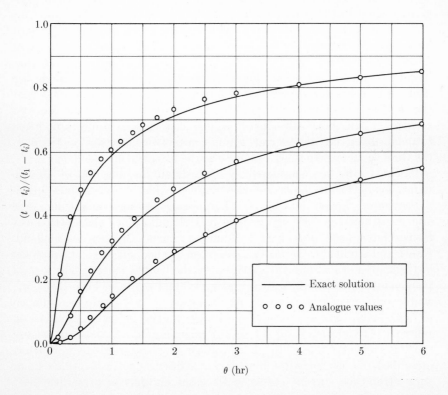

Fig. 13–29. Comparison between exact solution and network-analogue values for the temperature history at three sections in a suddenly heated semi-infinite solid. (Courtesy of D. I. Lawson.)

Accuracy. Lawson (39) discusses the inaccuracies involved in representing a long, continuously distributed thermal resistance by a long, iterated electrical cable. The approximation is shown to depend upon the number of sections per unit length in the lumped circuit, and the error at any section is shown to depend on the distance at which this section is located from the sending end of the cable. Lawson attributes the greater portion of the error shown in the analogue values of Fig. 13–29 to this iterated representation.

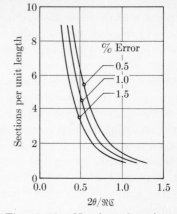

Fig. 13–30. Number of sections per unit length required in an iterated electrical cable. (Courtesy of D. I. Lawson.)

The absolute error is represented by the ratio of the potential at a given section to the potential which would be recorded at the same time and station in an uniterated $\Re$-$\mathfrak{C}$ cable. As expected, for a given instant θ this error is progressively reduced as the number of sections per unit length is increased as shown in Fig. 13–30. It is also suggested (39) that because of the time required for an impulse to be propagated along the cable, it is necessary to take rapid measurements of potential only near the sending end of the cable, and for a prescribed accuracy of the first section the length of subsequent sections can vary in direct proportion to the distance, i.e., the second section can be twice as coarse as the first, the third section three times as coarse as the first, and so on.

Paschkis (40) has considered in some detail the question of how to iterate a cable for the important cases represented by cylinders and spheres.

Permanent network analogues. Large-scale network analogues were first constructed in 1934 by Beuken in Holland. Since then permanent models have been developed by, among others, Gelissen in Holland, Fisher and Muller in Germany, Miroux in France, Jackson and Lawson in England, and Paschkis and McCann in the United States. The second Beuken model, as described by Gelissen (41) and shown in Figs. 13–31, 32, contains 15 groups of resistors and condensers (one group per lumped section) with resistance and capacitance ranges in each group being 100 to 1,111,000 ohms and 0.1 to 161 microfarads. A 300-volt battery supplies current either through a voltage divider for cases in which a prescribed temperature-time boundary condition is to be maintained, or an electron-tube current regulator for cases in which a prescribed heat input-time boundary condition is to be maintained. The Beuken model has been used almost exclusively for the study of problems in connection with the construction of intermittently operated electric furnaces.

The Paschkis model at Columbia University is similar to the Beuken model except for certain details as to decade arrangement of resistors and condensers, provisions for changing capacitances during an experiment, incorporation of simultaneous-recording electronic voltmeters, and the development of milliampere-minute meters for automatic integration of current-time data to give total heat flow. This model has been used in the study of a variety of problems in connection with the temperature history in the insulation of an intermittently operated steam pipe (42), in a rectangular bar (43), in composite walls (44), and in plates, cylinders, and spheres (45). Variations in thermal constants are dealt with either by assuming mean values or by manually changing circuit elements during the course of an experiment.

In England, Lawson (39) has developed an elaborate specialized model for handling problems characterized by rapid temperature-time variations. With the usual model a prescribed temperature-time boundary condi-

Fig. 13–31. Front view of the Beuken electrical network-analogue model. (Courtesy of Professor Gelissen.)

Fig. 13–32.   Rear view of the Beuken electrical network-analogue model.

tion is maintained by manual control, while in Lawson's model a wave-form generator develops the voltage wave forms for simulating the surface temperature rise. A cathode-ray oscillograph is used to display the temperature-time curve at any point in the circuit, and in this way the complete voltage distribution is built up by scanning each nodal point in turn.

An especially novel feature of the Lawson model is the incorporation of nonlinear resistors, which allows imitation of surface heat transfer by the combined effects of both convection and radiation, instead of the single mechanism of convection. This is accomplished by using a series circuit made up of a resistor and a resistance material called "Metrosil," which has essentially the same electrical characteristic as required for the representation of the fourth-power radiation function. The resistor and Metrosil circuit values are then matched in such proportion as to approximate the required convection-radiation cooling curve. Analogue results incorporating this feature have been found to agree quite well with measured temperature data.

13–15 Closure. There are several other useful analogues in addition to those already discussed. In 1936, for example, Moore (46) presented a liquid-flow analogue for cases of one-dimensional transient conduction. With this analogue the thermal system is replaced by an iterated distribution of water-filled standpipes, an analogy existing between thermal resistance and laminar-flow resistance, and between thermal capacity and standpipe capacity. This analogue has also been used successfully by Leopold (47), and a similar airflow analogue has been developed by Cole (48) for cases involving nonuniform thermal properties. Some attention is also being given to extending these analogues to include heating from a temperature-time medium, as well as to include the possibility of isothermal phase changes.

Still other analogies may be mentioned, and no doubt others will appear and existing ones will be greatly improved over the years.

13–16 Résumé. Our text has considered the solution of problems in heat conduction by analytical, numerical, and graphical means, and finally by the experimental analogic method. The reader will, by this time, recognize certain distinct advantages inherent in each of these methods, and will therefore avoid regarding any single approach with exclusive reverence. In many cases the method to be used is clearly indicated by the very nature of the problem itself. In other cases the selection of one method over another can only be made with confidence after a rather careful examination of the general difficulty and scope of the problem in question, the general level of accuracy required in the final results, the quantity and type of assistance available, and the allowable expenditures of both funds and time.

The analytical approach is clearly the preferred method of calculation whenever possible; indeed, it is the least expensive and most accurate method known. On the other hand, this approach is rarely, if ever, successful for systems complex in geometry and/or boundary conditions and, if it is, then the exact solution is usually so involved and unwieldy that the time and labor required in computing with it becomes prohibitive. This is especially the case when the result obtained does not explicitly display the wanted quantity, and auxiliary methods of computation must be introduced to evaluate the solution.

If the selection is narrowed down to a choice between a numerical and analogic approach, then the final selection will generally depend on the number of separate conditions to be studied. If a large number of conditions for the same system are of interest, then the numerical method loses favor, except in those instances where the time allotted for a solution is not too short and inexpensive help is readily available. If an analogue appears to represent the preferred approach, then funds must be available for its construction. In a good number of cases this construction expense is more than offset by the saving in time over some less expensive but lengthy method. It is known, for example, that it takes just about one-hundred times as long to reproduce some network analogue temperatures $t(x,\theta)$ by exact calculations.

As so often happens, the final selection is heavily influenced by the expense involved. For the solution of a limited number of problems in transient conduction, for example, the single investigator can rarely afford, in contrast to a ream of paper, several thousand resistors and condensers, multiple-stage amplifiers, oscillographs, and such a labyrinth of equipment as represents the permanent network analogue installation. And again, in many cases time and expense must be considered jointly. The turbine-blade analysis of Article 13–13 is a case in point; for this Ellerbrock (38) reported that the average cost of labor and materials for one analogue was approximately \$200 and the construction time was about 4 days. While a numerical solution might have been set up with much less expense and in a shorter time, Ellerbrock reported additionally that the time required to reproduce the temperature pattern for one blade in Fig. 13–26 was approximately one day with the analogue, as compared to one month of relaxation calculations. The numerical method, on the other hand, is readily adapted to high-speed digital and analogue computing machines. The expanding availability of such large-scale computing facilities has currently made it feasible to consider practical problems in conduction whose detailed numerical solutions were physically impossible only a few years ago.

A thoughtful assessment of all such factors is the chief ingredient of the so-called *efficient solution*.

REFERENCES

1. H. S. Hele-Shaw, A. Hay, and P. H. Powell, "Hydrodynamical and Electromagnetic Investigations Regarding the Magnetic Flux Distribution in Toothed-Core Armatures," *Journal of the Institute of Electrical Engineers*, Vol. 34, 1904–05, pp. 21–53.

2. A. D. Moore, "Fields from Fluid Flow Mappers," *Journal of Applied Physics*, Vol. 20, No. 8, Aug., 1949, pp. 790–804.

3. A. D. Moore, "The Further Development of Fluid Mappers," *Trans. AIEE*, Vol. 69 (2), 1950, pp. 1615–1624.

4. A. D. Moore, "Mapping Techniques Applied to Fluid Mapper Patterns," *Trans., AIEE*, Vol. 71, 1952.

5. A. D. Moore, "Soap-Film and Sandbed-Mapper Techniques," *Journal of Applied Mechanics, Trans., ASME*, Vol. 72, Sept., 1950, pp. 291–298.

6. J. P. Den Hartog, *Advanced Strength of Materials*. New York: McGraw-Hill, 1952, p. 22.

7. L. Prandtl, "Zur Torsion von prismatischen Stäben," *Z. Phys.* 4, 1902–03, pp. 758–759.

8. H. Anthes, "Versuchsmethode zur Ermittlung der Spannungsverteliung bei Torsion prismatischer Stäbe," *Dinglers Poly.*, J. 321 (Dissertation), Hannover, 1906.

9. T. J. Higgins, "Analogic Experimental Stress Analysis as Exemplified by Saint-Venant's Torsion Problem," *Experimental Stress Analysis*, Vol. II, No. 2, Oct., 1944, pp. 17–27.

10. L. H. Wilson and A. J. Miles, "Application of Membrane Analogy to the Solution of Heat Conduction Problems," *Journal of Applied Physics*, Vol. 21, June, 1950, pp. 532–535.

11. P. J. Schneider, "The Prandtl Membrane Analogy for Temperature Fields with Permanent Heat Sources or Sinks," *Journal of the Aeronautical Sciences*, (Reader's Forum), Vol. 19, No. 9, Sept., 1952, pp. 644–645.

12. A. A. Griffith and G. I. Taylor, "The Use of Soap Films in Solving Torsion Problems," *Proc. Institute of Mechanical Engineers*, Dec., 1917, pp. 755–809.

13. P. A. Cushman, "Shearing Stresses in Torsion and Bending by Membrane Analogy," *ASME Preprint* No. 1–5, June, 1932.

14. P. J. Schneider and A. B. Çambel, "Membrane Apparatus for Analogic Experiments," *The Review of Scientific Instruments*, Vol. 24, No. 7, July, 1953, pp. 513–514.

15. P. J. Schneider and A. B. Çambel, "Steady Temperature Fields in Electrical Coils by Membrane Analogy," *ASME Preprint* No. 53–SA–43, June, 1953.

16. K. Ikeda, "Soap Film Techniques for Solving Torsion Problems," *The Japan Science Review*, Vol. 2, No. 2, Aug., 1951, pp. 113–118.

17. G. Salet, "Nouvelle methode de mise en deuvre de l'analogie de la membrane pour l'étude de la torsion des poutre cylindrique," Bul. de l'Assn., *Technique Maritime et Aeronautique*, Vol. 43, 1939.

18. A. Piccard and L. Baes, "Mode experimental nouveau relatif à l'application des surfaces a courbure constante à la solution du problème de la torsion des barres primatiques," *Proc. Second International Congress for Applied Mechanics*, 1926, pp. 195–199.

19. C. Sunatani, T. Matuyama, and M. Hatamura, "The Solution of Torsion Problems by Means of a Liquid Surface," *The Technology Reports of the Tohoku Imperial University*, Vol. XII, 1938, pp. 374–396.

20. I. Langmuir, E. Q. Adams, and F. S. Meikle, "Flow of Heat Through Furnace Walls," *Trans., American Electrochemical Society*, Vol. 24, 1913, pp. 53–84.

21. L. Malavard, "The Use of Rheo-Electrical Analogies in Certain Aerodynamical Problems," *Journal of the Royal Aeronautical Society*, Vol. 51, 1947.

22. E. F. Relf, "An Electrical Method for Tracing Lines in the Two-Dimensional Motion of a Perfect Fluid," *Philosophy Magazine*, Vol. 48, Sept., 1924.

23. F. Cheers, W. G. Raymer, and R. G. Fowler, "Preliminary Tests on Electric Potential Flow Apparatus," *Aeronautical Research Council Tech. Report*, No. 2205, 1945.

24. P. G. Hubbard, "Application of the Electrical Analogy in Fluid Mechanics Research," *The Review of Scientific Instruments*, Vol. 20, No. 11, Nov., 1949, pp. 802–807.

25. H. K. Farr and F. R. Wilson, "Some Applications of the Electrolytic Field Analyzer," *Trans., AIEE*, Vol. 70 (2), 1951, pp. 1301–1309.

26. L. Malavard and J. Miroux, "Electrical Analogies for Heat Transfer Problems," *The Engineers Digest*, Vol. 13, Dec., 1952, pp. 416–420.

27. P. A. Einstein, "Factors Limiting the Accuracy of the Electrolytic Plotting Tanks," *British Journal of Applied Physics*, Vol. 2, Feb., 1951, pp. 49–55.

28. P. E. McNall, Jr. and J. E. Janssen, "An Electrolytic Analog Applied to the Solution of a Thermal Conduction Problem," *ASME Preprint* No. 54–SA–45, June, 1954.

29. E. R. Hartill, "The Electrolytic Tank and its Application to Engineering Design," *The Metropolitan-Vickers Gazette*, Vol. 24, April, 1952.

30. J. K. Mickelsen, "Automatic Equipment and Techniques for Field Mapping," *General Electric Review*, Vol. 52, 1949.

31. C. L. Beuken, "Die Warmestromung durch die Ecken von Ofenwandungen," *Warme- und Kaltetechnik*, Vol. 39 (7), p. 1.

32. J. H. Awberry and F. H. Schofield, "Effect of Shape on Heat-Loss through Insulation," *Fifth International Congress on Refrigeration*, 1928.

33. F. Bruckmayer, "Elektrische Modellversuche zur Losung warmetechnischer," *Archiv fur Warmewirtschaft und Dampfkesselwesen*, Heft 1, Bd. 20, Jan., 1939, pp. 23–25.

34. C. F. Kayan, "An Electrical Geometrical Analogue for Complex Heat Flow," *Trans., ASME*, Vol. 67, No. 8, Nov., 1945, pp. 713–716.

35. C. F. Kayan, "Temperature Patterns and Heat Transfer for a Wall Containing a Submerged Metal Member," *Refrigeration Engineering*, Vol. 51, June 1946, pp. 533–537, 568, 574, and 582.

36. C. F. Kayan, "Heat-Transfer Temperature Patterns of a Multicomponent Structure by Comparative Methods," *Trans., ASME*, Vol. 71, 1949, pp. 9–16.

37. "Instructions for Analog Field Plotter," Cat. No. 112L152G1 & G2, General Electric Company, Schenectady, N. Y.

38. H. H. Ellerbrock, Jr., E. F. Schum, and A. J. Nachtigall, "Use of Electric

Analogs for Calculation of Temperature Distribution of Cooled Turbine Blades,"
NACA TN No. 3060, Dec., 1953.

39. D. I. Lawson and J. H. McGuire, "The Solution of Transient Heat-Flow Problems by Analogous Electrical Networks," Proc. (A), *Institution of Mechanical Engineers*, Vol. 167, No. 3, 1953, pp. 275–287.

40. V. Paschkis and M. P. Heisler, "The Accuracy of Lumping in an Electric Circuit Representing Heat Flow in Cylindrical and Spherical Bodies," *Journal of Applied Physics*, Vol. 17, No. 4, April, 1946, pp. 246–254.

41. H. C. J. H. Gelissen, "Development of the Beuken Model for Analysis of Unsteady-State Heat Transfer," *Industrial Heating*, Vol. 15, No. 3, March, 1948, pp. 402–414.

42. V. Paschkis, "A Method for Determining Unsteady-State Heat Transfer by Means of an Electrical Analogy," *Trans., ASME*, Vol. 64, No. 2, Feb., 1942, pp. 105–110.

43. M. Avrami and V. Paschkis, "Application of an Electric Model to the Study of Two-Dimensional Heat Flow," *Trans., American Institute of Chemical Engineers*, Vol. 38, No. 3, June, 1942, pp. 631–652.

44. V. Paschkis, "Periodic Heat Flow in Building Walls Determined by Electrical Analogy Method," *Heating, Piping, and Air Conditioning* (Journal Section), Vol. 14, No. 2, Feb., 1942, pp. 133–138.

45. M. P. Heisler, "Temperature Charts for Induction and Constant-Temperature Heating," *Trans., ASME*, Vol. 69, April, 1947, pp. 227–236.

46. A. D. Moore, "A Hydrodynamic Calculating Machine for Solving Unsteady-State Problems in Heat Transfer and Other Types of Diffusion," *Industrial and Engineering Chemistry*, Vol. 28, No. 6, June, 1936, pp. 704–708.

47. C. S. Leopold, "Hydraulic Analogue for the Solution of Problems of Thermal Storage, Radiation, Convection, and Conduction," *Trans., ASHVE*, Vol. 54, 1948, pp. 389–401.

48. M. B. Cole, "An Air-Flow Analogy for the Solution of Transient Heat Conduction Problems," *British Journal of Applied Physics*, Vol. 2, Jan., 1951, pp. 12–17, (Also *ASME-AIE*, "General Discussion on Heat Transfer," 1951) pp. 265–267.

APPENDIX

COMPUTATION TABLES

TRIGONOMETRIC FUNCTION SIN φ

$\varphi°$	$0'$	$10'$	$20'$	$30'$	$40'$	$50'$	$60'$
0	0.0000	0029	0058	0087	0116	0145	0174
1	0.0174	0204	0233	0262	0291	0320	0349
2	0.0349	0378	0407	0436	0465	0494	0523
3	0.0523	0552	0581	0610	0640	0668	0698
4	0.0698	0727	0756	0785	0814	0843	0872
5	0.0872	0900	0930	0958	0987	1016	1045
6	0.1045	1074	1103	1132	1161	1190	1219
7	0.1219	1248	1276	1305	1334	1363	1392
8	0.1392	1420	1449	1478	1507	1536	1564
9	0.1564	1593	1622	1650	1679	1708	1736
10	0.1736	1765	1794	1822	1851	1880	1908
11	0.1908	1937	1965	1994	2022	2051	2079
12	0.2079	2108	2136	2164	2193	2221	2250
13	0.2250	2278	2306	2334	2363	2391	2419
14	0.2419	2447	2476	2504	2532	2560	2588
15	0.2588	2616	2644	2672	2700	2728	2756
16	0.2756	2784	2812	2840	2868	2896	2924
17	0.2924	2952	2979	3007	3035	3062	3090
18	0.3090	3118	3145	3173	3201	3228	3256
19	0.3256	3283	3311	3338	3366	3393	3420
20	0.3420	3448	3475	3502	3529	3556	3584
21	0.3584	3611	3638	3665	3692	3719	3746
22	0.3746	3773	3800	3827	3854	3880	3907
23	0.3907	3934	3961	3988	4014	4041	4067
24	0.4067	4094	4120	4147	4173	4200	4226
25	0.4226	4252	4279	4305	4331	4358	4384
26	0.4384	4410	4436	4462	4488	4514	4540
27	0.4540	4566	4592	4618	4643	4669	4695
28	0.4695	4720	4746	4772	4797	4823	4848
29	0.4848	4874	4899	4924	4950	4975	5000
30	0.5000	5025	5050	5075	5100	5125	5150
31	0.5150	5175	5200	5225	5250	5275	5299
32	0.5299	5324	5348	5373	5398	5422	5446
33	0.5446	5471	5495	5519	5544	5568	5592
34	0.5592	5616	5640	5664	5688	5712	5736

$\varphi°$	$0'$	$10'$	$20'$	$30'$	$40'$	$50'$	$60'$
35	0.5736	5760	5783	5807	5831	5854	5878
36	0.5878	5901	5925	5948	5972	5995	6018
37	0.6018	6041	6065	6088	6111	6134	6157
38	0.6157	6180	6202	6225	6248	6271	6293
39	0.6293	6316	6338	6361	6383	6406	6428
40	0.6428	6450	6472	6494	6517	6539	6561
41	0.6561	6582	6604	6626	6648	6670	6691
42	0.6691	6713	6734	6756	6777	6799	6820
43	0.6820	6841	6862	6884	6905	6926	6947
44	0.6947	6968	6988	7009	7030	7050	7071
45	0.7071	7092	7112	7133	7153	7173	7193
46	0.7193	7214	7234	7254	7274	7294	7314
47	0.7314	7333	7353	7373	7392	7412	7431
48	0.7431	7451	7470	7490	7509	7528	7547
49	0.7547	7566	7585	7604	7623	7642	7660
50	0.7660	7679	7698	7716	7735	7753	7772
51	0.7772	7790	7808	7826	7844	7862	7880
52	0.7880	7898	7916	7934	7951	7969	7986
53	0.7986	8004	8021	8039	8056	8073	8090
54	0.8090	8107	8124	8141	8158	8175	8192
55	0.8192	8208	8225	8241	8258	8274	8290
56	0.8290	8307	8323	8339	8355	8371	8387
57	0.8387	8403	8418	8434	8450	8465	8480
58	0.8480	8496	8511	8526	8542	8557	8572
59	0.8572	8587	8602	8616	8631	8646	8660
60	0.8660	8675	8689	8704	8718	8732	8746
61	0.8746	8760	8774	8788	8802	8816	8830
62	0.8830	8843	8857	8870	8884	8897	8910
63	0.8910	8923	8936	8949	8962	8975	8988
64	0.8988	9001	9013	9026	9038	9051	9063
65	0.9063	9075	9088	9100	9112	9124	9136
66	0.9136	9147	9159	9171	9182	9194	9205
67	0.9205	9216	9228	9239	9250	9261	9272
68	0.9272	9284	9293	9304	9315	9325	9336
69	0.9336	9346	9356	9367	9377	9387	9397
70	0.9397	9407	9417	9426	9436	9446	9455
71	0.9455	9465	9474	9483	9492	9502	9511
72	0.9511	9520	9528	9537	9546	9554	9563
73	0.9563	9572	9580	9588	9596	9605	9613
74	0.9613	9621	9628	9636	9644	9652	9659

$\varphi°$	0'	10'	20'	30'	40'	50'	60'
75	0.9659	9667	9674	9682	9689	9696	9703
76	0.9703	9710	9717	9724	9730	9737	9744
77	0.9744	9750	9757	9763	9769	9775	9782
78	0.9782	9788	9793	9799	9805	9811	9816
79	0.9816	9822	9827	9833	9838	9843	9848
80	0.9848	9853	9858	9863	9868	9872	9877
81	0.9877	9881	9886	9890	9894	9899	9903
82	0.9903	9907	9911	9914	9918	9922	9926
83	0.9926	9929	9932	9936	9939	9942	9945
84	0.9945	9948	9951	9954	9957	9959	9962
85	0.9962	9964	9967	9969	9971	9974	9976
86	0.9976	9978	9980	9981	9983	9985	9986
87	0.9986	9988	9989	9990	9992	9993	9994
88	0.9994	9995	9996	9997	9997	9998	9998
89	0.9998	9999	9999	0000	0000	0000	0000
90	1.0000						

Note that $\cos \varphi = \sin(\pi/2 \pm \varphi)$ and $\tan \varphi = \sin \varphi / \sin (\pi/2 \pm \varphi)$.

TABLE A–2.

EXPONENTIAL FUNCTIONS $e^{\pm u}$

u	e^u	e^{-u}	u	e^u	e^{-u}	u	e^u	e^{-u}
0.00	1.000	1.000	0.30	1.350	0.741	0.60	1.822	0.549
0.02	1.020	0.980	0.32	1.377	0.726	0.62	1.859	0.538
0.04	1.041	0.961	0.34	1.405	0.712	0.64	1.896	0.527
0.06	1.062	0.942	0.36	1.433	0.698	0.66	1.935	0.517
0.08	1.083	0.923	0.38	1.462	0.684	0.68	1.974	0.507
0.10	1.105	0.905	0.40	1.492	0.670	0.70	2.014	0.497
0.12	1.128	0.887	0.42	1.522	0.657	0.72	2.054	0.487
0.14	1.150	0.869	0.44	1.553	0.644	0.74	2.096	0.477
0.16	1.174	0.852	0.46	1.584	0.631	0.76	2.138	0.468
0.18	1.197	0.835	0.48	1.616	0.619	0.78	2.182	0.458
0.20	1.221	0.819	0.50	1.649	0.606	0.80	2.226	0.449
0.22	1.246	0.802	0.52	1.682	0.594	0.82	2.270	0.440
0.24	1.271	0.787	0.54	1.716	0.583	0.84	2.316	0.432
0.26	1.297	0.771	0.56	1.751	0.571	0.86	2.363	0.423
0.28	1.323	0.756	0.58	1.786	0.560	0.88	2.411	0.415

u	e^u	e^{-u}	u	e^u	e^{-u}	u	e^u	e^{-u}
0.90	2.460	0.407	1.70	5.474	0.183	2.50	12.18	0.082
0.92	2.509	0.398	1.72	5.584	0.179	2.52	12.43	0.080
0.94	2.560	0.391	1.74	5.697	0.176	2.54	12.68	0.079
0.96	2.612	0.383	1.76	5.812	0.172	2.56	12.94	0.077
0.98	2.664	0.375	1.78	5.930	0.169	2.58	13.20	0.076
1.00	2.718	0.368	1.80	6.050	0.165	2.60	13.46	0.074
1.02	2.773	0.361	1.82	6.172	0.162	2.62	13.74	0.073
1.04	2.829	0.353	1.84	6.296	0.159	2.64	14.01	0.071
1.06	2.886	0.346	1.86	6.424	0.156	2.66	14.30	0.070
1.08	2.945	0.340	1.88	6.554	0.153	2.68	14.58	0.069
1.10	3.004	0.333	1.90	6.686	0.150	2.70	14.88	0.067
1.12	3.065	0.326	1.92	6.821	0.147	2.72	15.18	0.066
1.14	3.127	0.320	1.94	6.959	0.144	2.74	15.49	0.065
1.16	3.190	0.313	1.96	7.099	0.141	2.76	15.80	0.063
1.18	3.254	0.307	1.98	7.243	0.138	2.78	16.12	0.062
1.20	3.320	0.301	2.00	7.389	0.135	2.80	16.44	0.061
1.22	3.387	0.295	2.02	7.538	0.133	2.82	16.78	0.060
1.24	3.456	0.289	2.04	7.691	0.130	2.84	17.12	0.058
1.26	3.525	0.284	2.06	7.846	0.127	2.86	17.46	0.057
1.28	3.597	0.278	2.08	8.004	0.125	2.88	17.81	0.056
1.30	3.669	0.272	2.10	8.166	0.122	2.90	18.17	0.055
1.32	3.743	0.267	2.12	8.331	0.120	2.92	18.54	0.054
1.34	3.819	0.262	2.14	8.499	0.118	2.94	18.92	0.053
1.36	3.896	0.257	2.16	8.671	0.115	2.96	19.30	0.052
1.38	3.975	0.252	2.18	8.846	0.113	2.98	19.69	0.051
1.40	4.055	0.247	2.20	9.025	0.111	3.00	20.08	0.050
1.42	4.137	0.242	2.22	9.207	0.109	3.10	22.20	0.045
1.44	4.221	0.237	2.24	9.393	0.106	3.20	24.53	0.041
1.46	4.306	0.232	2.26	9.583	0.104	3.30	27.11	0.037
1.48	4.393	0.228	2.28	9.777	0.102	3.40	29.96	0.033
1.50	4.482	0.223	2.30	9.974	0.100	3.50	33.11	0.030
1.52	4.572	0.219	2.32	10.176	0.098	3.60	36.60	0.027
1.54	4.665	0.214	2.34	10.381	0.096	3.70	40.45	0.025
1.56	4.759	0.210	2.36	10.591	0.094	3.80	44.70	0.022
1.58	4.855	0.206	2.38	10.805	0.093	3.90	49.40	0.020
1.60	4.953	0.202	2.40	11.023	0.091	4.00	54.60	0.018
1.62	5.053	0.198	2.42	11.246	0.089	4.20	66.69	0.015
1.64	5.155	0.194	2.44	11.473	0.087	4.40	81.45	0.012
1.66	5.259	0.190	2.46	11.705	0.085	4.60	99.48	0.010
1.68	5.366	0.186	2.48	11.941	0.084	4.80	121.51	0.008

u	e^u	e^{-u}	u	e^u	e^{-u}	u	e^u	e^{-u}
5.00	148.4	0.007	6.00	403.4	0.002	8.50	4914.8	0.000
5.20	181.3	0.006	6.50	665.1	0.002	9.00	8103.1	0.000
5.40	221.4	0.004	7.00	1096.6	0.001	9.50	13360.	0.000
5.60	270.4	0.004	7.50	1808.0	0.001	10.00	22026.	0.000
5.80	330.3	0.003	8.00	2981.0	0.000			

Note that $\sinh u = (e^u - e^{-u})/2$, $\cosh u = (e^u + e^{-u})/2$, and $\tanh u = (e^{2u} - 1)/(e^{2u} + 1)$.

TABLE A–3.

ZERO AND FIRST-ORDER BESSEL FUNCTIONS OF THE
FIRST KIND, $J_0(u)$ AND $J_1(u)$

u	$J_0(u)$	$J_1(u)$	u	$J_0(u)$	$J_1(u)$
0.0	1.0000	0.0000	2.0	0.2239	0.5767
0.1	0.9975	0.0499	2.1	0.1666	0.5683
0.2	0.9900	0.0995	2.2	0.1104	0.5560
0.3	0.9776	0.1483	2.3	0.0555	0.5399
0.4	0.9604	0.1960	2.4	0.0025	0.5202
0.5	0.9385	0.2423	2.5	−0.0484	0.4971
0.6	0.9120	0.2867	2.6	−0.0968	0.4708
0.7	0.8812	0.3290	2.7	−0.1424	0.4416
0.8	0.8463	0.3688	2.8	−0.1850	0.4097
0.9	0.8075	0.4059	2.9	−0.2243	0.3754
1.0	0.7652	0.4400	3.0	−0.2600	0.3391
1.1	0.7196	0.4709	3.1	−0.2921	0.3009
1.2	0.6711	0.4983	3.2	−0.3202	0.2613
1.3	0.6201	0.5220	3.3	−0.3443	0.2207
1.4	0.5669	0.5419	3.4	−0.3643	0.1792
1.5	0.5118	0.5579	3.5	−0.3801	0.1374
1.6	0.4554	0.5699	3.6	−0.3918	0.0955
1.7	0.3980	0.5778	3.7	−0.3992	0.0538
1.8	0.3400	0.5815	3.8	−0.4026	0.0128
1.9	0.2818	0.5812	3.9	−0.4018	−0.0272

u	$J_0(u)$	$J_1(u)$	u	$J_0(u)$	$J_1(u)$
4.0	-0.3971	-0.0660	8.0	0.1716	0.2346
4.1	-0.3887	-0.1033	8.1	0.1475	0.2476
4.2	-0.3766	-0.1386	8.2	0.1222	0.2580
4.3	-0.3610	-0.1719	8.3	0.0960	0.2657
4.4	-0.3423	-0.2028	8.4	0.0692	0.2708
4.5	-0.3205	-0.2311	8.5	0.0419	0.2731
4.6	-0.2961	-0.2566	8.6	0.0146	0.2728
4.7	-0.2693	-0.2791	8.7	-0.0125	0.2697
4.8	-0.2404	-0.2985	8.8	-0.0392	0.2641
4.9	-0.2097	-0.3147	8.9	-0.0652	0.2559
5.0	-0.1776	-0.3276	9.0	-0.0903	0.2453
5.1	-0.1443	-0.3371	9.1	-0.1142	0.2324
5.2	-0.1103	-0.3432	9.2	-0.1368	0.2174
5.3	-0.0758	-0.3460	9.3	-0.1577	0.2004
5.4	-0.0412	-0.3453	9.4	-0.1768	0.1816
5.5	-0.0068	-0.3414	9.5	-0.1939	0.1613
5.6	0.0270	-0.3343	9.6	-0.2090	0.1395
5.7	0.0599	-0.3241	9.7	-0.2218	0.1166
5.8	0.0917	-0.3110	9.8	-0.2323	0.0928
5.9	0.1220	-0.2951	9.9	-0.2403	0.0684
6.0	0.1506	-0.2767	10.0	-0.2459	0.0435
6.1	0.1773	-0.2559	10.1	-0.2490	0.0184
6.2	0.2017	-0.2329	10.2	-0.2496	-0.0066
6.3	0.2238	-0.2081	10.3	-0.2477	-0.0313
6.4	0.2433	-0.1816	10.4	-0.2434	-0.0555
6.5	0.2601	-0.1538	10.5	-0.2366	-0.0788
6.6	0.2740	-0.1250	10.6	-0.2276	-0.1012
6.7	0.2851	-0.0953	10.7	-0.2164	-0.1224
6.8	0.2931	-0.0652	10.8	-0.2032	-0.1422
6.9	0.2981	-0.0349	10.9	-0.1881	-0.1604
7.0	0.3001	-0.0047	11.0	-0.1712	-0.1768
7.1	0.2991	0.0252	11.1	-0.1528	-0.1913
7.2	0.2951	0.0543	11.2	-0.1330	-0.2038
7.3	0.2882	0.0826	11.3	-0.1121	-0.2143
7.4	0.2786	0.1096	11.4	-0.0902	-0.2224
7.5	0.2663	0.1352	11.5	-0.0677	-0.2284
7.6	0.2516	0.1592	11.6	-0.0446	-0.2320
7.7	0.2346	0.1813	11.7	-0.0213	-0.2333
7.8	0.2154	0.2014	11.8	0.0020	-0.2323
7.9	0.1944	0.2192	11.9	0.0250	-0.2290

u	$J_0(u)$	$J_1(u)$	u	$J_0(u)$	$J_1(u)$
12.0	0.0477	−0.2234	13.5	0.2150	0.0380
12.1	0.0697	−0.2158	13.6	0.2101	0.0590
12.2	0.0908	−0.2060	13.7	0.2032	0.0791
12.3	0.1108	−0.1943	13.8	0.1943	0.0984
12.4	0.1296	−0.1807	13.9	0.1836	0.1165
12.5	0.1469	−0.1655	14.0	0.1711	0.1334
12.6	0.1626	−0.1487	14.1	0.1570	0.1488
12.7	0.1766	−0.1307	14.2	0.1414	0.1626
12.8	0.1887	−0.1114	14.3	0.1245	0.1747
12.9	0.1988	−0.0912	14.4	0.1065	0.1850
13.0	0.2069	−0.0703	14.5	0.0875	0.1934
13.1	0.2129	−0.0488	14.6	0.0679	0.1998
13.2	0.2167	−0.0271	14.7	0.0476	0.2043
13.3	0.2183	−0.0052	14.8	0.0271	0.2066
13.4	0.2177	0.0166	14.9	0.0064	0.2069
			15.0	−0.0142	0.2051

TABLE A–4.

ZERO AND FIRST-ORDER BESSEL FUNCTIONS OF THE
SECOND KIND, $Y_0(u)$ AND $Y_1(u)$

u	$Y_0(u)$	$Y_1(u)$	u	$Y_0(u)$	$Y_1(u)$
0.0	$-\infty$	$-\infty$	1.5	0.3824	−0.4123
0.1	−1.5342	−6.4590	1.6	0.4204	−0.3476
0.2	−1.0811	−3.3238	1.7	0.4520	−0.2847
0.3	−0.8073	−2.2931	1.8	0.4774	−0.2237
0.4	−0.6060	−1.7809	1.9	0.4968	−0.1644
0.5	−0.4445	−1.4715	2.0	0.5104	−0.1070
0.6	−0.3085	−1.2604	2.1	0.5183	−0.0517
0.7	−0.1907	−1.1032	2.2	0.5208	0.0015
0.8	−0.0868	−0.9781	2.3	0.5181	0.0523
0.9	0.0056	−0.8731	2.4	0.5104	0.1005
1.0	0.0883	−0.7812	2.5	0.4981	0.1459
1.1	0.1622	−0.6981	2.6	0.4813	0.1884
1.2	0.2281	−0.6211	2.7	0.4605	0.2276
1.3	0.2865	−0.5485	2.8	0.4359	0.2635
1.4	0.3379	−0.4791	2.9	0.4079	0.2959

u	$Y_0(u)$	$Y_1(u)$	u	$Y_0(u)$	$Y_1(u)$
3.0	0.3768	0.3247	7.0	−0.0260	−0.3027
3.1	0.3431	0.3496	7.1	0.0042	−0.2995
3.2	0.3070	0.3707	7.2	0.0338	−0.2934
3.3	0.2691	0.3878	7.3	0.0628	−0.2846
3.4	0.2296	0.4010	7.4	0.0907	−0.2731
3.5	0.1890	0.4102	7.5	0.1173	−0.2591
3.6	0.1477	0.4154	7.6	0.1424	−0.2428
3.7	0.1061	0.4167	7.7	0.1658	−0.2243
3.8	0.0645	0.4141	7.8	0.1872	−0.2039
3.9	0.0234	0.4078	7.9	0.2065	−0.1817
4.0	−0.0169	0.3979	8.0	0.2235	−0.1581
4.1	−0.0561	0.3846	8.1	0.2381	−0.1332
4.2	−0.0938	0.3680	8.2	0.2501	−0.1072
4.3	−0.1296	0.3484	8.3	0.2595	−0.0806
4.4	−0.1633	0.3260	8.4	0.2662	−0.0535
4.5	−0.1947	0.3010	8.5	0.2702	−0.0262
4.6	−0.2235	0.2737	8.6	0.2715	0.0011
4.7	−0.2494	0.2445	8.7	0.2700	0.0280
4.8	−0.2723	0.2136	8.8	0.2659	0.0544
4.9	−0.2921	0.1812	8.9	0.2592	0.0799
5.0	−0.3085	0.1479	9.0	0.2499	0.1043
5.1	−0.3216	0.1137	9.1	0.2383	0.1275
5.2	−0.3312	0.0792	9.2	0.2245	0.1491
5.3	−0.3374	0.0445	9.3	0.2086	0.1691
5.4	−0.3402	0.0101	9.4	0.1907	0.1871
5.5	−0.3395	−0.0238	9.5	0.1712	0.2032
5.6	−0.3354	−0.0568	9.6	0.1502	0.2171
5.7	−0.3282	−0.0887	9.7	0.1279	0.2287
5.8	−0.3177	−0.1192	9.8	0.1045	0.2379
5.9	−0.3044	−0.1481	9.9	0.0804	0.2447
6.0	−0.2882	−0.1750	10.0	0.0557	0.2490
6.1	−0.2694	−0.1998	10.1	0.0307	0.2508
6.2	−0.2483	−0.2223	10.2	0.0056	0.2502
6.3	−0.2251	−0.2422	10.3	−0.0193	0.2471
6.4	−0.2000	−0.2596	10.4	−0.0437	0.2416
6.5	−0.1732	−0.2741	10.5	−0.0675	0.2337
6.6	−0.1452	−0.2857	10.6	−0.0904	0.2236
6.7	−0.1162	−0.2945	10.7	−0.1122	0.2114
6.8	−0.0864	−0.3002	10.8	−0.1326	0.1973
6.9	−0.0562	−0.3029	10.9	−0.1516	0.1813

u	$Y_0(u)$	$Y_1(u)$	u	$Y_0(u)$	$Y_1(u)$
11.0	−0.1688	0.1637	13.0	−0.0782	−0.2101
11.1	−0.1843	0.1446	13.1	−0.0569	−0.2152
11.2	−0.1977	0.1243	13.2	−0.0352	−0.2182
11.3	−0.2091	0.1029	13.3	−0.0134	−0.2190
11.4	−0.2183	0.0807	13.4	0.0085	−0.2176
11.5	−0.2252	0.0579	13.5	0.0301	−0.2140
11.6	−0.2299	0.0348	13.6	0.0512	−0.2084
11.7	−0.2322	0.0114	13.7	0.0717	−0.2007
11.8	−0.2322	−0.0118	13.8	0.0913	−0.1912
11.9	−0.2298	−0.0347	13.9	0.1099	−0.1798
12.0	−0.2252	−0.0571	14.0	0.1272	−0.1666
12.1	−0.2184	−0.0787	14.1	0.1431	−0.1520
12.2	−0.2095	−0.0994	14.2	0.1575	−0.1359
12.3	−0.1986	−0.1190	14.3	0.1703	−0.1186
12.4	−0.1858	−0.1371	14.4	0.1812	−0.1003
12.5	−0.1712	−0.1538	14.5	0.1903	−0.0810
12.6	−0.1551	−0.1689	14.6	0.1974	−0.0612
12.7	−0.1375	−0.1821	14.7	0.2025	−0.0408
12.8	−0.1187	−0.1935	14.8	0.2056	−0.0202
12.9	−0.0989	−0.2028	14.9	0.2066	0.0005

TABLE A–5.

ZERO AND FIRST-ORDER MODIFIED BESSEL FUNCTIONS OF THE FIRST KIND, $I_0(u)$ AND $I_1(u)$

u	$I_0(u)$	$I_1(u)$	u	$I_0(u)$	$I_1(u)$
0.0	1.0000	0.0000	1.0	1.2661	0.5652
0.1	1.0025	0.0501	1.1	1.3262	0.6375
0.2	1.0100	0.1005	1.2	1.3937	0.7147
0.3	1.0226	0.1517	1.3	1.4693	0.7973
0.4	1.0404	0.2040	1.4	1.5534	0.8861
0.5	1.0635	0.2579	1.5	1.6467	0.9817
0.6	1.0920	0.3137	1.6	1.7500	1.0848
0.7	1.1263	0.3719	1.7	1.8640	1.1963
0.8	1.1665	0.4329	1.8	1.9896	1.3172
0.9	1.2130	0.4971	1.9	2.1277	1.4482

u	$I_0(u)$	$I_1(u)$	u	$I_0(u)$	$I_1(u)$
2.0	2.280	1.591	4.0	11.30	9.76
2.1	2.446	1.746	4.1	12.32	10.69
2.2	2.629	1.914	4.2	13.44	11.71
2.3	2.830	2.098	4.3	14.67	12.82
2.4	3.049	2.298	4.4	16.01	14.05
2.5	3.290	2.517	4.5	17.48	15.39
2.6	3.553	2.755	4.6	19.09	16.86
2.7	3.842	3.016	4.7	20.86	18.48
2.8	4.157	3.301	4.8	22.79	20.25
2.9	4.503	3.613	4.9	24.91	22.20
3.0	4.881	3.953	5.0	27.24	24.34
3.1	5.294	4.326	5.1	29.79	26.68
3.2	5.747	4.734	5.2	32.58	29.25
3.3	6.243	5.181	5.3	35.65	32.08
3.4	6.785	5.670	5.4	39.01	35.18
3.5	7.378	6.206	5.5	42.70	38.59
3.6	8.028	6.793	5.6	46.74	42.33
3.7	8.739	7.436	5.7	51.17	46.44
3.8	9.517	8.140	5.8	56.04	50.95
3.9	10.369	8.913	5.9	61.38	55.90

TABLE A–6.

ZERO AND FIRST-ORDER MODIFIED BESSEL FUNCTIONS
OF THE SECOND KIND, $K_0(u)$ AND $K_1(u)$

u	$\dfrac{2}{\pi}K_0(u)$	$\dfrac{2}{\pi}K_1(u)$	u	$\dfrac{2}{\pi}K_0(u)$	$\dfrac{2}{\pi}K_1(u)$
0.0	∞	∞	1.0	0.268	0.383
0.1	1.545	6.270	1.1	0.233	0.324
0.2	1.116	3.040	1.2	0.203	0.277
0.3	0.874	1.946	1.3	0.177	0.237
0.4	0.710	1.391	1.4	0.155	0.204
0.5	0.588	1.054	1.5	0.136	0.177
0.6	0.495	0.829	1.6	0.120	0.153
0.7	0.420	0.669	1.7	0.105	0.133
0.8	0.360	0.549	1.8	0.093	0.116
0.9	0.310	0.456	1.9	0.082	0.102

u	$\frac{2}{\pi}K_0(u)$	$\frac{2}{\pi}K_1(u)$	u	$\frac{2}{\pi}K_0(u)$	$\frac{2}{\pi}K_1(u)$
2.0	0.072	0.089	3.0	0.022	0.026
2.1	0.064	0.078	3.1	0.020	0.023
2.2	0.057	0.069	3.2	0.018	0.020
2.3	0.050	0.060	3.3	0.016	0.018
2.4	0.045	0.053	3.4	0.014	0.016
2.5	0.040	0.047	3.5	0.012	0.014
2.6	0.035	0.042	3.6	0.011	0.013
2.7	0.031	0.037	3.7	0.010	0.011
2.8	0.028	0.032	3.8	0.009	0.010
2.9	0.025	0.029	3.9	0.008	0.009

TABLE A–7.

FIRST FIVE LEGENDRE POLYNOMIALS OF THE FIRST KIND, $P_n(u)$

u	$P_1(u)$	$P_2(u)$	$P_3(u)$	$P_4(u)$	$P_5(u)$
0.00	0.0000	−0.5000	0.0000	0.3750	0.0000
0.01	0.0100	−0.4998	−0.0150	0.3746	0.0187
0.02	0.0200	−0.4994	−0.0300	0.3735	0.0374
0.03	0.0300	−0.4986	−0.0449	0.3716	0.0560
0.04	0.0400	−0.4976	−0.0598	0.3690	0.0744
0.05	0.0500	−0.4962	−0.0747	0.3657	0.0927
0.06	0.0600	−0.4946	−0.0895	0.3616	0.1106
0.07	0.0700	−0.4926	−0.1041	0.3567	0.1283
0.08	0.0800	−0.4904	−0.1187	0.3512	0.1455
0.09	0.0900	−0.4878	−0.1332	0.3449	0.1624
0.10	0.1000	−0.4850	−0.1475	0.3379	0.1788
0.11	0.1100	−0.4818	−0.1617	0.3303	0.1947
0.12	0.1200	−0.4784	−0.1757	0.3219	0.2101
0.13	0.1300	−0.4746	−0.1895	0.3129	0.2248
0.14	0.1400	−0.4706	−0.2031	0.3032	0.2389
0.15	0.1500	−0.4662	−0.2166	0.2928	0.2523
0.16	0.1600	−0.4616	−0.2298	0.2819	0.2650
0.17	0.1700	−0.4566	−0.2427	0.2703	0.2769
0.18	0.1800	−0.4514	−0.2554	0.2581	0.2880
0.19	0.1900	−0.4458	−0.2679	0.2453	0.2982

u	$P_1(u)$	$P_2(u)$	$P_3(u)$	$P_4(u)$	$P_5(u)$
0.20	0.2000	-0.4400	-0.2800	0.2320	0.3075
0.21	0.2100	-0.4338	-0.2918	0.2181	0.3159
0.22	0.2200	-0.4274	-0.3034	0.2037	0.3234
0.23	0.2300	-0.4206	-0.3146	0.1889	0.3299
0.24	0.2400	-0.4136	-0.3254	0.1735	0.3353
0.25	0.2500	-0.4062	-0.3359	0.1577	0.3397
0.26	0.2600	-0.3986	-0.3461	0.1415	0.3431
0.27	0.2700	-0.3906	-0.3558	0.1249	0.3453
0.28	0.2800	-0.3824	-0.3651	0.1079	0.3465
0.29	0.2900	-0.3738	-0.3740	0.0906	0.3465
0.30	0.3000	-0.3650	-0.3825	0.0729	0.3454
0.31	0.3100	-0.3558	-0.3905	0.0550	0.3431
0.32	0.3200	-0.3464	-0.3981	0.0369	0.3397
0.33	0.3300	-0.3366	-0.4052	0.0185	0.3351
0.34	0.3400	-0.3266	-0.4117	0.0000	0.3294
0.35	0.3500	-0.3162	-0.4178	-0.0187	0.3225
0.36	0.3600	-0.3056	-0.4234	-0.0375	0.3144
0.37	0.3700	-0.2946	-0.4284	-0.0564	0.3051
0.38	0.3800	-0.2834	-0.4328	-0.0753	0.2948
0.39	0.3900	-0.2718	-0.4367	-0.0942	0.2833
0.40	0.4000	-0.2600	-0.4400	-0.1130	0.2706
0.41	0.4100	-0.2478	-0.4427	-0.1317	0.2569
0.42	0.4200	-0.2354	-0.4448	-0.1504	0.2421
0.43	0.4300	-0.2226	-0.4462	-0.1688	0.2263
0.44	0.4400	-0.2096	-0.4470	-0.1870	0.2095
0.45	0.4500	-0.1962	-0.4472	-0.2050	0.1917
0.46	0.4600	-0.1826	-0.4467	-0.2226	0.1730
0.47	0.4700	-0.1686	-0.4454	-0.2399	0.1534
0.48	0.4800	-0.1544	-0.4435	-0.2568	0.1330
0.49	0.4900	-0.1398	-0.4409	-0.2732	0.1118
0.50	0.5000	-0.1250	-0.4375	-0.2891	0.0898
0.51	0.5100	-0.1098	-0.4334	-0.3044	0.0673
0.52	0.5200	-0.0944	-0.4285	-0.3191	0.0441
0.53	0.5300	-0.0786	-0.4228	-0.3332	0.0204
0.54	0.5400	-0.0626	-0.4163	-0.3465	-0.0037
0.55	0.5500	-0.0462	-0.4091	-0.3590	-0.0282
0.56	0.5600	-0.0296	-0.4010	-0.3707	-0.0529
0.57	0.5700	-0.0126	-0.3920	-0.3815	-0.0779
0.58	0.5800	0.0046	-0.3822	-0.3914	-0.1028
0.59	0.5900	0.0222	-0.3716	-0.4002	-0.1278

u	$P_1(u)$	$P_2(u)$	$P_3(u)$	$P_4(u)$	$P_5(u)$
0.60	0.6000	0.0400	-0.3600	-0.4080	-0.1526
0.61	0.6100	0.0582	-0.3475	-0.4146	-0.1772
0.62	0.6200	0.0766	-0.3342	-0.4200	-0.2014
0.63	0.6300	0.0954	-0.3199	-0.4242	-0.2251
0.64	0.6400	0.1144	-0.3046	-0.4270	-0.2482
0.65	0.6500	0.1338	-0.2884	-0.4284	-0.2705
0.66	0.6600	0.1534	-0.2713	-0.4284	-0.2919
0.67	0.6700	0.1734	-0.2531	-0.4268	-0.3122
0.68	0.6800	0.1936	-0.2339	-0.4236	-0.3313
0.69	0.6900	0.2142	-0.2137	-0.4187	-0.3490
0.70	0.7000	0.2350	-0.1925	-0.4121	-0.3652
0.71	0.7100	0.2562	-0.1702	-0.4036	-0.3796
0.72	0.7200	0.2776	-0.1469	-0.3933	-0.3922
0.73	0.7300	0.2994	-0.1225	-0.3810	-0.4026
0.74	0.7400	0.3214	-0.0969	-0.3666	-0.4107
0.75	0.7500	0.3438	-0.0703	-0.3501	-0.4164
0.76	0.7600	0.3664	-0.0426	-0.3314	-0.4193
0.77	0.7700	0.3894	-0.0137	-0.3104	-0.4193
0.78	0.7800	0.4126	0.0164	-0.2871	-0.4162
0.79	0.7900	0.4362	0.0476	-0.2613	-0.4097
0.80	0.8000	0.4600	0.0800	-0.2330	-0.3995
0.81	0.8100	0.4842	0.1136	-0.2021	-0.3855
0.82	0.8200	0.5086	0.1484	-0.1685	-0.3674
0.83	0.8300	0.5334	0.1845	-0.1321	-0.3449
0.84	0.8400	0.5584	0.2218	-0.0928	-0.3177
0.85	0.8500	0.5838	0.2603	-0.0506	-0.2857
0.86	0.8600	0.6094	0.3001	-0.0053	-0.2484
0.87	0.8700	0.6354	0.3413	0.0431	-0.2056
0.88	0.8800	0.6616	0.3837	0.0947	-0.1570
0.89	0.8900	0.6882	0.4274	0.1496	-0.1023
0.90	0.9000	0.7150	0.4725	0.2079	-0.0411
0.91	0.9100	0.7422	0.5189	0.2698	0.0268
0.92	0.9200	0.7696	0.5667	0.3352	0.1017
0.93	0.9300	0.7974	0.6159	0.4044	0.1842
0.94	0.9400	0.8254	0.6665	0.4773	0.2744
0.95	0.9500	0.8538	0.7184	0.5541	0.3727
0.96	0.9600	0.8824	0.7718	0.6349	0.4796
0.97	0.9700	0.9114	0.8267	0.7198	0.5954
0.98	0.9800	0.9406	0.8830	0.8089	0.7204
0.99	0.9900	0.9702	0.9407	0.9022	0.8552
1.00	1.0000	1.0000	1.0000	1.0000	1.0000

TABLE A–8.

VALUES OF THE PLATE SERIES $P(\Theta)$

Θ	$P(\Theta)$	Θ	$P(\Theta)$	Θ	$P(\Theta)$
0.020	1.00000	0.180	0.80884	0.340	0.55004
0.024	0.99999	0.184	0.80148	0.344	0.54466
0.028	0.99996	0.188	0.79414	0.348	0.53932
0.032	0.99984	0.192	0.78684	0.352	0.53404
0.036	0.99961	0.196	0.77956	0.356	0.52881
0.040	0.99919	0.200	0.77231	0.360	0.52363
0.044	0.99850	0.204	0.76510	0.364	0.51850
0.048	0.99750	0.208	0.75793	0.368	0.51342
0.052	0.99614	0.212	0.75080	0.372	0.50838
0.056	0.99439	0.216	0.74372	0.376	0.50340
0.060	0.99222	0.220	0.73668	0.380	0.49846
0.064	0.98962	0.224	0.72968	0.384	0.49357
0.068	0.98661	0.228	0.72274	0.388	0.48873
0.072	0.98318	0.232	0.71584	0.392	0.48394
0.076	0.97936	0.236	0.70900	0.396	0.47919
0.080	0.97516	0.240	0.70220	0.400	0.47449
0.084	0.97061	0.244	0.69546	0.404	0.46983
0.088	0.96572	0.248	0.68877	0.408	0.46522
0.092	0.96052	0.252	0.68214	0.412	0.46066
0.096	0.95504	0.256	0.67555	0.416	0.45614
0.100	0.94930	0.260	0.69903	0.420	0.45166
0.104	0.94333	0.264	0.66256	0.424	0.44723
0.108	0.93715	0.268	0.65614	0.428	0.44284
0.112	0.93078	0.272	0.64978	0.432	0.43849
0.116	0.92424	0.276	0.64347	0.436	0.43419
0.120	0.91755	0.280	0.63722	0.440	0.42992
0.124	0.91072	0.284	0.63103	0.444	0.42570
0.128	0.90379	0.288	0.62489	0.448	0.42152
0.132	0.89675	0.292	0.61881	0.452	0.41738
0.136	0.88963	0.296	0.61278	0.456	0.41329
0.140	0.88244	0.300	0.60680	0.460	0.40923
0.144	0.87519	0.304	0.60088	0.464	0.40521
0.148	0.86788	0.308	0.59502	0.468	0.40124
0.152	0.86055	0.312	0.58921	0.472	0.39729
0.156	0.85318	0.316	0.58346	0.476	0.39339
0.160	0.84580	0.320	0.57776	0.480	0.38953
0.164	0.83840	0.324	0.57211	0.484	0.38571
0.168	0.83100	0.328	0.56651	0.488	0.38192
0.172	0.82360	0.332	0.56097	0.492	0.37817
0.176	0.81622	0.336	0.55548	0.496	0.37446

Θ	P(Θ)	Θ	P(Θ)	Θ	P(Θ)
0.500	0.37078	0.660	0.24984	0.900	0.1382
0.504	0.36714	0.664	0.24739	0.920	0.1315
0.508	0.36353	0.668	0.24496	0.940	0.1252
0.512	0.35996	0.672	0.24256	0.960	0.1192
0.516	0.35643	0.676	0.24017	0.980	0.1134
0.520	0.35293	0.680	0.23781	1.000	0.1080
0.524	0.34946	0.684	0.23548	1.020	0.1028
0.528	0.34603	0.688	0.23317	1.040	0.0978
0.532	0.34263	0.692	0.23088	1.060	0.0931
0.536	0.33927	0.696	0.22861	1.080	0.0886
0.540	0.33593	0.700	0.22636	1.100	0.0844
0.544	0.33264	0.704	0.22414	1.120	0.0803
0.548	0.32937	0.708	0.22194	1.140	0.0764
0.552	0.32613	0.712	0.21976	1.160	0.0728
0.556	0.32293	0.716	0.21760	1.180	0.0693
0.560	0.31976	0.720	0.21546	1.200	0.0659
0.564	0.31662	0.724	0.21335	1.240	0.0597
0.568	0.31351	0.728	0.21125	1.280	0.0541
0.572	0.31043	0.732	0.20918	1.320	0.0490
0.576	0.30738	0.736	0.20712	1.360	0.0444
0.580	0.30436	0.740	0.20509	1.400	0.0402
0.584	0.30138	0.744	0.20307	1.440	0.0365
0.588	0.29841	0.748	0.20108	1.480	0.0330
0.592	0.29548	0.752	0.19910	1.520	0.0299
0.596	0.29258	0.756	0.19715	1.560	0.0271
0.600	0.28971	0.760	0.19521	1.600	0.0246
0.604	0.28686	0.764	0.19330	1.680	0.0202
0.608	0.28405	0.768	0.19140	1.760	0.0166
0.612	0.28126	0.772	0.18952	1.840	0.0136
0.616	0.27850	0.776	0.18766	1.920	0.0112
0.620	0.27576	0.780	0.18581	2.000	0.0092
0.624	0.27305	0.784	0.18399	2.080	0.0075
0.628	0.27037	0.788	0.18218	2.160	0.0062
0.632	0.26772	0.792	0.18039	2.240	0.0051
0.636	0.26509	0.796	0.17862	2.320	0.0042
0.640	0.26248	0.800	0.1769	2.400	0.0034
0.644	0.25990	0.820	0.1684	2.480	0.0028
0.648	0.25735	0.840	0.1602	2.560	0.0023
0.652	0.25482	0.860	0.1525	2.640	0.0019
0.656	0.25232	0.880	0.1452	2.720	0.0016

TABLE A-8.—(Continued)

Θ	P(Θ)	Θ	P(Θ)	Θ	P(Θ)
2.800	0.0013	3.200	0.0005	3.600	0.0002
2.880	0.0010	3.280	0.0004	3.680	0.0001
2.960	0.0009	3.360	0.0003	3.760	0.0001
3.040	0.0007	3.440	0.0003	3.840	0.0001
3.120	0.0006	3.520	0.0002	4.000	0.0001

TABLE A-9.

VALUES OF THE CYLINDER SERIES $C(\Theta)$

Θ	C(Θ)	Θ	C(Θ)	Θ	C(Θ)
0.020	0.99999	0.140	0.69798	0.260	0.35577
0.024	0.99994	0.144	0.68339	0.264	0.34767
0.028	0.99974	0.148	0.66897	0.268	0.33975
0.032	0.99921	0.152	0.65475	0.272	0.33201
0.036	0.99813	0.156	0.64073	0.276	0.32444
0.040	0.99627	0.160	0.62692	0.280	0.31704
0.044	0.99345	0.164	0.61332	0.284	0.30981
0.048	0.98951	0.168	0.59996	0.288	0.30275
0.052	0.98439	0.172	0.58683	0.292	0.29584
0.056	0.97806	0.176	0.57392	0.296	0.28909
0.060	0.97054	0.180	0.56126	0.300	0.28249
0.064	0.96189	0.184	0.54883	0.304	0.27604
0.068	0.95219	0.188	0.53664	0.308	0.26973
0.072	0.94152	0.192	0.52468	0.312	0.26358
0.076	0.93000	0.196	0.51297	0.316	0.25756
0.080	0.91772	0.200	0.50149	0.320	0.25167
0.084	0.90478	0.204	0.49024	0.324	0.24592
0.088	0.89129	0.208	0.47922	0.328	0.24030
0.092	0.87733	0.212	0.46844	0.332	0.23481
0.096	0.86299	0.216	0.45788	0.336	0.22945
0.100	0.84836	0.220	0.44755	0.340	0.22420
0.104	0.83349	0.224	0.43743	0.344	0.21908
0.108	0.81846	0.228	0.42753	0.348	0.21407
0.112	0.80333	0.232	0.41785	0.352	0.20918
0.116	0.78813	0.236	0.40838	0.356	0.20440
0.120	0.77293	0.240	0.39912	0.360	0.19973
0.124	0.75776	0.244	0.39005	0.364	0.19516
0.128	0.74265	0.248	0.38119	0.368	0.19070
0.132	0.72763	0.252	0.37253	0.372	0.18634
0.136	0.71273	0.256	0.36405	0.376	0.18208

Θ	$C(\Theta)$	Θ	$C(\Theta)$	Θ	$C(\Theta)$
0.380	0.17792	0.500	0.0887	0.800	0.0157
0.384	0.17385	0.520	0.0792	0.850	0.0117
0.388	0.16988	0.540	0.0704	0.900	0.0088
0.392	0.16599	0.560	0.0628	0.950	0.0066
0.396	0.16220	0.580	0.0560	1.000	0.0049
0.400	0.1585	0.600	0.0499	1.050	0.0037
0.410	0.1496	0.620	0.0444	1.100	0.0028
0.420	0.1412	0.640	0.0396	1.150	0.0021
0.430	0.1332	0.660	0.0352	1.200	0.0016
0.440	0.1258	0.680	0.0314	1.250	0.0012
0.450	0.1187	0.700	0.0280	1.300	0.0009
0.460	0.1120	0.720	0.0249	1.350	0.0007
0.470	0.1057	0.740	0.0222	1.400	0.0005
0.480	0.0998	0.760	0.0198	1.500	0.0003
0.490	0.0942	0.780	0.0176	1.700	0.0001

TABLE A-10.

VALUES OF THE ERROR FUNCTION $S(X) = \mathrm{erf}(X)$

X	$S(X)$	X	$S(X)$	X	$S(X)$	X	$S(X)$
0.00	0.00000	0.20	0.22270	0.40	0.42839	0.60	0.60386
0.01	0.01128	0.21	0.23352	0.41	0.43797	0.61	0.61168
0.02	0.02256	0.22	0.24430	0.42	0.44747	0.62	0.61941
0.03	0.03384	0.23	0.25502	0.43	0.45689	0.63	0.62705
0.04	0.04511	0.24	0.26570	0.44	0.46622	0.64	0.63459
0.05	0.05637	0.25	0.27633	0.45	0.47548	0.65	0.64203
0.06	0.06762	0.26	0.28690	0.46	0.48466	0.66	0.64938
0.07	0.07886	0.27	0.29742	0.47	0.49374	0.67	0.65663
0.08	0.09008	0.28	0.30788	0.48	0.50275	0.68	0.66378
0.09	0.10128	0.29	0.31828	0.49	0.51167	0.69	0.67084
0.10	0.11246	0.30	0.32863	0.50	0.52050	0.70	0.67780
0.11	0.12362	0.31	0.33891	0.51	0.52924	0.71	0.68467
0.12	0.13476	0.32	0.34913	0.52	0.53790	0.72	0.69143
0.13	0.14587	0.33	0.35928	0.53	0.54646	0.73	0.69810
0.14	0.15695	0.34	0.36936	0.54	0.55494	0.74	0.70468
0.15	0.16800	0.35	0.37938	0.55	0.56332	0.75	0.71116
0.16	0.17901	0.36	0.38933	0.56	0.57162	0.76	0.71754
0.17	0.18999	0.37	0.39921	0.57	0.57982	0.77	0.72382
0.18	0.20094	0.38	0.40901	0.58	0.58792	0.78	0.73001
0.19	0.21184	0.39	0.41874	0.59	0.59594	0.79	0.73610

X	S(X)	X	S(X)	X	S(X)	X	S(X)
0.80	0.74210	1.20	0.91031	1.60	0.97635	2.00	0.995322
0.81	0.74800	1.21	0.91296	1.61	0.97721	2.02	0.995720
0.82	0.75381	1.22	0.91553	1.62	0.97804	2.04	0.996086
0.83	0.75952	1.23	0.91805	1.63	0.97884	2.06	0.996424
0.84	0.76514	1.24	0.92050	1.64	0.97962	2.08	0.996734
0.85	0.77067	1.25	0.92290	1.65	0.98038	2.10	0.997020
0.86	0.77610	1.26	0.92524	1.66	0.98110	2.12	0.997284
0.87	0.78144	1.27	0.92751	1.67	0.98181	2.14	0.997525
0.88	0.78669	1.28	0.92973	1.68	0.98249	2.16	0.997747
0.89	0.79184	1.29	0.93190	1.69	0.98315	2.18	0.997951
0.90	0.79691	1.30	0.93401	1.70	0.98379	2.20	0.998137
0.91	0.80188	1.31	0.93606	1.71	0.98441	2.22	0.998308
0.92	0.80677	1.32	0.93806	1.72	0.98500	2.24	0.998464
0.93	0.81156	1.33	0.94002	1.73	0.98558	2.26	0.998607
0.94	0.81627	1.34	0.94191	1.74	0.98613	2.28	0.998738
0.95	0.82089	1.35	0.94376	1.75	0.98667	2.30	0.998857
0.96	0.82542	1.36	0.94556	1.76	0.98719	2.32	0.998966
0.97	0.82987	1.37	0.94731	1.77	0.98769	2.34	0.999065
0.98	0.83423	1.38	0.94902	1.78	0.98817	2.36	0.999155
0.99	0.83851	1.39	0.95067	1.79	0.98864	2.38	0.999237
1.00	0.84270	1.40	0.95228	1.80	0.98909	2.40	0.999311
1.01	0.84681	1.41	0.95385	1.81	0.98952	2.42	0.999379
1.02	0.85084	1.42	0.95538	1.82	0.98994	2.44	0.999441
1.03	0.85478	1.43	0.95686	1.83	0.99035	2.46	0.999497
1.04	0.85865	1.44	0.95830	1.84	0.99074	2.48	0.999547
1.05	0.86244	1.45	0.95970	1.85	0.99111	2.50	0.999593
1.06	0.86614	1.46	0.96105	1.86	0.99147	2.55	0.999689
1.07	0.86977	1.47	0.96237	1.87	0.99182	2.60	0.999764
1.08	0.87333	1.48	0.96365	1.88	0.99216	2.65	0.999822
1.09	0.87680	1.49	0.96490	1.89	0.99248	2.70	0.999866
1.10	0.88020	1.50	0.96610	1.90	0.99279	2.75	0.999899
1.11	0.88353	1.51	0.96728	1.91	0.99309	2.80	0.999925
1.12	0.88679	1.52	0.96841	1.92	0.99338	2.85	0.999944
1.13	0.88997	1.53	0.96952	1.93	0.99366	2.90	0.999959
1.14	0.89308	1.54	0.97059	1.94	0.99392	2.95	0.999970
1.15	0.89612	1.55	0.97162	1.95	0.99418	3.00	0.999978
1.16	0.89910	1.56	0.97263	1.96	0.99443	3.20	0.999994
1.17	0.90200	1.57	0.97360	1.97	0.99466	3.40	0.999998
1.18	0.90484	1.58	0.97455	1.98	0.99489	3.60	1.000000
1.19	0.90761	1.59	0.97546	1.99	0.99511		

Note that $\text{erfc}(X) = 1 - \text{erf}(X)$.

FIRST FIVE ROOTS M_n OF $J_m(M_n) = 0$

m	M_1	M_2	M_3	M_4	M_5
0	2.4048	5.5201	8.6537	11.7915	14.9309
1	3.8317	7.0156	10.1735	13.3237	16.4706
2	5.1356	8.4172	11.6198	14.7960	17.9598
3	6.3802	9.7610	13.0152	16.2235	19.4094
4	7.5883	11.0647	14.3725	17.6160	20.8269

TABLE A–12.

FIRST FIVE ROOTS M_n OF $M_n \tan M_n = C$

C	M_1	M_2	M_3	M_4	M_5
0.000	0.0000	3.1416	6.2832	9.4248	12.5664
0.002	0.0447	3.1422	6.2835	9.4250	12.5665
0.004	0.0632	3.1429	6.2838	9.4252	12.5667
0.006	0.0774	3.1435	6.2841	9.4254	12.5668
0.008	0.0893	3.1441	6.2845	9.4256	12.5670
0.010	0.0998	3.1448	6.2848	9.4258	12.5672
0.020	0.1410	3.1479	6.2864	9.4269	12.5680
0.040	0.1987	3.1543	6.2895	9.4290	12.5696
0.060	0.2425	3.1606	6.2927	9.4311	12.5711
0.080	0.2791	3.1668	6.2959	9.4333	12.5727
0.100	0.3111	3.1731	6.2991	9.4354	12.5743
0.200	0.4328	3.2039	6.3148	9.4459	12.5823
0.300	0.5218	3.2341	6.3305	9.4565	12.5902
0.400	0.5932	3.2636	6.3461	9.4670	12.5981
0.500	0.6533	3.2923	6.3616	9.4775	12.6060
0.600	0.7051	3.3204	6.3770	9.4979	12.6139
0.700	0.7506	3.3477	6.3923	9.4983	12.6218
0.800	0.7910	3.3744	6.4074	9.5087	12.6296
0.900	0.8274	3.4003	6.4224	9.5190	12.6375
1.000	0.8603	3.4256	6.4373	9.5293	12.6453
1.500	0.9882	3.5422	6.5097	9.5801	12.6841
2.000	1.0769	3.6436	6.5783	9.6296	12.7223
3.000	1.1925	3.8088	6.7040	9.7240	12.7966
4.000	1.2646	3.9352	6.8140	9.8119	12.8678
5.000	1.3138	4.0336	6.9096	9.8928	12.9352
6.000	1.3496	4.1116	6.9924	9.9667	12.9988
7.000	1.3766	4.1746	7.0640	10.0339	13.0584
8.000	1.3978	4.2264	7.1263	10.0949	13.1141
9.000	1.4149	4.2694	7.1806	10.1502	13.1660
10.000	1.4289	4.3058	7.2281	10.2003	13.2142
15.000	1.4729	4.4255	7.3959	10.3898	13.4078
20.000	1.4961	4.4915	7.4954	10.5117	13.5420
30.000	1.5202	4.5615	7.6057	10.6543	13.7085
40.000	1.5325	4.5979	7.6647	10.7334	13.8048
50.000	1.5400	4.6202	7.7012	10.7832	13.8666
100.000	1.5552	4.6658	7.7764	10.8871	13.9981

FIRST FIVE ROOTS M_n OF $M_n J_1(M_n)/J_0(M_n) = C$

C	M_1	M_2	M_3	M_4	M_5
0.00	0.0000	3.8317	7.0156	10.1735	13.3237
0.02	0.1995	3.8369	7.0184	10.1754	13.3252
0.04	0.2814	3.8421	7.0213	10.1774	13.3267
0.06	0.3438	3.8473	7.0241	10.1794	13.3282
0.08	0.3960	3.8525	7.0270	10.1813	13.3297
0.10	0.4417	3.8577	7.0298	10.1833	13.3312
0.20	0.6170	3.8835	7.0440	10.1931	13.3387
0.30	0.7465	3.9091	7.0582	10.2029	13.3462
0.40	0.8516	3.9344	7.0723	10.2127	13.3537
0.50	0.9408	3.9594	7.0864	10.2225	13.3611
0.60	1.0184	3.9841	7.1004	10.2322	13.3686
0.70	1.0873	4.0085	7.1143	10.2419	13.3761
0.80	1.1490	4.0325	7.1282	10.2516	13.3835
0.90	1.2048	4.0562	7.1421	10.2613	13.3910
1.00	1.2558	4.0795	7.1558	10.2710	13.3984
2.00	1.5994	4.2910	7.2884	10.3658	13.4719
3.00	1.7887	4.4634	7.4103	10.4566	13.5434
4.00	1.9081	4.6018	7.5201	10.5423	13.6125
5.00	1.9898	4.7131	7.6177	10.6223	13.6786
6.00	2.0490	4.8033	7.7039	10.6964	13.7414
7.00	2.0937	4.8772	7.7797	10.7646	13.8008
8.00	2.1286	4.9384	7.8464	10.8271	13.8566
9.00	2.1566	4.9897	7.9051	10.8842	13.9090
10.00	2.1795	5.0332	7.9569	10.9363	13.9580
15.00	2.2509	5.1773	8.1422	11.1367	14.1576
20.00	2.2880	5.2568	8.2534	11.2677	14.2983
30.00	2.3261	5.3410	8.3771	11.4221	14.4748
40.00	2.3455	5.3846	8.4432	11.5081	14.5774
50.00	2.3572	5.4112	8.4840	11.5621	14.6433
100.00	2.3809	5.4652	8.5678	11.6747	14.7834

TABLE A–14.

FIRST FIVE ROOTS M_n OF $1 - M_n \cot M_n = C$

C	M_1	M_2	M_3	M_4	M_5
0.000	0.0000	4.4934	7.7253	10.9041	14.0662
0.005	0.1224	4.4945	7.7259	10.9046	14.0666
0.010	0.1730	4.4956	7.7265	10.9050	14.0669
0.020	0.2445	4.4979	7.7278	10.9060	14.0676
0.030	0.2991	4.5001	7.7291	10.9069	14.0683
0.040	0.3450	4.5023	7.7304	10.9078	14.0690
0.050	0.3854	4.5045	7.7317	10.9087	14.0697
0.060	0.4217	4.5068	7.7330	10.9096	14.0705
0.070	0.4551	4.5090	7.7343	10.9105	14.0712
0.080	0.4860	4.5112	7.7356	10.9115	14.0719
0.090	0.5150	4.5134	7.7369	10.9124	14.0726
0.100	0.5423	4.5157	7.7382	10.9133	14.0733
0.200	0.7593	4.5379	7.7511	10.9225	14.0804
0.300	0.9208	4.5601	7.7641	10.9316	14.0875
0.400	1.0528	4.5822	7.7770	10.9408	14.0946
0.500	1.1656	4.6042	7.7899	10.9499	14.1017
0.600	1.2644	4.6261	7.8028	10.9591	14.1088
0.700	1.3525	4.6479	7.8156	10.9682	14.1159
0.800	1.4320	4.6696	7.8284	10.9774	14.1230
0.900	1.5044	4.6911	7.8412	10.9865	14.1301
1.000	1.5708	4.7124	7.8540	10.9956	14.1372
1.500	1.8366	4.8158	7.9171	11.0409	14.1724
2.000	2.0288	4.9132	7.9787	11.0856	14.2075
3.000	2.2889	5.0870	8.0962	11.1727	14.2764
4.000	2.4557	5.2329	8.2045	11.2560	14.3434
5.000	2.5704	5.3540	8.3029	11.3349	14.4080
6.000	2.6537	5.4544	8.3914	11.4086	14.4699
7.000	2.7165	5.5378	8.4703	11.4773	14.5288
8.000	2.7654	5.6078	8.5406	11.5408	14.5847
9.000	2.8044	5.6669	8.6031	11.5994	14.6374
10.000	2.8363	5.7172	8.6587	11.6532	14.6870
11.000	2.8628	5.7606	8.7083	11.7027	14.7335
16.000	2.9476	5.9080	8.8898	11.8959	14.9251
21.000	2.9930	5.9921	9.0019	12.0250	15.0625
31.000	3.0406	6.0831	9.1294	12.1807	15.2380
41.000	3.0651	6.1311	9.1987	12.2688	15.3417
51.000	3.0801	6.1606	9.2420	12.3247	15.4090
101.000	3.1105	6.2211	9.3317	12.4426	15.5537

INDEX

Accuracy: of electrical network analogue, 354; of fluid-flow analogue, 322; of membrane analogue, 330; of solid geometrical analogue, 344; of steady-state numerical solutions, 153, 157, 161, Probs. 7-2, 7-7, 7-9; of transient numerical solutions, 297, 298-301, 304, 310, Probs. 12-2, 12-9, 12-10

Adiabatic: boundary condition, 7; surface temperature, 311

Adiabatic structures, 120, 128, 181, 237, 253, 287, 295, 306, Probs. 6-1, 6-2, 6-10, 10-5, 10-16, 12-5

Adiabatic trace: in a filleted corner, Prob. 6-15; in a heating wall, 142; in a long solid semicylinder, 139; in a ribbed wall, Prob. 6-14; in a semi-infinite adiabatic plate, 128; in a square corner, 145, Probs. 6-12, 6-13; in a transistor, 342; in a wall of odd shape, 140, 320

Aerodynamic heating, 310

Age of the earth, 243

Airflow analogue: see Experimental solutions

ALLEN, D. N. de G., 150, 159, 292

Allowable temperature: in electrical coils, 186; in turbine blades, 36

Amplitude: of periodic temperature oscillations, 276, Prob. 11-6; of a series, 97

Analogies: see Experimental solutions

Analogues, 318

Analogy, experimental solutions by, 318

Anisotropic conductivity, 13, 262

ANTHES, H., 325

AVRAMI, M., 91, 355

AWBERRY, J. H., 345

Azimuthal symmetry, 6

Bessel equation, 46; see also Differential equation

Bessel functions: expansion in a series

of, 57, Probs. 3-12, 3-13; graphs of, 50, 56; modified, 54; of negative integral order, 53; of nonintegral order, 54; recurrence formulas for derivatives of, 50; relief of, 49; values of, Tables A-3, A-4, A-5, A-6; of zero order, first kind, 48; of zero order, second kind, 48; zeros of, Table A-11

BEUKEN, C. L., 345

BEWLEY, L. V., 125

Binder-Schmidt: see Graphical method (transient)

BOELTER, L. M. K., 181

Boundary conditions, *steady*, 7: adiabatic, 7; convection, 17; in electrical network analogues, 351; homogeneous, 112; isothermal, 7; in membrane analogues, 325, 329, 333; radiation, 182

Boundary conditions, *transient*, 272, 304: linear, 274, 304; periodic, 276

Boundary layer, on extended surfaces, 81

BRUCKMAYER, F., 345

Capacity lag: in heating and cooling, 257; in a thermocouple, Prob. 10-15

CARRIER, W. H., 91

CARSLAW, H. S., 108, 113, 264, 267, 273

Cauchy, convergence test of, 47, 99, 122

Cauchy-Riemann, equations of, 123

ÇETINKALE, T. N., 21

CHEERS, F., 343

CHURCHILL, R. V., 113, 116

Circular harmonics, 132, 208

Coils: see Electrical coils

Cold working, allowable time for, Prob. 10-1

COLE, M. B., 357

Complementary error function, 265

Complex functions, 123